Evolving Auckland

THE CITY'S ENGINEERING HERITAGE

To John & Judy
with best wishes &
my appreciation for your
contribution to the
success of New Zealand
Steel

Yours Rosemary & John

21/8/12

Ingram

Evolving Auckland

THE CITY'S ENGINEERING HERITAGE

IPENZ Engineering Heritage Auckland Chapter

Edited by
John La Roche

WILY PUBLICATIONS

Dedicated to Sir John Ingram for his huge contribution to our book and the nation

Published by
Wily Publications Ltd
302 Lake Terrace Road
Shirley
Christchurch 8061
New Zealand
Email: jjhaworth@xtra.co.nz

ISBN 978-1-927167-03-8

Cover design from a concept by Sue La Roche, with full title design by Erica Pitt
Book design and page layout by Quentin Wilson, Christchurch
          wilson.quentin@gmail.com
Printed by Choice Company, Taiwan

Contents

FOREWORD *by Sir Ron Carter*   9

EDITORIAL NOTES *by John La Roche*   11

CHAPTER ONE
People and Engineering

1.1   Introduction *by Judy McDonald*   15

1.2   From 1840 to the Present – an Overview *by Bryan Bartley*   16

1.3   Development of Professional Engineering Education and
Engineering Institutions in New Zealand
by John La Roche   22

CHAPTER TWO
Water and Wastewater

2.1   Auckland's Water Supply *by John La Roche*   27

2.2   Auckland Wastewater *by John Fitzmaurice*   51

2.3   North Shore Sewerage *by John Fitzmaurice*   78

CHAPTER THREE
Harbour Development

3.1   Development of Auckland Ports *by Les Jones*   87

CHAPTER FOUR
Roads and Motorways

4.1   Roads *by Bryan Bartley*   105

4.2   Auckland Motorways *by Mike Lancaster and John La Roche*   110

CHAPTER FIVE
Ferries and Trams

| 5.1 | Auckland Ferries *by John Duder* | 117 |
| 5.2 | Auckland Trams *by Colin Zeff* | 120 |

CHAPTER SIX
Railways

| 6.1 | A Brief History of Auckland's Railways *by Rhys Thomas* | 127 |

CHAPTER SEVEN
Bridges

7.1	Auckland Harbour Bridge *by Mike Lancaster*	149
7.2	Grafton Bridge *by Bryan Bartley*	158
7.3	Mangere Bridge *by Mike Lancaster and John La Roche*	161
7.4	Newmarket Viaduct *by Mike Lancaster and John La Roche*	168
7.5	Tamaki River Bridge, Panmure *by John La Roche*	171

CHAPTER EIGHT
Telecommunications

8.1	Telecommunications in Auckland *by Neil Mander and John La Roche*	175
8.2	Musick Point Radio Station *by Rhys Thomas*	181
8.3	Warkworth Satellite Earth Station *by Neil Mander*	188
8.4	COMPAC Submarine Telephone Cable System *by Neil Mander*	195

CHAPTER NINE
Aviation

| 9.1 | Walsh Brothers Flying School *by Colin Zeff* | 203 |
| 9.2 | Mangere – Auckland International Airport *by Mike Lancaster* | 206 |

CHAPTER TEN
Military Protection

10.1	Albert Barracks Wall *by Rhys Thomas*	211
10.2	Albert Park Air Raid Shelters *by Rhys Thomas, Bryan Bartley and Elizabeth Aitken Rose*	216
10.3	North Head: Engineering Auckland's Victorian Defences *by David Veart*	220

10.4   Stony Batter: Auckland's Last Fortress *by David Veart*   223
10.5   Mt Eden Shot Tower *by Bryan Bartley*   226

CHAPTER ELEVEN
Energy Supplies

11.1   The Auckland Gas Company *by David Veart*   229
11.2   Auckland City Destructor *by Bryan Bartley and*
        Elizabeth Aitken Rose   234
11.3   A Brief History of Electricity in Auckland *by Bryan Leyland*   237

CHAPTER TWELVE
Industrial Development

12.1   Steel from Ironsand *by Sir John Ingram*   245
12.2   Slurry Transportation Ironsand Concentrate – Mine Site to
        Glenbrook *by Sir John Ingram*   261
12.3   Chelsea Sugar Works *by Alec Aitken and John La Roche*   264
12.4   Winstone's Lunn Avenue Quarry, Mt Wellington,
        Auckland *by Bryan Bartley*   269
12.5   Kawau Mining *by John Duder*   278
12.6   The Cement Works of Northland *by Andrew Marriott and*
        John La Roche   281

CHAPTER THIRTEEN
Buildings

13.1   Heritage Buildings *by Bryan Bartley and Colin Nicholas*   287
13.2   Auckland Town Hall *by Bryan Bartley,*
        Elizabeth Aitken Rose and Mark Hedley   290
13.3   Auckland High Court *by Elizabeth Aitken Rose*   293
13.4   Civic Theatre *by Elizabeth Aitken Rose and Mark Hedley*   *294*
13.5   Auckland War Memorial Museum *by Mark Hedley*   297
13.6   Auckland Chief Post Office *by Mark Hedley*   300
13.7   Auckland City Art Gallery *by Mark Hedley*   304
13.8   Sky Tower *by Dale Turkington*   307

BIOGRAPHIC INFORMATION ABOUT WRITERS   319
ACKNOWLEDGEMENTS   327
INDEX   331

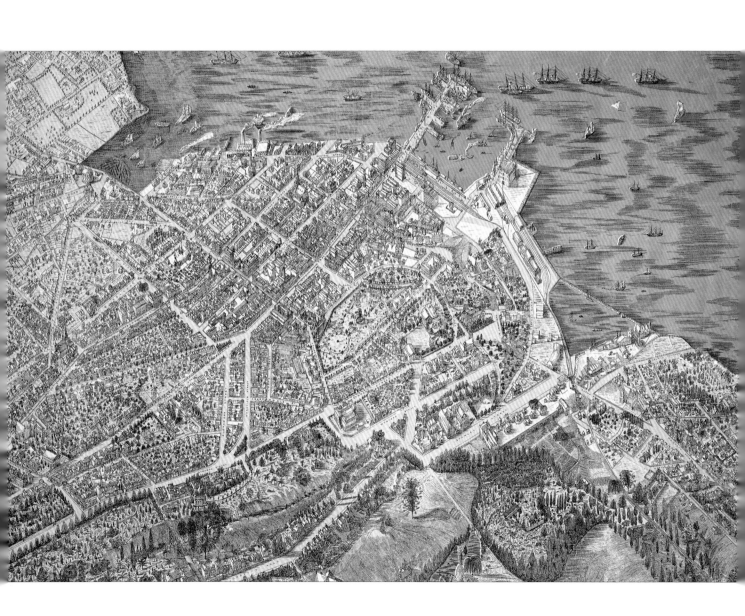

FOREWORD

By any measure Auckland is a youthful city. At the time of writing this account just 171 years have elapsed since Auckland was founded. The Institution of Professional Engineers New Zealand (IPENZ) has been able to draw on the experience of long-serving members whose careers started in the 1950s and who met or worked for some outstanding engineers who started shortly after the First World War. This gives the text personal experience, rather than just literature research, at a very opportune time in recording Auckland's engineering history.

Not only do the authors describe the engineering aspects of so much of Auckland's heritage infrastructure, they also intertwine the technical with the inevitable political issues. Frequently the political, financial and ownership aspects of major projects dominate historical records and diminish the importance of the excellent engineering involved. This book sets the balance right and does so in a way that will interest the lay person as well as the professional.

Much of our infrastructure is unseen. Consider the water supply. Large dams, water mains, purification plants, service reservoirs, reticulation and metering. All are reliable, economic and capable of meeting the needs of an expanding population. Similarly the disposal of sewage, wastewater and stormwater is effective, reliable and largely unseen.

Consider how much of our high standard of living, in this one example of water supply, we owe to the profession of engineering, with their high standards of economic design, execution safety, maintenance and development. For over 100 years it has been sustainable and with environmental impacts such that few are aware of the infrastructure that makes it possible. The book covers the background and development of the many services that make up our standard of living, including trams, ferries, trains and the motorway system.

The development of Auckland's infrastructure continues apace. These

by
Sir Ron Carter

Opposite page: An 1886 'birds-eye' perspective drawing of Auckland by George Tracy Stevens who imagined he was at a point 1,000 feet above Auckland Public Hospital.

Courtesy Sir George Grey Special Collections, Auckland Libraries NZ Map 374 works of today will become the heritage of tomorrow. Projects are of a scale that demands increasing public involvement, global standards of technology and sophisticated methods of construction. In particular, projects of the 21st century demand efficient management and a far wider range of skills than we used 100 years ago.

The value of this record is to enable future generations to look back with respect for those who created the foundations on which Auckland is built. *Evolving Auckland: The City's Engineering Heritage* provides the retrospective which will allow the 20th century infrastructure to take its place in the history of our city.

Ron Carter

Editorial Notes

The idea of publishing a book about Auckland's engineering heritage began in 2006 after the Auckland Chapter of IPENZ Engineering Heritage Committee had successfully published a 48-page booklet entitled *Heritage Walks – The Engineering Heritage of Auckland*. This booklet has been greatly appreciated by many people and used as an example for a series of other walks' booklets produced by Auckland City and other engineering chapters in Wellington and Dunedin. The heritage engineering described in the booklet was limited by the distance of a three-hour walk around engineering heritage sites in the central city – but there was so much to write about. There was a much wider region, and so many other fascinating engineering heritage stories that we wanted to describe. We have a very enthusiastic committee of 19 mainly retired engineers who have all been involved in a wide range of projects in the Auckland region. We are therefore able to relate the 'inside' story about the projects we are writing about. Now, five years later, we are all elated that we have produced our book.

Our Foreword is written by one of New Zealand's most distinguished engineers, Sir Ron Carter. After reading a number of draft chapters, Sir Ron made some very pertinent observations. He suggested we include more about present-day engineering, the engineering that will be the heritage of future years. Much of present-day engineering is complex, leading-edge design done by teams of specialists. They use sophisticated computer programmes and complex analysis. We older engineers did our calculations with slide rules and seven-figure log tables, using tee squares and drawing boards to show what we had designed. We marvel at what can now be achieved with sophisticated electronic equipment. Perhaps we need another book!

Another comment made by Sir Ron was the importance of partnerships with Maori, who have a rich cultural heritage and beliefs that are now required

by
John La Roche

to be incorporated into large engineering programmes. As chairman of the Committee for Auckland, Sir Ron said he had much satisfaction over the last three years in coordinating a number of meetings between our network of business leaders and the leaders of Maori business. This work is partly funded by the Maori Development Corporation, Te Puni Kokiri. Such cooperation shows huge promise, not only for successful use of Maori assets, but also for developing Maori business education, combining wealth for the benefit of society. Most importantly it is creating a better understanding of Maori and non-Maori sectors of New Zealand.

Maori could be credited as being the first engineers in New Zealand. They carried out massive earthworks to build pa sites from where tribes could defend themselves against other tribal invaders. Most of Auckland's volcanic cones have terraces originally formed by pre-European Maori.

Although New Zealand is blessed with our founding Treaty of Waitangi, it is only since the Waitangi Tribunal was established in 1975 and the legislation incorporating the principles of the treaty became law in 1986, that Maori interests have been taken into consideration and given the importance they deserve. There have been many engineering decisions that have ignored Maori interests, causing hardship and grievance. Auckland's drainage system is a case in point. At Okahu Bay the sewer was built across the beach foreshore on Ngati Whatua land, blocking their beach access. They were treated very badly at that time. At the Mangere Sewage Treatment Plant, oxidation ponds were built in 1960 across the traditional food gathering areas for the local Iwi only with their reluctant consent. Waikato-Tainui and Maori of the local Makaurau Marae were full of praise for Watercare Services in 2002 when the oxidation ponds were removed after new processes had been installed to treat Auckland's sewage to much higher standards than were possible with the oxidation ponds. As you will read in John Fitzmaurice's writing about Auckland's wastewater, the Huakina Development Trust was involved in consultation processes from 1994 when it was decided that major changes were necessary at Mangere Wastewater Treatment Plant.

Sir John Ingram, a member of our committee and formerly Managing Director of New Zealand Steel, has written a fascinating account of many of the challenges that the company had to overcome to produce a highly efficient steel manufacturing industry for New Zealand. Sir John was deeply involved with local whanau from 1970 in negotiating rights to mine raw ironsand at Taharoa and also in the ground-breaking Waitangi Tribunal Manukau Harbour hearing in 1984. As a member of the Waitangi Tribunal from 1993 Sir John became well aware of Maori grievances. He saw it as his duty to talk to many groups who had little or no understanding of the shocking injustice many Maori have suffered.

No major engineering project can now proceed without genuine consultation and partnership with Maori. New graduates in engineering include an increasing number of Maori who bring their cultural wisdom to our profession. Appreciating and taking into account a diverse range of views and cultures is now a very important part of engineering in New Zealand.

We hope you will enjoy reading about the engineering projects our committee have enjoyed writing about. We will welcome your observations and comments after reading our book.

CHAPTER ONE

People and Engineering

This book records milestones in engineering history in the wider Auckland region. It covers the earliest pioneering days until quite recent times, outlining major challenges faced and triumphs achieved. It also chronicles some opportunities lost.

Since our colonial beginnings, engineers have made it possible for us to travel readily on land by road or rail; to transport goods in and out of the region by sea; to communicate across ever-increasing distances. Their skills have allowed us to deal safely with human waste; to take for granted clean and available water; even to guard against the fear of attack by land or air. Nationally significant industries have been developed, based on local materials. Civic buildings have enabled individuals to come together for cultural activities, for political rallies, or to exercise judicial functions: in short, to become citizens in a fully functioning urban society.

1.1

Introduction

by
Judy McDonald

Auckland in 1852 – from Queen Street Wharf looking up a muddy Queen Street.

Courtesy NZ Fine Prints
www.prints.co.nz

All around us are monuments to engineering's power to change our lives for the better, our legacy from generations of engineers. To fully understand and appreciate that legacy, some historical context is vital. The great achievements described in the following chapters have often been completed against all odds, in spite of extraordinary practical difficulties or prolonged and bitter infighting – or even both. Political careers have been made and reputations lost on issues as disparate as sewerage and steel. Some stories, like Auckland rail, go on and on.

These accounts of Auckland's heritage are written by engineers at the forefront of their profession, often with inside knowledge of 'what really happened'. They make an inspiring story of vision, technical innovation and determination to overcome extraordinary obstacles.

To read these chapters on Auckland's engineering heritage is to see the region with new eyes.

1.2

From 1840 to the Present – an Overview

by
Bryan Bartley

Engineering was defined in the past as 'the application of Science for the benefit of Mankind'. Another definition suggested 'the art of directing the great sources of power in Nature for the use and convenience of Man'. Today, we need a more inclusive definition: engineering is about the beneficial use of applied science, materials and the forces of nature.

The first widespread impact of engineering on the Auckland region took place after the signing of the Treaty of Waitangi in 1840, when Lieutenant Governor Captain William Hobson determined that the new capital would be at the Waitemata Harbour and named it after the First Lord of the Admiralty and later Governor of India, Lord Auckland.

In the absence of adequate governance, early settlers had a hard time getting shelter, water, food and fuel. It was 31 years after the signing of the Treaty of Waitangi before the city council was established as a stable local government. Roads for horses and carts were mostly muddy tracks in winter. Scoria cone hills provided the first easily-won road material and 60 years later, at the turn of the 20th century, horses were still the main form of transport and transportation of goods.

In such an environment, it is no wonder that every new bridge had an official opening, with speeches by the mayor to a cheering crowd. The engineer would be complimented on the design and supervision of the project, carried out by either council staff or a building contractor. The jubilation was because

such an event represented another rise in the standard of living. The bridge would have reduced the travel distance, or replaced an inadequate boat or ferry. All the infrastructure developments described in this book are steps up in the standard of living of citizens: for example, the reticulated water supply, sewage treatment, transportation, electricity and refrigeration.

Greys Avenue in 1870 – just a muddy track!

Sir George Grey Special Collections, Auckland Libraries 4-11270

A large crowd gathered to see the first electric trams in Queen Street, 1902.

Sir George Grey Special Collections, Auckland Libraries 7-A92

Arising out of the industrial revolution, steam power was the essential driver as Auckland became established. Steam ships progressively replaced sail. Steam drove the early saw mills, flour mills and water pumps, and provided heating for hospitals and many industrial processes, including the dairy industry. Former ships' engineers, skilled in the use of steam and keen to settle in the colony, provided much of the management and design of the early equipment. Many had trained in Scottish shipyards.

'Coal was King' as the main fuel for boilers; its supply was an essential industry based on coastal shipping and horse and cart transport. It was used to heat houses on an open fire or in the old coal and wood range for cooking.

As time went on, solid coal fuel was partly superseded by the manufacture of gas from West Coast bituminous coal at the gasworks in Freemans Bay, reticulated to most of the early suburbs. Gas stoves and water heaters ('califonts'), then gas lighting, brought great benefits, while the gasworks also provided tar for roads and coke for industry and home heating.

The Auckland Electric Tramway Co. Ltd was early on the world scene using electricity as a form of traction for trams (1902) and brought electricity generation from steam to the colony. Steam-driven power stations were the source of electricity for Auckland until 1930, when the switch over to hydropower from Arapuni was made.

Unloading coal in wicker baskets from ships into horse and dray, c. 1910.

B. Bartley painting based on *NZ Herald* photo

All these developments were made possible by an influx of skills. Professional engineers, mostly from the United Kingdom, were amongst the immigrants. They brought the skills of civil engineering design (civil as distinct from military) and were to the fore in design and development of infrastructure such as ports, roads, bridges and water supply. Most were employed by the government (later in the Ministry of Works), or by the city, as city engineers or staff. Road boards, which later became boroughs, also employed these engineers and many were employed in industry.

Some of the immigrant engineers set up as consulting engineers in private practice by virtue of their qualifications and their practical experience, mostly gained in Britain but also from working elsewhere around the world. They provided their services to local government, builders, industries and individuals.

The big step forward in the demand for the profession of civil engineers came after the devastating earthquakes of Murchison in 1929 and Napier in 1931. The latter destroyed most of the brick buildings, including the Napier hospital, with a death toll of 256 people.

Devastation after the 1931 Napier earthquake.

Sir George Grey Special Collections, Auckland Libraries 248-11

As a result, the building codes used by professional engineers and designers since 1935 have included design for earthquake resistance, focused on the interests of personal safety, with higher standards required for hospitals and such places as halls or theatres which people may use in an emergency. Buildings can be designed to be earthquake proof, but the general requirement is for them to be earthquake resistant, maintaining the integrity of the structure, although often allowing minor, repairable damage to occur, providing a good standard of safety for people in the building.

Immediately after the Second World War, an industrial boom produced many labour-saving devices formerly available only to the financially well off. A prime example was the motorcar. Henry Ford's pioneering concept of mass production was used widely during and after the war from 1914, leading to magnificent cars being available to many families. Thus the standard of living was raised by greater convenience, safety in an emergency, security from perceived troublemakers on city streets, cheap family transport, privacy and mobility for family holidays. Often overlooked is that people no longer needed horses, which required considerable personal effort to maintain.

Social attitudes began changing in the post-1918 war period. Before this time, perhaps until the beginning of the Second World War, New Zealand, and in turn Auckland society, had seen itself as engaged in a struggle against the forces of nature; a struggle in the name of progress in which engineers played an admired and vital role.

That was then. What is the mood of society in such matters now? Our built environment is commonly seen as ugly. Changes and development draw protests and attempts to stop them, especially if they are likely to impinge too far on the natural environment. Some think the standard of living is too high and we should be constrained to a simpler way of life, with fewer cars, more public transport and walking. A sea change has taken place in society's values. It comes from a high standard of living that enables the luxury of concern for the environment, which is not seen in less developed countries.

The role of engineers in government service, both central and local, has also

Motorway retaining walls are now adorned with attractive designs.

J. La Roche

changed. In the years of great advances in our standard of living the Ministry of Works was all-powerful. It looked after all the main road systems, hydro dams, electricity generation and supply; in fact all works paid for by taxpayers. The Ministry of Works has now been shut down and in effect privatised (1996).

The local government engineer used to be the right-hand man of the mayor, attending to all works, getting things done and taking responsibility for the expenditure of ratepayers' money on works, control of all building permits and inspections. He, or indeed today possibly she, is no longer employed in that way. Town clerks who formerly attended to correspondence, council meetings, records keeping and rates have mostly become city managers or chief executive officers and the role of the chief engineer has been greatly reduced. Consulting engineering practices have taken over design of the major projects while all maintenance and services are now let out on contract under the control of the city manager.

Nevertheless engineering in New Zealand has never been stronger, with outstanding projects being developed to meet the needs of our society. Environmental and sustainability considerations have generally been involved in engineering decisions, along with safety and economy, but in recent times other professionals such as planners and contract managers have been involved.

Engineering as a profession has moved on in so many ways, such as applying new science, new materials, gaining economic advances, raising quality standards and safety. Computer science has greatly improved calculations regarding strength of materials and structural analysis of complex designs. It has also greatly improved the communication with contractors and builders and advanced the rates of teaching and learning.

The Institution of Professional Engineers New Zealand (IPENZ), the professional body that represents professional engineers from all disciplines in the country, continues to gain in strength of membership and international standing. The university schools of engineering in Auckland and Christchurch continue to provide graduates of recognised academic ability, as do additional degree programmes now available in several other institutions. IPENZ maintains an overview of their practical experience and admits only those found suitable for membership.

A young engineer applying for a scholarship recently described engineering in these terms: 'To me this profession was a hidden secret; every single person from every walk of life relies on civil engineering to provide the infrastructure supporting their existence, yet most are oblivious to the energy and intelligence to which they owe their quality of life.'

Recording places of engineering heritage for the benefit of future generations, and thus honouring those who were outstanding in their profession, helps to open our eyes to this 'hidden secret'. The engineering profession has transformed Auckland – from the mud of the pioneer settlers to the modern city we enjoy.

References and further reading

Furkert, F. W., *Early New Zealand Engineers,* A. H. & A. W. Reed, Wellington, 1953.

Newnham, W. L., *Learning Service Achievement: Fifty years of engineering in New Zealand*, New Zealand Institution of Engineers, Wellington, 1971.

Noonan, Roslyn J., *By Design: a brief history of the Public Works Department Ministry of Works 1870–1970*, NZ Government, Wellington, 1975.

The Institution of Professional Engineers New Zealand, *Engineering to 1990,* Engineering Publications Co. Ltd, Wellington, 1990.

Wright, Matthew, *New Zealand's Engineering Heritage, 1870–2000*, Reed Books, Auckland, 1999.

Wright, Matthew, *Big Ideas, 100 Wonders of New Zealand Engineering*, Random House, 2009.

1.3

Development of Professional Engineering Education and Engineering Institutions in New Zealand

by
John La Roche

Institution of Civil Engineers building, Great George Street, London.

Courtesy Institution of Civil Engineers

The early engineers in New Zealand had usually learned their professional skills in the United Kingdom before leaving there for New Zealand. The Institution of Civil Engineers with headquarters in London was the professional body to which many early engineers belonged with the qualification AMICE – Associate Member of the Institution of Civil Engineers, or MICE – Member of the Institution of Civil Engineers.

In the early 18th century engineers were almost always military men and there was no identifiable profession of engineering. John Smeaton and a group of colleagues formed the Smeatonian Society of Civil Engineers in Britain in 1771; they met informally over dinner to discuss technical subjects of interest and it is suggested they had a library of sorts. According to Garth Watson's *The Civils – the Story of the Institution of Civil Engineers*, 'the title "civil engineer" had been used by John Smeaton to distinguish his profession from that of the military engineer, the original "Ingeniator", from the time of the Norman Conquest, if not earlier'.

The Institution of Civil Engineers was founded in 1818, and under its first President Thomas Telford developed its professional qualifications. Early engineers were usually trained by older experienced engineers. William Weaver (1828–1868), Engineer in Chief of the Auckland Provincial Council from 1864 to 1867, was educated in England. He was a pupil of Brassey and Peto of Bristol, and from 1846 was trained in the office of Isambard Kingdom Brunell and later R. I. Ward, MICE. He worked on the Great Western Railway. To be admitted to the Institution the applicant had to be at least 25 years of age, to have been engaged in the practice of a civil engineer for at least five years and to have gained considerable eminence therein.

Other branches of engineering in Britain developed later with the Institution of Mechanical Engineers being formed in 1847 and the Institution of Electrical Engineers in 1871.

There was a desperate shortage of skilled engineers in New Zealand in the 1870s when Sir Julius Vogel brought in his grand plan to open up the country with new roads and railways. In her book *By Design* describing the history of the Ministry of Works, Rosslyn Noonan states, 'In the Public Works statement for 1874 the Minister said there had been no periods during the year when staff was sufficient to meet the requirements of the department. Very serious difficulty has been found in procuring Engineers who have had experience in railway surveying and construction. Many works have been retarded for want of Engineers.'

The first school of engineering was established at Canterbury University in 1887, when 22 students were enrolled, with two part-time lecturers: Edward Dobson, the first Provincial Engineer in Canterbury, and Robert Julian Scott.

Far left: The first Auckland University School of Engineering.

Courtesy University of Auckland

Left: University of Auckland School of Engineering in 2010.

J. La Roche

At Auckland University the Engineering School was originally the School of Mines, established in 1906, but students could only complete two years at Auckland before going to Canterbury to complete their degree. It was 1949 before a full degree course was offered at Auckland University. Degrees were awarded by the University of New Zealand, the engineering schools of Canterbury and Auckland being part of Canterbury University College and Auckland University College until these became autonomous in 1962.

Mining was a very important industry in the 1800s, requiring many levels of technical competence. By the 1870s quartz reef gold mining in Otago and the Hauraki region required the ore to be crushed before the gold could be recovered. There were many technical skills required, so in 1872 the University of Otago appointed Professor James Black to teach chemistry and mineralogy. James MacAndrew, the Provincial Superintendent, saw the need for a formal School of Mines, which was established in 1876. William Larnach, Minister of Mines from 1885 to 1887, saw the need for additional schools of mines. In 1885 Black was asked to tour mining centres around the country, lecturing to miners about scientific methods for gold recovery. With the success of these lectures 29 schools of mines were established but by 1898 only six remained due to the general decline in gold mining activity.

Local body engineers felt the need to discuss engineering works of common interest and formed the Institute of Local Government Engineers of New Zealand in 1912. New Zealand members of the Institution of Civil Engineers also felt the need for a New Zealand organisation more representative than just local body engineers so in 1914 the Institute of Local Government

Institution of Professional
Engineers New Zealand
Wellington building
in 2010.

J. La Roche

Engineers was wound up in favour of the New Zealand Society of Civil Engineers, the forerunner of the New Zealand Institution of Engineers, now called the Institution of Professional Engineers New Zealand, or IPENZ.

Formal training and examinations were important for maintaining recognised standards for those engaged in the engineering profession. By 1897 the Institution of Civil Engineers (ICE) had established its own examinations for use both in Britain and the British Dominions. These examinations were accepted by most of the British colonies, including New Zealand. University degrees could be used to exempt students from the preliminary examinations. Special courses were instituted at technical colleges such as Seddon Memorial Technical College for those who wished to study at night classes while working under the direction of qualified engineers.

Although for many years the New Zealand Institution had two acceptable means of training, it is now accepted that a university degree in engineering is a necessary prerequisite to further practical training and examinations for becoming a qualified engineer. The Institution accepted the University BE degrees as a suitable measure of academic ability but those degrees are appraised by Institution on a regular basis. The reviews are very thorough and demanding.

While the ICE and 'Home Institutions' courses and examinations were required to recognise academic ability there is a further step to being accepted as a member and that is the Professional Interview. A small committee of senior members interviews each applicant to determine that they:

- have demonstrated practical experience on construction projects and
- are of sound mind and of sober disposition to be able to fairly represent the Institution, its standards and ethics in the future.

Engineers who have qualified to become chartered professional engineers are now required to maintain 'continuing professional development' by undertaking refresher courses and reading to ensure they keep up to date with the latest worldwide developments in engineering practice relating to their particular specialty. The New Zealand Institution of Professional Engineers has always endeavoured to maintain its membership qualifications in line with the best international standards. The Washington Accord, signed in 1989, is an international agreement among bodies responsible for accrediting engineering degree programmes. It recognises the substantial equivalency of programmes accredited by those bodies and recommends that graduates of programmes accredited by any of the signatory bodies be recognised by the other bodies as having met the academic requirements for entry to the practice of engineering.

Attendance at meetings to hear or deliver addresses on engineering and technical subjects has long been an important mechanism for an engineer to keep up to date. The Royal Society of New Zealand (known as the New Zealand Institute before 1933) was founded in Wellington in 1851 'to foster science and technology'. The Royal Society is a professional body of scientists. Since engineering is an applied science, many engineers have been associated with the Royal Society of New Zealand. In Auckland, the Auckland Institute (now the Auckland Institute and Museum) is the Auckland regional branch of the Royal Society of New Zealand. James Stewart (1832–1914), a civil engineer who came to Auckland from Scotland in 1859, was responsible for many engineering works in the region. He was an enthusiastic member of the Auckland Institute and for a time its President. He presented and had published 15 papers in the Proceedings of the New Zealand Institute between 1868 and 1909, many of which described engineering works.

Very comprehensive proceedings with written accounts, diagrams and pictures were published by the British engineering institutions from 1837, including contributions from New Zealand authors. These were obviously an important source of information for engineers working in New Zealand. Proceedings of the British and other engineering institutions, including the Institution of Professional Engineers of NZ (IPENZ) and other world engineering organisations, continue to be important sources of historical and up-to-date information about engineering practice and projects. In addition, regional branches of IPENZ and its affiliated 28 specialist Technical Groups or Collaborating Technical Societies now hold meetings on their own particular engineering topics in many locations.

Today IPENZ accredited engineering degrees can be undertaken at Auckland University of Technology, Manukau Institute of Technology, Massey University, Unitec, University of Auckland, University of Canterbury and University of Waikato.

References and further reading

Bassett, Judith, *Prospero's Island: A History of the School of Engineering at the University of Auckland,* University of Auckland Faculty of Engineering, Auckland, 2003.

Furkert, F. W., *Early New Zealand Engineers*, A. W. & A. H. Reed, Wellington, 1953.

IPENZ website http://www.ipenz.org.nz/ipenz/Education_career/accreditation/four_year.cfm

Mace, Tania and Ngati Maru Rununga, *Thames School of Mines Conservation Plan*, Mathews & Mathews, Auckland, June 2006.

Newnham, W. L., *Learning Service Achievement: Fifty Years of Engineering in New Zealand*, The New Zealand Institution of Engineers, Wellington, 1971.

Noonan, Rosslyn J., *By Design: A Brief History of the Public Works Department Ministry of Works 1870–1970*, Ministry of Works and Development, Wellington, 1975.

Watson, Garth, *The Civils: The story of the Institution of Civil Engineers,* Thomas Telford, London, 1988.

CHAPTER TWO

Water and Wastewater

uckland has many advantages that make it such a popular place to live. It was greatly prized and fought over by Maori before being chosen by Governor William Hobson as the site for the capital of New Zealand in 1840. The close proximity of two very sheltered harbours, Waitemata and Manukau, streams and springs with clear running water, and fertile land made Auckland very attractive to the European settlers who began arriving as soon as the first 1,214 hectares were purchased from Ngati Whatua chiefs.

The Waihoritu Stream, originating from a swampy area near the present Aotea Square, ran with clear water down the gully that is now Queen Street and served the settlement's immediate needs. At that time and for the next 30 years, public amenities provided by the authorities in the rapidly growing town were minimal because of a lack of finance.

The first piped water supply in 1866 came from the Domain springs. It soon proved totally inadequate for the growing population. Most people had to rely on rain water, springs or wells for their water. There were five public wells with pumps also used for fire fighting in the city in the early 1860s, two

2.1

Auckland's Water Supply

by
John La Roche

Auckland's first water supply from the Domain Springs.

Courtesy Watercare Services

in Queen Street, one in Albert Street, one in Kitchener Street and another in Wellesley Street East, near the old Albert Barracks wall. Residents would rise at 5 o'clock in the morning, often queuing to collect and carry their buckets of water from the wells to their homes. These water supplies became particularly scarce in dry summers, with wells drying up or becoming polluted from refuse and nearby pit toilets. Charcoal filters were recommended to purify the water. The Waihoritu stream, now called the Ligar Canal, had become foul smelling and severely polluted by the rapidly growing businesses along Queen Street. Responding to public pressure, the Queen Street Sewer was progressively constructed along the eastern side of Queen Street.

Auckland's wooden buildings were very vulnerable to fire in the 1860s.

Sir George Grey Special Collections, Auckland Libraries 4-415

Fires in the wooden buildings of the day and the lack of a pressure water system were major problems. Fifty buildings were destroyed in 1858 by fire that started in the Osprey Inn, High Street. On 6 September 1873 a fire destroyed 54 buildings on the western side of Queen Street, causing £70,000 worth of damage. Five weeks later another fire in lower Queen Street caused £50,000 worth of damage.

There was great agitation for the authorities to act. In 1864 the Auckland Provincial Council commissioned civil engineer Henry Wrigg AMICE to report on water supply to the town. He recommended a gravity scheme from the Nihotupu River to Khyber Pass Road, including filters and service reservoirs, at a cost of £82,771 0s 4d.

It was estimated it would take 18 months to complete. The mayor, Mr P. A. Phillips, petitioned Parliament in 1871 for £80,000 to provide a water

Left: Queen Street/Wellesley Street corner after an 1873 fire. The pub was quickly rebuilt!

Sir George Grey Special Collections, Auckland Libraries 4-87

supply for the city. Although the petition was favourably received, no action was taken. Water shortages continued to worsen with a severe drought in the summer of 1871–72. To help alleviate the drought, 66 cubic metres per day from Seccombe's Well in Khyber Pass Road was added to the Domain supply, but this was not nearly enough for the growing population.

This led to the development of the Western Springs supply.

Western Springs

Mr Edward O. Moriaty, civil engineer, was engaged by the City in 1874 to report on all possible sources of water for Auckland. After a thorough investigation of many sources he recommended a pumped supply from Western Springs.

Having raised a loan, the City purchased the Western Springs property from Low and Motion in 1875. Consulting engineer William Errington was engaged to prepare working plans and specifications for a steam-powered beam engine, buildings and reservoirs at Ponsonby and Khyber Pass. Errington (1832–1894)

Above: Henry Wrigg (1824– 1879), consulting engineer.

Auckland Council Archives from *Cyclopaedia of NZ*, Vol. 2, Auckland Provincial District, 1902

Left: Low and Motion flour mill, Western Springs 1874.

Sir George Grey Special Collections, Auckland Libraries 80-Bin 304

learned his engineering skills in steam engines and railways in England before immigrating to Australia at 22 years of age. In Australia he became superintendent of a large iron foundry where one of Australia's first railway locomotives was built. Having prepared the plans and supplied the machinery for the largest pump made in Australia at the time, he came to Thames in 1871 to supervise the installation of this 'Big Pump' for dewatering gold mines. He also designed and supervised construction and associated pumping equipment for the Auckland Graving Dock near Lower Albert Street and the Calliope Dock at Devonport.

Pumphouse and Western Springs in 1924.

Sir George Grey Special Collections, Auckland Libraries 1-W514

Pumping head to Ponsonby Reservoir	71.6 metres
Pump Bore	609 millimetres diameter
Maximum pumping capacity (two pumps)	580 cubic metres per hour

Engineering to 1990, a booklet compiled by the Institution of Professional Engineers New Zealand (IPENZ), describes the Western Springs pumphouse and machinery which opened in 1877: 'The pumping machinery is the finest in New Zealand that is still in demonstrable working order. The pumps are housed in a mid-Victorian brick structure with internal beams and columns of cast iron. The pumps drew water from the artesian source at Western Springs and supplied the growing city of Auckland from 1877 to 1936.' The pumphouse and its machinery are preserved in working order at the Museum of Transport and Technology (MOTAT). A 530 millimetre diameter cast iron pipe connects the pump to Ponsonby Reservoir, 71.6 metres above Western Springs. At Ponsonby a further pump provided water to Khyber Reservoir 25.9 metres higher.

The new water supply system made a huge difference to the health of Aucklanders. The annual death rate in the city was 248 in 1876, dropping to 181 in 1877 and 173 in 1878. The majority of residents purchased a permit to collect water from standpipes, at between 5 shillings and 10 shillings per month depending on usage. Water usage increased as the City provided more water mains, and those residents who could afford the £10 connection fee obtained

Western Springs beam engine
pump.

J. La Roche

piped water connections. People who could raise the money were installing water closet toilets, and using water to flush sewer pipes and to water streets to keep the dust down. By 1886, 24-hour pumping was sometimes needed at Western Springs. While initially the supply was good, it deteriorated over time, attracting increasing complaints. The District Health Officer warned of the risk of typhoid in 1899. The need for yet another new supply of water had become obvious.

Water from the Waitakeres

In February 1883 the *New Zealand Herald* describes visits by the mayor and councillors to the Waitakere Falls and the Nihotupu River to look at possible water sources. Although there was much talk about water from the Waitakere Ranges, it was only a water crisis in 1898 that forced the council to act. The *New Zealand Observer* refers sarcastically to Council doing 'something' in January 1898:

> That something usually takes the form of a series of pleasant picnics to all the creeks and water falls within a radius of thirty miles. They [the councillors] gaze upon the beauties of nature and discuss the gastronomic charm of succulent ham sandwiches washed down with libations of sparkling champagne, as they lie a-basking in the sun after the exertions of climbing to the falls.

Various schemes to bring Waitakere water to the city were proposed and investigated by the council. To meet the water crisis a decision was made in 1900 to proceed with the collection of water from the Waitakere Ranges. This was facilitated by a gift of land from Mr Henry Atkinson in Titirangi for part of the pipeline route. Timber dams were built on Nihotupu Steam and on Quinns Creek to provide a temporary water supply conveyed through light-gauge wrought iron pipes to Western Springs from 1902. The Nihotupu wooden dam was demolished in 1914 during the building of the present Upper Nihotupu dam. From this time, the council adopted a policy of continually planning the future provision of water for an ever growing city.

Auckland City Councillors at a picnic in the Waitakere Ranges, February 1906.

Sir George Grey Special Collections, Auckland Libraries 7-A4869

Waitakere Dam

Waitakere dam and falls 1917.

Sir George Grey Special Collections,
Auckland Libraries 1-W1611

Type	Gravity mass concrete
Maximum height of original dam, completed 1910	20.4 metres
Maximum height of raised dam, completed 1927	25.3 metres
Length of raised dam	175 metres
Reservoir storage	1,850,000 cubic metres

Consulting engineer H. Munro Wilson, and James Carlaw, the city Waterworks
Engineer, were asked to report on how best to develop the Waitakere water
sources. They recommended building a concrete gravity dam at the Waitakere
Falls and tenders were called in 1905, with work starting in 1906. There were
many construction difficulties. The pipeline route and access tramline travelled
around rocky bluffs and through tunnels. George's Tunnel, 693 metres long, had

Waitakere wooden dam 1908.

Courtesy Watercare Services

Above: Waitakere dam during construction, 1909.

Courtesy Watercare Services

Above right: Pipe track – George's Tunnel to Waitakere Falls.

Auckland Council Archives ACC 015 Record No 2136/1

Below: Waitakere dam nearing completion, 1910.

Courtesy Watercare Services

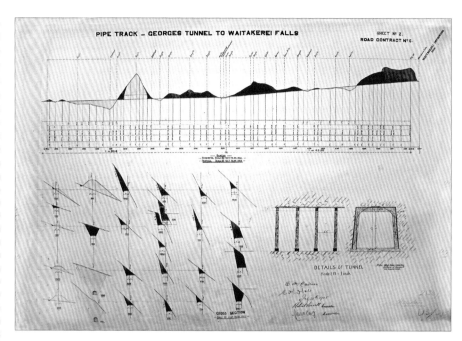

to be constructed under the main Waitakere ridge. Supplies were brought by rail to Swanson railway station and then delivered to the dam site by horse-drawn trucks along the access tramline. Progress was hampered by wet weather and a shortage of labour. Twenty-five kilometres of 533 millimetre and 686 millimetre diameter locking bar steel pipes were manufactured by Mephan Ferguson, a Wanganui company that established a factory in New Lynn. Once these pipes were laid by April 1907, water supply from two temporary timber dams, one on the Waitakere River and the other on Kelly's Creek, provided water to the city.

Right: First Waitakere dam, completed 1910.

Sir George Grey Special Collections, Auckland Libraries 1-W1612

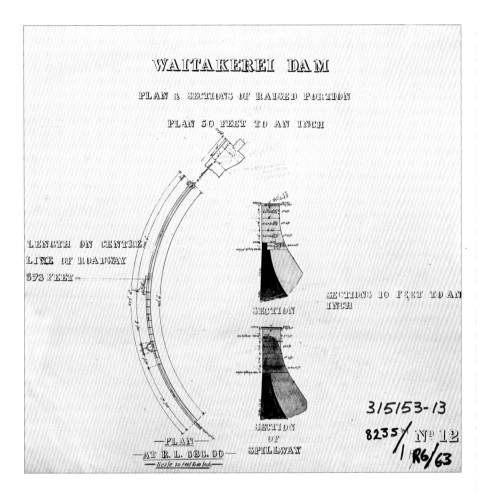

Drawing of raised Waitakere dam.

Auckland Council Archives ACC 015 Record No 8235/1

Construction of the main dam continued to be slow, causing the original contractor to withdraw. A new contractor took over, but progress remained slow because of wet weather and supply problems. A major storm in May 1910 brought down a large slip of earth and trees on to the temporary dam. The weight of trees and debris caused the temporary dam to collapse, sweeping away tools and boxing from the partially completed permanent dam just downstream. At the aggregate quarry beside the entrance to George's Tunnel a slip blocked the tunnel and broke the water supply pipes. Continuing water shortages in the city reinforced urgency. However, by mid December 1910 the new dam was completed and water again flowed to the city. Subsequent raising of the dam by 4.8 metres in 1925 more than doubled the storage capacity. In recent years it has been strengthened by drilling down to the foundation rock strata and tying the dam to the rock with prestressed cables.

Upper Nihotupu Dam

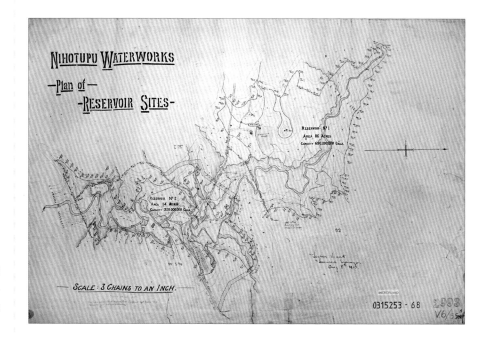

Nihotupu waterworks, plan of reservoir sites in 1910.

Auckland Council Archives ACC 015 Record No 2993/1

Type	Gravity mass concrete
Maximum height dam, completed 1923	50.3 metres
Length of dam	162 metres
Reservoir storage	2,363,000 cubic metres

Nihotupu wooden dam being demolished in 1914 for construction of the new dam.

Sir George Grey Special Collections, Auckland Libraries 4-2456

Although the pending completion of Waitakere Dam promised relief, by 1909 it was obvious to the city Waterworks Engineer that more water would soon be required. A permanent dam at Nihotupu was the next choice. Slips in the steep country along the temporary pipeline route and deterioration of the light-gauge wrought iron pipes caused frequent disruption of the water supply from the temporary Nihotupu wooden dams. To alleviate this problem, between 1911 and 1913 tunnels were dug under intervening ridges on the pipeline route, shortening the pipe length by four kilometres and making it less vulnerable to slip damage. A two-foot gauge tramline (now used as a public attraction by Watercare's Rain Forest Express as well as for maintenance of the pipeline) was laid for the installation of 609 millimetre and 533 millimetre diameter cast iron pipes imported from Britain.

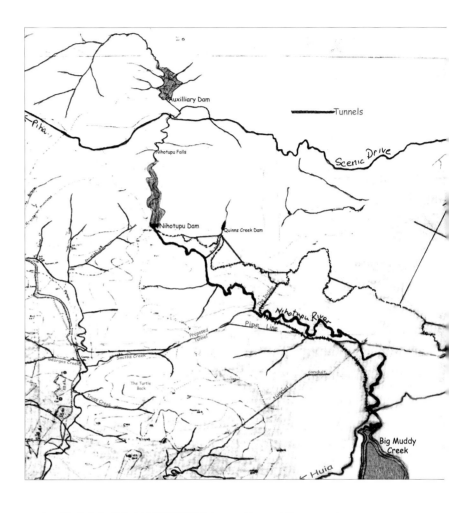

Above: Nihotupu pipeline route.

Auckland Council Archives based on ACC 015 Record No 6525/2

Left: Big Muddy Creek wharf for unloading and storage of cement and sand in 1921.

Sir George Grey Special Collections, Auckland Libraries 1-W1819

The City Engineer, Walter Bush, favoured a site on the Nihotupu River north of Piha Road where he considered an earth dam could be built with good storage capacity. However, when consulting engineer Henry Metcalfe (1851–1918) was engaged to report on Bush's proposal, foundation difficulties were uncovered. A site further down the valley just above the main Nihotupu Falls was recommended, where a concrete dam could be built. Bush then designed the dam and tenders were called in 1915. The contract to construct the Upper Nihotupu dam, as it is now called, was awarded to Gisborne firm Langlands and Company.

Construction supplies were brought by boat across the Manukau Harbour to a special wharf and storage hoppers at Big Muddy Creek. A tramline was constructed up the Nihotupu Valley to 'The Incline'. Here a steep ascent required trucks to be hauled up to the pipeline track by a steam-powered hauler. A quarry site for aggregate was cleared at the head of the reservoir and a tramline constructed to the dam site. But in March 1916 a freak accident occurred during blasting for this tramline. A rock flying from 100 metres away crashed through the roof of the site office, killing the contractor, William Langlands. The contract continued under the control of Langlands' partner.

However, progress was very slow after very heavy rainfall and flooding of the site, with washouts and tunnel collapses causing delay in materials being transported. This compounded the major shortages of men and materials caused by World War I. By 1919 only foundation trenches had been dug and the first concrete poured.

The continuing installation of flush toilets in the city and new consumers joining the supply meant the amount of water used was growing rapidly and the council became increasingly concerned about the slow progress. To speed up the process of providing more water storage, James Tyler, the Assistant City Engineer, designed a 19.8 metre high concrete slab and buttress dam at Bush's first dam site north of Piha Road. Under urgency, this buttress dam was completed by June 1921, providing 313,000 cubic metres of storage.

Langlands' contract continued to get further behind. A request for an extension of time in January 1921 was refused and the council took over control of the work using its own engineering

Above: Nihotupu auxiliary dam completed June 1921.

Sir George Grey Special Collections, Auckland Libraries 1-W339

Far left: Nihotupu dam site showing excavation of cut-off trench, the concrete batching plant, flume for diverting river flows and pipeline for run-of-stream water to the city.

Sir George Grey Special Collections, Auckland Libraries 1-W1794

Above left: Nihotupu cut-off trench in 1918, showing rock 'plums' ready for placing in the concrete. Note three workmen standing beside the trench.

Sir George Grey Special Collections, Auckland Libraries 1-W1800

Far left: City Engineer Walter Bush and James Tyler at Nihotupu cut-off trench for the first pour of concrete in February 1919.

Sir George Grey Special Collections, Auckland Libraries 1-W1814

Above right: Nihotupu concrete batching plant in 1918.

Sir George Grey Special Collections, Auckland Libraries 1-W1788

staff and day labour. James Tyler was directed to complete the dam by 1923. He reorganised the whole project with separate supply contracts for cement and sand; he re-graded the tramway from Big Muddy Creek and replaced the wooden rails with steel from the Waitakere tramline; and he reorganised the quarry and purchased new locomotives along with other improvements. Exceptionally heavy rainfall and gales on the Manukau Harbour continued to

Above: Gibbons and Harris steam engine at Nihotupu quarry.

Courtesy Watercare Services

Above right: Official opening of Nihotupu dam on 14 April 1923.

Courtesy Watercare Services

Far right: Aerial view of Upper Nihotupu dam, 1990s.

Courtesy Watercare Services

Above right: Mason & Porter vertical boiler steam engine, known as "The Rat", crossing bridge on lower tramway.

Sir George Grey Special Collections, Auckland Libraries 1-W1803

cause supply difficulties. However, by February 1923 the last concrete had been poured and the dam was officially opened by the Hon. J. G. Coates, Minister of Works, on 14 April 1923.

The need for filtration

Auckland Health Officer Dr T. J. Hughes condemned Western Springs water in December 1920 as 'unfit for human consumption'. Soon afterwards he informed the council that 'Waitakere water is very impure and falls outside the limit of organic purity'. Faecal coliforms were detected in both Western Springs and Nihotupu water. In response, the council stopped public access to the water catchments and the boundaries were fenced. By 1922 chlorination plants had been installed at Titirangi and Western Springs. In 1924 the council decided to install filtration for all water supplied to the city. The Candy Filter Company of London was awarded the contract for filter stations at Titirangi (Nihotupu) and Waitakere. This company had already installed Candy 'Dechlor' pressure filters at the Captain Cook Brewery in Khyber Pass in 1912 and at Onehunga and One Tree Hill Boroughs in 1916. By July 1927 both filter stations at Nihotupu and Waitakere were brought into service using aluminium sulphate to coagulate the suspended organic matter in the water, followed by filtration through 1.06 metre deep beds of sand and gravel. Water was dosed with lime and chlorine after the sand filtration.

At this time the Upper Huia Dam was under construction. The Candy Filter Company was awarded the contract to provide a filter station for Huia water in Titirangi, not far from the Nihotupu filter station. Upper Huia Dam, another gravity mass concrete dam, was completed in 1929, with storage capacity of 520,000,000 gallons (2,436,000 m³).

Far left: Huia Filter Station, 1990s.

Courtesy Watercare Services

Lower Nihotupu Dam

Type	Rolled fill earth and rock
Maximum height dam, completed 1948	24.7 metres
Length of dam	381 metres
Reservoir storage	4,805,000 cubic metres

City Engineer Walter Bush had first recommended the Lower Nihotupu dam in 1915. The Upper Nihotupu Dam had been completed in 1923 when the council adopted a policy to use in turn the Upper Huia, Lower Nihotupu and Lower Huia catchments. Preliminary investigations had been undertaken in 1929 at the Lower Nihotupu site, including a contour survey and test shafts at 30 metre intervals to rock foundations along the proposed dam centre-line. Reduced consumption of water in the early 1930s caused by the economic depression enabled a pause in further work. Water use was again increasing by 1938 and investigations were resumed. The outbreak of World War II and the military enlistment of most of the city's technical staff interrupted work

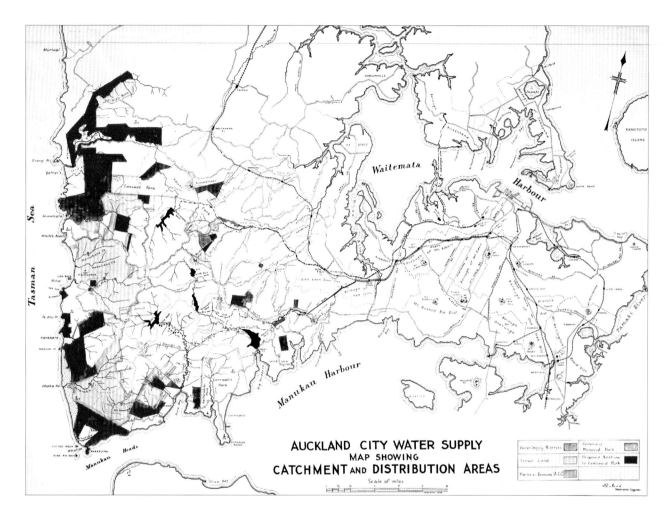

AUCKLAND CITY WATER SUPPLY
MAP SHOWING
CATCHMENT AND DISTRIBUTION AREAS

Above: Auckland city water supply, 1938.

Auckland War Memorial Museum G9048

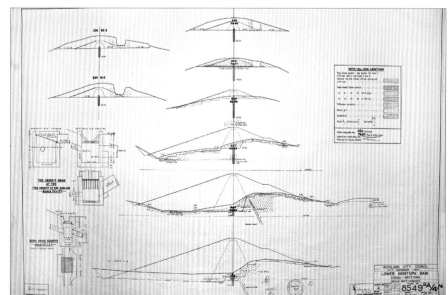

Right: Cross sections of Lower Nihotupu dam.

Auckland Council Archives ACC 015 Record No 8549/4

Above: Lower Nihotupu dam spillway channel under construction, showing diversion tunnel.

Courtesy Watercare Services

Aerial view of completed Lower Nihotupu dam, 1948.

Auckland War Memorial Museum 1 M60 116

again. The very dry summer of 1942–43 and the arrival of American troops and activity associated with the war effort again brought severe water shortages. Completing the Lower Nihotupu dam became urgent.

Lower Nihotupu Dam was the first roll fill earth dam constructed in New Zealand, designed in accord with modern soil mechanics theory and testing of soil materials for the dam. Tractor-drawn scrapers and sheepsfoot rollers were used to achieve the desired levels of compaction and low permeability. Although many earth dams had been constructed prior to this time, they were built with either a concrete core wall or a puddled clay core to ensure water-tightness. Puddle clay had been used since Roman times for waterproofing canal linings and the core of earth dams. Traditionally, puddle clay compaction was achieved by manual 'heeling' or using flocks of sheep. New Zealand dams built this way included the 1867 Ross Creek Dam for Dunedin's water supply and the Lower Karori Dam in 1874.

Cyril Firth (1903–2003), later to become Auckland City Council Chief Engineer Water, and Director of the Auckland Regional Authority, carried out the geological investigations and designed the Lower Nihotupu earth dam. Firth completed an MSc in geology, his thesis describing the geology of the Hunua Ranges. After working as an engineer at Manukau and Franklin County Councils, he joined the Superior Oil Company in 1939, prospecting for oil in Taranaki. During World War II he was seconded by the New

Above: Cyril Firth.

NZ Herald

Arthur Mead at Upper
Nihotupu dam.

Courtesy Watercare Services

Zealand Government for oil exploration in the lower North Island. He joined Auckland City Council Waterworks Department in 1943. Cyril Firth's knowledge of geology was passed on to many engineers who learned their skills at Auckland University School of Engineering, where he lectured part-time. He received many awards from engineering organisations, and at the age of 94 was recognised as a Distinguished Fellow of IPENZ.

Laboratory tests on the soils at Lower Nihotupu showed that ample water tightness could be obtained by appropriate control of soil grading, moisture content and compaction. As an alternative to an earth dam, a multiple-arch concrete gravity dam was also designed. Tenders were called for both designs and in March 1945 Downer & Co were awarded the contract to build an earth dam for £287,789, 10 per cent less than the tendered price for a concrete dam.

A comprehensive paper on the design and construction of the Lower Nihotupu Dam was written by Arthur Mead in the Proceedings of the New Zealand Institution of Engineers. Arthur Mead, Chief Engineer Water from 1929 until he retired in 1953, was responsible for the planning and development of much of Auckland's water supply. He was a man of many talents and interests. An ardent conservationist, he wrote a booklet, 'The Native Flora of the Waitakere Range Auckland', listing all the species of trees and plants found in the Waitakere Ranges, and was awarded the prestigious Loader Cup in 1972 for his conservation work. He is commemorated by the Arthur Mead Environmental Award, given to an Institution of Engineers Auckland engineer whose submission for a predominantly engineering work best exemplifies care for, and consideration of environmental values. Arthur Mead joined the City Waterworks department as a junior engineer in 1910 after graduating BE from Canterbury University College. He served as an infantryman and was awarded the Military Medal in World War I. After his return he completed much of the design work for the Upper Nihotupu dam. In the early 1930s he undertook a survey of the Hunua Ranges, providing the future plan for the water supply development of the area. The map he produced of the Hunua Ranges was very popular with trampers of that time.

Hunua Dams

The Hunua Ranges, well to the south, had long been eyed as a source of water for Auckland and work commenced on a dam at Cosseys Creek in 1946. Held up by staff and material shortages, it was not finished until 1956. When the 5.6 kilometres of tunnels and 24 kilometres of pipeline were completed, the first Hunua water became available to the City in 1953 from the flow of stream at Cosseys Creek. Many far-sighted engineers have been involved in waterworks construction for Auckland and formed part of Cyril Firth's design and management teams. Bruce Smithson, George Hutchinson, Ron Sharp, Don Wilson, Tom Torrens and Bruce Duffield were responsible for much of the construction and design work in the Hunua ranges and later became leaders in the waterworks department and the engineering profession.

To keep ahead of the need for water supply to the region, new roll-fill earth dams were steadily constructed, all under Firth's direction. Upper Mangatawhiri dam was completed in 1965, Lower Huia in 1971, Wairoa in 1975 and Mangatangi in 1977. But Auckland continues to grow and now the Waikato River is being used as another source of water.

Ardmore Filter Station

Ardmore Filter Station is the largest water filtration plant in New Zealand, with a capacity of 350,000 cubic metres per day. It is significant because when commissioned between 1956 and 1961 it was the first major water treatment plant to use vertical flow clarification tanks and automatic filter back-washing.

The first four tanks were brought into service at Ardmore in 1956 after many complaints from 1953 onwards about the discolouration of unfiltered Hunua water from Cosseys Creek. The design of the 8.8 metre square vertical flow clarifier tanks with 60 degree sloped hopper bottoms had been developed in the United Kingdom by the Candy Filter Company in 1939. Aluminium sulphate added upstream flocculates (clots) the fine particles in the incoming water, forming a floc blanket in the tank through which clarified water emerges. The Candy hopper bottomed tank is designed to have a more turbulent zone to promote flocculation at the lowest apex point where the incoming flow

Ardmore Filter Station.

Courtesy Watercare Services

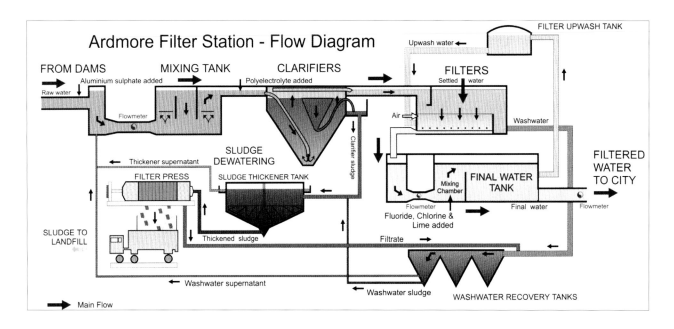

Ardmore Filter Station - Flow Diagram

Ardmore Filter Station flow diagram, 2010.

Courtesy Watercare Services

Dennis Mansergh, Managing Director Candy Filters, 1928–1967.

Courtesy D. Peate

enters the tank. As the flow rises the velocity and turbulence reduce, promoting the formation of a blanket of alum floc. The minute particles making the water turbid are trapped in the floc blanket and are removed by periodic 'bleeding'. Installing these tanks was very successful and gradually more tanks were added. There are now 76 of them in service at Ardmore. Polyelectrolytes are now added with the aluminium sulphate, permitting increased flow rates in each tank.

Sand-media filters and automated filter washing were then introduced. The first six filters were brought into service in 1961. Automation was very new at this time. A Lockheed high-pressure oil system was used to automatically open and close valves using electrical post-office type relays and sensing equipment commonly used in aircraft of the period. A centralised control room enabled the operators to monitor the plant operation using information transmitted from the filters indicating when washing was needed. Automation could be overridden if needed. Now with computer technology the need for large control rooms has disappeared, but the pioneering use of automation at Ardmore has proved its worth in terms of labour saving and consistent control. Auckland's filter stations have provided a high standard of water quality to the region.

Although much of the treatment plant design for Ardmore was done by the Candy Filter Company in London, it was Candy Filter Company's Dennis Mansergh and Des Peate, based in Auckland, who were responsible for commissioning the Ardmore filter station. Between them they played a major role in water treatment technology throughout New Zealand for many years. They were highly respected engineers and the treatment systems they installed have provided high quality water supplies for many cities and towns throughout the country.

Since 1953 there have been progressive additions and changes to the Ardmore Filter Station. Additional capacity was needed as new Hunua dams were brought into service. The sludge removed from settling tanks is now treated and de-watered through filter presses. Dirty water from the filter washing is also treated and returned to the station inlet so there is zero waste-water discharge from the Filter Station. Changes to the New Zealand Drinking Water Standards require more stringent turbidity standards and safeguarding against potential threats from cryptosporidium and giardia. To meet the new requirements, all sand filters have recently been upgraded and operated with increased upflow backwash rates.

Des Peate, Managing Director Paterson Candy International, 1967–1981.

Courtesy D. Peate

Reticulation (Pipe Network) Systems

Along with the many storage dams at water sources, followed by the filter stations where water is treated, providing piped water to over 1.2 million people in greater Auckland requires considerable investment in reticulation and treated water storage reservoirs. There is a history of innovative engineering in providing these largely unseen services. Arthur Mead's submerged pipeline crossing the Waitemata Harbour from Westmere to Birkenhead in 1934 was a particularly ingenious use of rotating joints, underwater trenching and careful placement of the pipeline in strong tidal currents. Bringing Hunua water to the city through large 1900 millimetre diameter concrete lined steel pipes, tunnels and aqueduct systems was also a major engineering achievement.

New water mains continue to be laid and reservoirs to be built. In 2008, Watercare Services Limited, now responsible for Auckland's water supplies,

Train crossing water main construction at Remuera.

Sir George Grey Special Collections, Auckland Libraries 580-3290

looks after 545 kilometres of water mains, 53 treated water reservoirs and 31 pumping stations. Unlike many other towns and cities in New Zealand, Auckland has universal metering that provides fair and impartial charging and encourages efficient water use. Aucklanders on average use only 68 per cent of the average unmetered use in Christchurch.

Controlling Organisations

Auckland Provincial Government built the first Auckland water supply from the Domain in 1866. Auckland City Council, after its formation in 1871, became responsible for the provision of water to its residents. After water from Western Springs was provided in 1877 there were significantly increasing demands on the city's supply as the surrounding boroughs or road boards sought to either join or purchase water from Auckland City. Although there were often arguments about the price charged by Auckland City, a Royal Commission in 1927 stated that the price charged by the City for bulk water was reasonable.

Auckland Regional Authority, formed in April 1965, took over bulk water supply responsibilities from Auckland City. Auckland Regional Authority became Auckland Regional Council in 1989. Watercare Services Limited took over responsibility after its formation as a 'council-controlled organisation' under the Local Government Act of 1989. Ownership is now vested in Watercare Services Ltd which is a Council Controlled Organisation belonging to the combined local bodies of the Auckland Council formed in 2010. Watercare Services Limited is responsible for all bulk water supplies and waste water systems in the Auckland region, including the Mangere Wastewater Treatment Plant.

Waikato River Treatment

The severe drought of 1994 was a wake-up call for the politicians when the storage dams in the Waitakere and Hunua ranges emptied or became very low, causing severe water restrictions to be put in place. Although there had been much investigation work about using the Waikato before the drought, it became obvious that drawing water from the Waikato River was urgently needed.

Auckland does not stop growing! Watercare Services Limited has to plan decades in advance for increased supplies. Public consultation is required for all new developments. Auckland's population is estimated to double in the next 25 years. To provide for future water supplies, a site on the Waikato River at Whangarata near Tuakau was chosen, based on investigations carried out by local consultants KRTA Ltd in partnership with the British water supply specialists Binnie and Partners. Cyril Firth, now retired from his position as the first Director of Works of the Auckland Regional Authority, was retained as a specialist adviser. Ensuring the highest water quality standards from the river requires a four-stage treatment process including membrane filtration and granular activated carbon.

Watercare Services Limited 2002 Annual Report describes the plant as follows:

The $155 million Project Waikato incorporates leading-edge filtration technology that produces a high standard of water. The technology uses a four-stage multi-barrier process, making the plant the most sophisticated of its kind in the Southern Hemisphere.

In the first stage, coagulant is added to the water to form floc, which is easily removed during clarification. The second stage sees the water treated by state-of-the-art membrane filtration technology, which international experts consider to be an effective barrier to pathogenic organisms in water and guarantees against contamination from parasites such as giardia, cryptosporidium and most waterborne viruses.

From there the water from the membranes is passed through granular activated carbon filters. This removes organic compounds, pesticides, any remaining oestrogenic substances and unpleasant tastes and odours. Finally the water is treated with chlorine to kill any remaining waterborne viruses and prevent bacterial growth during transportation and storage. Water treated by the new plant is as good as or better than water from Auckland's existing sources.

The new Waikato source provides greater flexibility in the management of water sources and ensures that the required 1-in-200-year drought security standard is maintained.

Below: Waikato Water Treatment Plant and the Waikato River.

Courtesy Watercare Services

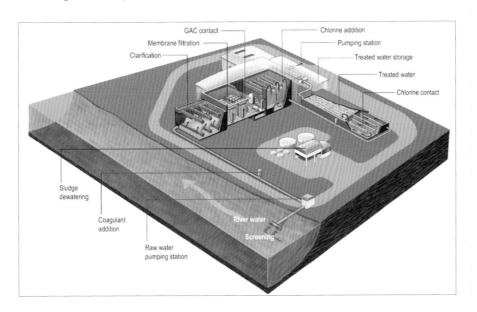

Left: Diagrammatic view of Waikato Water Treatment Plant.

Courtesy Watercare Services

Glossary of Technical Terms

Turbidity is a measure of the amount of very fine suspended particles, or the 'dirtiness' of water.

Flocculation is the process used in water treatment where the turbidity or fine particles suspended in the water are coagulated with chemicals and gentle agitation into a 'floc blanket'. This blanket is usually suspended in the flocculation tank and is periodically 'bled' to remove the suspended turbidity from the water supply.

Post-office-type relays are an electrical device where a small electrical current is used to switch a larger current to another circuit. They were common in tele-communications before the advent of electronic circuitry.

References and further reading

Barr, John, *Municipal and Official Handbook of the City of Auckland,* Auckland City Council, 1922.

Bush, G. W. A., *Decently and In Order: The Centennial History of the Auckland City Council 1840–1971,* Auckland City Council, Collins, Auckland, 1971.

Bush, W. E., *The Water Supply Undertaking of Auckland City Council,* NZ Institution of Engineers Proceedings, Volume 13, pp 181–213.

Firth, Norman, 'Engineer saw vision fulfilled', Obituary for Cyril Firth, *New Zealand Herald,* October 2003.

Firth, C. W., *A Century of Water Supply for Auckland,* Auckland Regional Authority, 1967.

Furkert, F. W., *Early New Zealand Engineers,* A. W. & A. H. Reed, Wellington, 1953.

Institution of Professional Engineers New Zealand, *Engineering to 1990,* Engineering Publications Ltd, Wellington, 1990.

Mead, A. D., *Submerged Pipeline Crossing Auckland Harbour,* NZ Society of Civil Engineers Proceedings, 1934–35, Volume 21, pp 353–369.

Mead A. D., *The Lower Nihotupu Water Supply for the City of Auckland,* NZ Institution of Engineers Proceedings, Volume 35, pp 289–343.

Murdoch, G. J., *The Water Supply of Metropolitan Auckland,* unpublished history, property of Watercare Services Ltd, Auckland, 1990.

Museum of Transport and Technology, *The Beam Engine and Western Springs Pumping Station,* MOTAT, 2008.

Offer, R. E., *Walls for Water: Pioneer Dam Building in New Zealand,* Dunmore Press, Palmerston North, 1997.

Watercare Services Ltd, *Annual Sustainability Report 2002,* Watercare Services, 2002.

Watercare Services Ltd, *Project Waikato: Information on the new major water supply for Auckland,* Watercare Services Ltd, 2002.

Watercare Services Ltd, *Annual Report 2008,* Watercare Services, 2008.

Wilson, Loraine M., *An Iron Essay: A Short History of the Beam Engine and Western Springs Waterworks Auckland,* Museum of Transport and Technology, Auckland, 1994.

Worldwide, major wastewater schemes have often attracted controversy. New Zealand has not been immune. The greatest of these local controversies, in terms of size and population, and the most traumatic, in terms of political drama and time for resolution, is that of Auckland.

That resolution has taken a long time is aptly summed up in the 1956 Majority Report of the overseas panel of engineering experts, of which we shall hear more. The report stated: 'The sewerage problem appears first to have become manifest in 1878 and, during the next thirty years, at least six engineering reports dealing with the matter were sought and received.' And this was for only part of Auckland, since the North Shore, then in its infancy, was not included in these deliberations.

Dealing with Auckland's sewerage has seen the reputation of many engineers trampled on, and the enhancement of the careers of others. This review is written by an engineer who took part at the time of the ongoing controversy which saw the current scheme adopted in its emergent form.

Prior to any attempts by its early settlers to put in place a proper sewerage scheme, the central area of Auckland was drained naturally by the Ligar Canal, which ran down Queen Street to the Waitemata Harbour. Conditions were deplorable and work on constructing a sewer up lower Queen Street, while commenced in 1854, proceeded very slowly. As late as 1870, it was described by the *New Zealand Herald* as 'That abomination, the Ligar Canal…still a pestiferous ditch, the receptacle of every imaginable filth, bubbling in the noonday sun'. However, even at that time, there were ambitious thoughts as to the possible beneficial use of sewage. The *Herald* in 1871 advanced the idea that, by purifying the water, the solid residue could be used as a fertiliser, turning sewage into an asset rather than a liability.

Interestingly, about this time (1850s) the city of London, with a population of 10 million, was experiencing severe pollution, with outbreaks of deadly cholera attributed to sewage odours. The River Thames was its Ligar Canal but on a far greater scale. The interceptor sewer scheme of the London Board of Works engineer Joseph Bazalgette – collecting sewage from drains previously discharging directly to the Thames and transporting wastes downstream for holding in collection tanks for discharge on the outgoing tide – alleviated these odours when commissioned in 1865. While it did not abate the cholera, it did eliminate sewage odours as the cause, thus exposing contamination of drinking water as the vector of transmission. As you read on, it can be perceived that Bazalgette's work in England influenced the thinking of engineers giving advice in New Zealand soon after that time.

To alleviate the foul conditions in the Ligar Canal, construction of the Queen Street sewer was progressively extended up the eastern side of Queen

2.2

Auckland Wastewater

by John Fitzmaurice

Construction of Queen Street sewer at Fort Street corner, 1863.

Sir George Grey Special Collections, Auckland Libraries 4-400

Street, roughly parallel to the canal. The sewer was constructed as an oval-shaped conduit with a bluestone base and triple layers of tapered bricks forming an arch some two metres in height at its downstream end, reducing in height as it progressed upstream. At the same time as the sewer was being constructed the downstream reach of the canal was covered over to permit adjacent building construction. The canal was finally covered completely in 1873. A 2008 upgrade of the Queen Street landscape commemorates the Ligar Canal by a footpath-level trail of solar-powered lights supposedly following its course.

General sanitary conditions were still deplorable. In 1878, under pressure from the *Herald*, the Auckland City Council requested the advice of a visiting British hydraulics engineer, William Clark, who recommended a temporary scheme comprising a sewer which would intercept a number of drains to the harbour and terminate at Stanley Street. From there, treated effluent would be pumped to discharge into adjacent St Georges Bay. In particular, the interceptors would eliminate the by-then-notorious Wharf Outfall at the foot of Queen Street. Clark envisaged that, ultimately, sewage would be processed at Hobson Bay into farm manure. Notwithstanding the relative economy of the scheme, city councillors did not act. By 1885 the country was gripped by depression, and lack of finance meant that no public works of any great cost could proceed.

The return of better times and mounting intolerance of the system of night-soil collection saw the commissioning in 1903 of Wellington civil engineer R. L. Mestayer, who recommended the separation of stormwater and sewage, with sewage being piped up-harbour to a septic tank at Coxs Creek. Again cost dismayed the council and a second opinion was sought of English engineer G. Midgley Taylor, who scorned the proposal for strategic reasons and claimed costs had been grossly underestimated. He recommended the discharge of screened sewage on the out-going tide, off Takapurawha Point at Okahu Bay at the harbour entrance. The council was confused by the conflicting advice and awaited the appointment in 1906 of the new City Engineer, Walter E. Bush.

The forceful and optimistic Bush threw his support behind the Okahu Bay scheme. In 1908 Midgley Taylor was recalled to progress the scheme, which was now, in cost, well beyond the resources of one local body. This led to the successful promotion that year of a parliamentary bill creating the Auckland and Suburban Drainage Board to service the drainage needs of the several local bodies in the area. Construction of the Orakei works then progressed well and the main outfall works were opened in March 1914 with appropriate pomp and ceremony.

In the discussion on the technical paper on the scheme presented by Walter Bush to the Institution of Civil Engineers in 1920, Mr G. M. C. Taylor said

Orakei sewage holding tanks under construction in 1911, now Kelly Tarlton's Underwater World.

Courtesy Watercare Services

his father, Midgley Taylor, chose the outfall location at Orakei because it was the narrowest point in the harbour and would benefit from the mass of water discharged from the harbour each tide. Accordingly, he did not favour Mestayer's Coxs Creek scheme as it did not have this advantage and, furthermore, discharged effluent would flow past the city before it found its way out of the harbour and into the open sea. Also mentioned in the paper and lauded in the discussion was the fact that the scheme was built for less than Midgley Taylor's estimated cost – a tribute both to him and to Bush, under whose direction the scheme was built.

Some of the features of the scheme are interesting both technically and historically. Sewers of quite large diameter were built because of the enormous

Main interceptor sewer to
Orakei, crossing Okahu Bay
foreshore in 1914.

Sir George Grey Special Collections,
Auckland Libraries 4-4258

volumes of stormwater as well as sanitary wastes they were required to convey
to the outfall works. The main intercepting sewer runs 13,500 metres at a grade
of one in 3,000 from Avondale in the west to Orakei. It is of egg-shape cross
section, gradually increasing from 1.05 metres height by 0.7 metres width to
2.6 metres by 1.75 metres. To carry the sewage from those areas not able to be
drained by gravity into the main sewer, four pumping stations were constructed
as part of the scheme.

The Orakei outfall comprised twin 1200 millimetres diameter cast iron
pipes 380 metres long on cast iron cradles, discharging seven metres below
ordinary low tide. The storage tanks were divided into three longitudinal compartments of total capacity 37,000 cubic metres. In anticipation of the Tamaki
foreshore roadway, not constructed at that time, the reinforced concrete roofs
to the storage tanks were built strong enough to carry tram traffic – the electric
tram system, extending to the suburbs of Auckland, having been inaugurated
in 1902. While tram traffic never eventuated, the tanks now sustain heavy
road traffic.

Today, a portion of the storage tanks has been converted into Kelly Tarlton's
Underwater World, where Auckland's citizens, most of them unknowingly,
view sharks where their sewage wastes were once held for tidal discharge. The
screenings building – described by Bush as a handsome brick building on a
stone base – housed a detritus removal plant, of bucket dredge type, three sets
of 100 millimetre screens followed by mechanically cleaned 15 millimetre
screens, and a screenings incinerator with its conspicuous chimney. Many
were the false teeth sets recovered (and sometimes claimed from those on
display). In the earlier, quieter, less technological times an operator wended
his way by bicycle the length of the holding tanks to the valve house (now part
of a popular café) to manually open the outfall penstocks on each outgoing

tide. The screenings building itself (without chimney) is today a fashionable seafood restaurant.

When the Orakei Scheme opened, it served 88,693 out of a total population of some 100,000. It was capable of being extended to serve 300,000. In opening the works, the Mayor of Auckland, James Parr, optimistically asserted that it would 'hold good' until Auckland attained a population of half a million.

As Auckland grew, its boundaries increased and sewerage reticulation kept pace. By 1920 it was apparent that the waters around the Orakei outfall and adjacent shores were polluted and the Medical Officer of Health considered that the effluent was a menace to health. Also, the expanding reticulation saw an increasing number of sewage outfalls into both the Waitemata and Manukau harbours. The Auckland City Council finally persuaded the Drainage Board to undertake its own investigations. The board's engineer-secretary, Mr. H. H. Watkins, was dispatched overseas in 1929 to study the various methods of sewage disposal then available. He investigated a large number of sewerage schemes and noted that the 'dilution method' – untreated discharge into a large body of water – was the choice most commonly preferred and also the most economical system available.

Mr Watkins' comprehensive report of December 1931 proposed to abandon the Orakei outfall and replace it with treatment works on Browns Island, some 2.5 kilometres offshore, with discharge of screened and settled sewage to an outfall in the adjacent Motukorea Channel. The works would be connected to the reticulation system by an underwater sewer. It was proposed to service the North Shore separately, with its own treatment works discharging into the Hauraki Gulf.

Top: Proposed Browns Island scheme.
Bottom left: The outfall in Waitemata harbour.
Bottom right: The existing Orakei screening building.
Insert: H. H. Watkins.

Sir George Grey Special Collections, Auckland Libraries 7-A12173

While Browns Island was much more remote than Orakei, the discharge would still be within the outer harbour. The board did not want a repeat of the Orakei experience, which had fallen well short of the prediction that it would be adequate until Auckland's population reached the half million expected by 1970. Moreover the financial implications were enormous. Before it committed itself, it was imperative that the board could feel totally confident that Watkins' scheme would work, especially as it foreshadowed the formation of a re-constituted, elective, metropolitan-wide Drainage Board.

Had the board immediately adopted the Watkins report, it probably could have proceeded with little criticism, but the board had sufficient misgivings to request government to set up a committee of inquiry to review the proposal. It recommended a comprehensive drainage district and indicated a preference for an outfall into the Tasman Sea (an option revisited, fleetingly, in 2000). Watkins submitted a supplementary report in July 1933 which dismissed the feasibility of the Tasman outfall as well as sewage farms and the commercial production of manure from sludge. The board also took notice of the committee's recommendation for a comprehensive drainage district and set about drawing in the outer local body areas, as well as pressing on with the Browns Island scheme.

There was some opposition. It came principally from those parties who could see themselves likely to be affected by the discharge. The Tamaki Ratepayers and Residents Association protested, as did the Tamaki Yacht Club, which postulated that conditions would be little better than the existing Orakei outfall. The Auckland Yacht and Motor Boat Association added its concerns. However, public dissatisfaction with the existing system, which by now was serving 158,000 and under considerable strain, muted these objections. Notwithstanding, outer local bodies showed no enthusiasm to join the board and share its impending costs.

The election in 1935 of Ernest Davis (later Sir Ernest), brewery baron, as mayor, and thus board chairman, was expected to accelerate developments. Encouraged, Watkins advocated a metropolitan board be formed without delay; but Davis, sensing trouble, had the board resolve to call in outside experts to review all proposals yet again.

The Drainage Engineer to the Melbourne and Metropolitan Board of Works, 41-year-old E. F. Borrie, and G. A. Hart, who was about to retire as Wellington City Engineer, were commissioned for this task and reported in February 1936. They ruled out the Manukau Heads or other locations on the west coast as discharge points and endorsed the Browns Island scheme; but subject to float tests to confirm the anticipated movement of the effluent field.

The Borrie and Hart report did not please everyone – instead of uniting behind a cause to achieve a community-desired outcome, the 'Auckland disease' again manifested itself with the *Herald* advocating an outlet at Huia towards the mouth of the Manukau Harbour and others still advocating a west coast outfall. By May 1937 the completed float tests, independently checked, were reported on, confirming the efficacy of the proposed Browns Island outfall and dismissing the need for the discharge to be disinfected, although it did recommend chlorination be available for use during prolonged periods of dry weather.

The Frazer Commission, chaired by Sir Francis Frazer, was set up in late 1937 to determine the appropriate area for a greater metropolitan drainage authority. Once it had been assessed, the board sought a bill to establish its extended boundaries. However, Parliament dithered, possibly in response to lobbying by the Harbour Preservation Society, a new voice on the block. With unacceptable changes proposed, the board withdrew its bill. With the Depression receding the government subsidy on labour costs was withdrawn, further checking enthusiasm. Then the outbreak of World War II put all such projects on hold.

Only after the course of the war turned decisively in favour of the Allies was it possible to revisit the issue. Meanwhile, Watkins chafed at not being able to implement a scheme which to his mind would avert the ever-increasing pollution by meatworks discharges to the Manukau and cope with burgeoning state house expansion in the eastern suburbs. In 1943, under the chairmanship of Mayor J. A. C. Allum (later Sir John), the board again put forward its bill for a metropolitan drainage authority. It was passed in 1944, notwithstanding a petition which branded the Browns Island proposal 'a serious blunder and permanent disfigurement of the most beautiful harbour in the Pacific'. Thus the Auckland & Suburban Drainage Board expired on 31 January and the Auckland Metropolitan Drainage Board came into being on 1 February 1945. Watkins, who had served the previous board since its inception 36 years previously, looked forward to long-deferred progress.

Opposition seemingly waned. Behind the scenes, however, trouble still stirred. The Harbour Preservation Society commissioned engineer Andrew Murray OBE to check the data that Watkins had used to estimate the costs of his Browns Island scheme compared with pumping sewage to be discharged near Manukau Heads. Murray was a respected engineer, both military, having being in command of 3rd Division Royal New Zealand Engineers in the Pacific, and civil, being principal of Andrew Murray, Consulting Engineer, later to become Andrew Murray and Partners, then Murray North Partners. To the disappointment of the society, Murray found the data both adequate and fairly applied.

There was another dissenting party, the Auckland and Suburban Drainage League. Small and ineffectual initially, it was resurrected from the waning

Harbour Preservation Society. To its ranks it attracted a significant figure, one Dove-Myer Robinson (later Sir Dove-Myer).

Robinson was a businessman, until that time little interested in civic affairs, but destined, through his initial interest in the sewerage controversy, to become the longest-serving mayor in Auckland's history. At the time he was managing director of Childware Ltd, a children's clothing manufacturer, and owned a prestigious home in Glendowie, overlooking the Hauraki Gulf and Browns Island. His son contracted meningitis, thought by his father to be due to swimming at the foreshore near his home, and spent several weeks convalescing in hospital.

Having attended one of the initial meetings of the Drainage League, he quickly became its central and dynamic figure. Its goals were to prevent the Browns Island scheme coming to fruition unless supported by independent professional opinion, and to promote a complete, adequate and permanent drainage scheme for the board's district.

The league sought a meeting with the board, at which league members were treated with disdain by Chairman Allum. They retired unheard and resentful. This hardened the league's resolve and Robbie (as he later came to be affectionately known) vowed a personal crusade to make the harbour waters free of pollution.

Robinson worked on the public's prejudices against 'swimming in their own excreta'. He became conversant in sewage treatment methodology, and developed an allied interest in waste composting. The league's first honorary engineer, T. A. F. Stone, a retired civil and mechanical engineer, touted a 'Triple Scheme' of disposal comprising sewage lakes, sunlight photosynthesis and compost production. This was adversely reported on by the City Engineer, Arthur J. Dickson.

The league continued to elicit support, floating a petition criticising the Browns Island proposal, formulated as far ago as 1931 and now 14 years old, as obsolete, and stressing its similarity to the discredited Orakei Scheme. They hammered for alternatives to be considered. However, the press and general public were apathetic about the league's endeavours at this time and no support was forthcoming from the New Zealand Institution of Engineers.

League spirits were raised by a letter from R. P. Worley, a well-known local consulting engineer, giving his opinion that Browns Island was the centre of 'a great slow-moving whirlpool' which would guarantee that Watkins' scheme would pollute the Waitemata Harbour. Ralph Worley was from an engineering family, prominent in Auckland engineering circles, his brother Rupert being the chief engineer of the Auckland Gas Company. Ralph's practice was to become Worley, Downey, Muir & Partners, more recently assimilated into international consultants Maunsell AECOM.

A request from the league for the support of the Auckland University College received a rebuttal from the Dean of the faculty of engineering, Professor T. J. Leach, who advised that the Browns Island scheme was technically and economically sound. Tom Leach was an energetic and charismatic Australian whose unusual background included scientific work for the Snowy Mountains hydro schemes and secret wartime experimental work testing explosions to create destructive tsunami waves for assisting attacks against Pacific Islands held by the Japanese. He was much revered by Auckland engineering students of the time and later students too, once the engineering school transferred to Ardmore.

A league petition of 43,000 presented to Parliament in September 1945 failed, although compensation rights for injurious effects were extended to embrace properties other than those directly intruded upon by drainage works, the league's oblique aim being to include adverse foreshore effects.

Robinson continued his public education campaign, drawing to his support V. J. Chapman and K. B. Cumberland, lecturers recently appointed from England by Auckland University College to teach, respectively, botany and geography. Robinson assumed presidency of the league in 1946.

When a second parliamentary petition was presented in that year, a parliamentary committee was appointed to enquire into the composting of wastes for soil fertiliser. The league was pleased when in November A. T. Simmons, a design engineer with Auckland City, presented a report to Council on composting of refuse, although expressing strong reservations about how viable it would be for large-scale application. Nevertheless, a small pilot plant was set up in Upland Road where the local refuse landfill, well remembered by the writer, is now a recreational playground – Little Rangitoto Reserve.

The league's overriding fear was that planning for the Browns Island scheme would proceed beyond the point of no return. However, the inconvenient location of the proposed treatment plant on an island and the board's lack of skilled staff made progress slow. Watkins was in his final year before retirement and was described as 'frayed and careworn' at the frustration of delay. He retired in September 1947, creating a further hiatus. W. L. Mynott was promoted to acting engineer. Even if he could have exerted dynamic leadership, which does not appear to have been the case, material shortages in the early post-war days further inhibited progress.

Re-elected league president in 1947, Robinson promoted the idea of all sewage being directed to Westfield. Sludge would be retrieved from sedimentation tanks and the effluent held in an artificial lake formed by building a low retaining dam beneath the Mangere Bridge. Profits would accrue from harvesting water hyacinths and mixing these with the settled sludge to form compost for sale.

The 1947 local body elections saw a focus on fixing the Orakei system. Yachties deplored it. It was said they covered their mouths with handkerchiefs when passing the outfall. At the same time, in the upper Manukau, fish became a rarity and fumes from the industrial effluent discoloured houses, prompting train passengers through Westfield to dub it 'Lavender Flat'.

In October 1947 the first case of a new epidemic of poliomyelitis (infantile paralysis) was noted. It was thought, but not conclusively proved, that bathing in polluted seawaters was the cause and bathing was prohibited at all inner-harbour beaches. By the end of November the first death had occurred. All Auckland schools closed and, by the time they reopened a month later than usual in March 1948, 113 positive cases had been hospitalised. There had been eight deaths.

The previous year's elections had seen Allum easily elected to his third successive term as mayor and subsequently re-elected chairman of the Drainage Board.

The board needed to expedite progress on the Browns Island scheme but lacked drive with only an acting engineer. It was several months before a permanent engineer, selected from lists of both local and overseas engineers, prepared by an advisory panel of Auckland engineers, was appointed. Significantly, Bill Mynott, the assistant and acting chief engineer who had worked with Watkins on the detailed design of the Browns Island scheme for all those years, was passed over.

James P. Porter BSc MICE, aged 51, whose earlier upbringing had been in New Zealand and whose recent work experience was with the London County Council meant he was familiar with discharge of sewage to tidal waters, was appointed Chief Engineer on 6 June 1948. Porter found that little had been accomplished since the retirement of Watkins nine months earlier and no doubt was dismayed at how little technical help was available – the board's staff at that time comprising only Bill Mynott, the acting Chief Engineer, John Rowntree, a well qualified engineer later to become President of the New Zealand Institution of Engineers, Jack Lee, a surveyor, and a few other staff. (So well qualified was John Rowntree that David Chandler FIPENZ recently described his first sight of Rowntree's office as 'being wallpapered in diplomas'.)

Porter and staff quickly set about reviewing the Browns Island scheme. His end of July report identified that, with the population growth since the scheme was first mooted, it would serve Auckland's needs only if the Westfield industries treated their own wastes. Otherwise, the Browns Island scheme could serve only immediately contiguous residential areas plus these industries, and additional satellite schemes would necessarily be required. As to the Browns Island proposal itself, while supportive of it, Porter was concerned at the lack of test-boring geological investigation of the submarine sewer route to the island.

While Porter's report was no consolation to the Drainage League, the board laboured at this time under the shadow of a parliamentary commission of inquiry into the scheme, vigorously espoused by T. E. Skinner, the member for Tamaki (the Tom Skinner who was later to become famous as President of the Federation of Labour and ultimately to be awarded a knighthood). Allum dismissed the suggestions that work be deferred pending the outcome of the commission and, with increased staff, by the end of 1948 significant progress with design was being accomplished.

Underwater borings on the alignment of the Browns Island sewer were carried out in early 1949. The Auckland Harbour Board agreed discharge standards and the Department of Health approved these, requiring them to be achieved beyond 'a half-mile off the shores' of the island, with such standards to apply other than on the ebb or outgoing tide.

Porter unveiled a modified Dual Scheme in January 1949 that retained the Browns Island proposal for the urban area tributary to the Waitemata and included a separate plant to serve the Manukau industries and the southern area. He was still concerned about the feasibility of the underwater sewer, particularly as the borings had identified an infilled valley on the sewer alignment. The advice of Sir William Halcrow, a renowned British engineer who had been retained to act on Auckland's underground railway, was sought. He advocated a tunnel under the seabed with a light railway for construction of the sewer.

In recognition of the seriousness of the industrial waste problem, Ronald Hicks, a chemist, was appointed in May 1949. Aged 43, Hicks had been manager of sewage purification works at Hamilton, Scotland. As will be seen, he was to prove a 'hick-up'.

The period 1949–1951 was consumed by political activity involving the commission of inquiry into the board's scheme and attempts to get legislation passed to enable it to be carried out. The commission completely endorsed Porter's Dual Scheme and trampled on the league's ambitions for ponds and recovery of nutrients by water hyacinths – indeed, going further, and condemning oxidation ponds. The 1950 triennial local body elections gave Allum a massive victory, an unprecedented fourth term as mayor and, of course, renewed chairmanship of the board. In March 1951 the board approved the Dual Scheme and by the end of the year had its enabling legislation, as did the North Shore with its own act, each board tacitly agreeing not to sully each other's nest.

By this time the need for a scheme was desperate, Orakei being only one of over two dozen outfalls discharging raw wastes into the Waitemata and Manukau harbours. Fourteen of these served industries around the

Westfield-Penrose area including the freezing works, which alone were equivalent to a population of 300,000 persons.

The board was not over all its hurdles yet. Hicks had broken ranks, publicly disagreeing with the board's scheme at the Local Bills Committee hearing in October 1951, saying that the scheme's bacteriological standards would fall distinctly short of what was acceptable. Porter was livid – and pointed out that the effluent was to be discharged only on the out-going tide and standards applied only to incoming tide.

Hicks was silenced. But to his dissent was added engineering criticism. Despite Halcrow's assurances regarding the submarine sewer, Ralph Worley, about to become the newly formed North Shore Drainage Board's first consultant, and Hugh Vickerman DSO OBE, ex Deputy Chief Engineer of the Public Works Department and a past President of the New Zealand Institution of Engineers, condemned the project in the December 1951 issue of *NZ Engineering*.

The Drainage League was awakened and Robbie saw his chance when a casual vacancy in the council occurred early in 1952. He ran, his win ordaining that he be appointed to the Drainage Board. There he found he was hamstrung by standing orders introduced at the behest of Porter to restrain Hicks from access to information other than with the approval of the chairman.

Robbie then turned to advocating his alternative scheme, aggressively deprecating Porter's expertise, both at the board table and in public. Professional convention prevented rebuttal, Porter having to rely on the scant protection accorded by the board chairman.

Matters came to a head when the City Council, expecting the Browns Island scheme to be implemented, proposed to utilise a planned trunk sewer serving the Glendowie area as a temporary septic tank. Discharge would take place at the Karaka Bay foreshore until such time as it could be connected to the submarine sewer to the island. The announcement that swimming at Karaka Bay would be prohibited galvanised a large public meeting protesting at the proposal. Mynott and Rowntree had to bear the brunt of uncivil criticism expressed at the meeting.

The sequence to this meeting was the league's unveiling of a now updated and amended proposal. This provided for all sewage to be treated by oxidation ponds located between Puketutu Island and the Mangere foreshore in the Manukau Harbour. The author, the league divulged, was none other than R. P. Worley MSc AMICE MNZIE. A public meeting, advertised by the league with the theme 'The Great Drainage Mystery', attracted a large audience some weeks later in November 1952. Typical of league meetings, it was protracted. While it is said the audience dwindled to half by the time resolutions were passed, insisting that the Department of Health resist any reduction in purity standards and that the board adopt Porter's alternative Manukau scheme. The recollection of Bryan Bartley ONZM Dist. FIPENZ is that those not in sympathy with the league's proposals had slunk away before the voting, leaving him exposed to Robbie's sarcasm as the sole dissenter. The meeting, portentously, also suggested a panel of overseas experts review all proposals.

Other schemes popped up. A Citizens Sewage Committee put forward a proposal by W. Y. Agnew, a New York consulting engineer, for treatment on Maori land at Orakei and in Hobson Bay. Those residents at the end of Victoria Avenue were not amused at the use of Hobson Bay and few of other citizens wanted a continuing operation at Orakei, Maori land or not. Both Porter and Hicks condemned the proposal on engineering and chemical grounds respectively.

Then doubt again arose regarding the submarine sewer, Sir William Halcrow's major report to the board in September saying the proposal was probably reasonable as long as the probability of earth tremors was low. The board's staff began to lose confidence, particularly when tenders for initial works greatly exceeded estimates.

Following considerable turmoil at board level, in March 1953 the board reviewed competing schemes in a debate which extended over two days. The Agnew scheme to use Orakei and Hobson Bay was supported at this hearing by B. H. Kingston, one of the leaders in the Glendowie protest. This and the league's scheme were rejected. In a last 10-minute flurry, the meeting reaffirmed the Browns Island scheme and awarded to Etude et Enterprises Ltd, which had been invited to re-tender following unacceptable earlier tenders, a contract to construct access works, the submarine sewer and the Browns Island outfall for the sum of £1,914,332.

In order to achieve such progress, the board had taken on additional engineering staff. Charles C. Collom BSc (Eng) MICE, later to become Chief Engineer, took up his appointment as Senior Civil Engineer in November 1951. Along with the appointment of a number of young graduate engineers then and in early 1952, including the writer, this gave rise to a buoyant morale in the engineering office. Collom was an Englishman in his mid-forties, with some 20 years experience in Malaya and Singapore. He was made a prisoner-of-war when the Japanese overran Singapore and tells the story of how, in an act of rebellion against their captors, the British engineers charged with the operation of the sewage treatment plant for the Japanese, merely continued to recirculate the plant's contents for some years. On discovery, Collom and others were transferred to the notorious Changi prison, where sustenance was poor and sanitary conditions pitiful.

Auckland Metropolitan
Drainage Board in session,
with Robbie (Dove-Myer
Robinson) at helm,
W. L. Mynott,
John Rowntree and
Ronald Hicks
at rear table.

Sparrow Industrial Pictures Ltd

Robinson continued his criticism of the scheme and particularly of Porter, going so far as to move the board request a public investigation into the affairs of the board over the period of Porter's tenure. Even at the ceremony marking the commencement of construction, he expressed an aside to Collom that 'the scheme could still be stopped'.

At the 1953 local body elections league members fielded city council candidates under the banner of the United Independents. Allum, seeking a fifth term as mayor, narrowly lost to Luxford. Several United Independents, including Robbie, were appointed to the board and at its first meeting in February 1954 Robbie was elected chairman. Immediately he led the board into an intensive review of all aspects of the then-adopted seven-fold scheme (Porter's Dual Scheme having expanded to include minor satellite plants, four to Waitemata Harbour and one additional to Manukau Harbour). The review included particular scrutiny of the submarine tunnel, since abandoned in favour of a seabed trench. Most board members appreciated that proper technical consideration was beyond their competence and, in the face of wavering confidence by staff and the intractable position Porter had got himself into, opted to slow down the Browns Island scheme and seek review by an overseas panel of experts.

From a short-list of 21 nominations prepared by staff, the March meeting of the board selected a panel of four engineers, three from the west coast of the United States, two of whom had previously worked together, one from England and one chemist from Britain. There were considerable allegations of bias in the selection as the US engineers had a heavily weighted background in development of oxidation ponds; Dr David H. Caldwell's firm Brown & Caldwell had designed sewage treatment plants based on this process for several Californian communities. Also, he had had a past close-working association with the oldest septuagenarian member of the panel, Professor Charles G. Hyde. The selection of A. M. Rawn, Chief Engineer and General Manager of Los Angeles County Sanitation District and an internationally renowned expert in tunnelling for ocean outfalls, was free of criticism, as was the choice of John T. Calvert, senior partner John Taylor & Sons, London.

Notwithstanding the shadow over selection, the panel worked very fast. Within a month of arrival it delivered on 18 April an interim opinion on the proposed scheme, saying that it could not comply with the official discharge standards set by the Harbour Board as approved by the Department of Health. Calvert, in a minority report, advocated a reduction in standards, even though those adopted were now to apply at bathing beaches rather than adjacent to the discharge, and supported the Browns Island Scheme, as against others, on the grounds of cost, ability to proceed immediately and on the principle he favoured of dealing with wastes of an area within its own watershed. As to reduced standards, all except Calvert said it would require further testing, which would take up to a year. Calvert said there was a reasonable chance, but the only way to be certain was to put the scheme into operation and find out.

The premature leaking of Calvert's minority report, which, it had been agreed, would only be released with the panel's majority report, refuelled the dispute. Calvert's services were dispensed with, his fee being met only after hesitation. His intimation that he would not report further unless additional fees were paid earning the riposte that 'nothing more was wanted'.

Porter's position, too, had become untenable. He had been humiliated by the board and its antagonistic chairman. At the March meeting he was stripped of his role as Chief Executive Officer and Hicks was vested with the right to report directly on sewage purification and treatment. At its meeting on 19 May 1954 Porter tendered his resignation. At the same meeting the board, ignoring criticism of its predisposition to jettison previous plans on any pretext, resolved not to proceed with its seven-fold scheme.

The press revelled in the dispute, which was notable for the courage of the number of local engineers who spoke up to criticise the board for precipitately abandoning the scheme: Lloyd Mandeno, retired professor of engineering Sidney Lamb, his successor Neil Mowbray and Greville Walker. However, they in turn were not without critics – one writer suggesting that Lamb's claim that the Orakei system had worked to the intentions of its designer was akin to the surgeon's apology that 'the operation was successful, but the patient died'.

Meanwhile the panel of overseas engineers laboured industriously and by 1 July had completed its report. On 7 July the board adopted the panel's recommendation for the Manukau Scheme on lines very close to the Drainage League's concept. All sewage was to be treated in a plant on the shores of the Manukau and in four oxidation ponds lying between Puketutu Island and the mainland near Ihumatao. A high-quality effluent was expected. Treatment would comprise pre-aeration and grit removal, primary sedimentation, oxidation by trickling filters as required and recirculation through the extensive oxidation ponds, some 550 hectares in area, before discharge to the harbour on the outgoing tide. Sludge from the sedimentation tanks would be digested, and captured methane gas used to generate electricity in dual-fuel engines, with excess generation being fed to the national grid.

Both Collom, who had worked alongside the panel, and Hicks supported the scheme. Other prominent personalities, including Arthur Dickson, the City Engineer, also welcomed this solution. A rearguard action was mounted by some local engineers, critical of the cost estimates and concerned with delay and with the unknown performance of such large-scale oxidation ponds. However, this failed to dampen widespread acceptance.

Scheme as adopted by Auckland Metropolitan Drainage Board.

Auckland Metropolitan Drainage Board

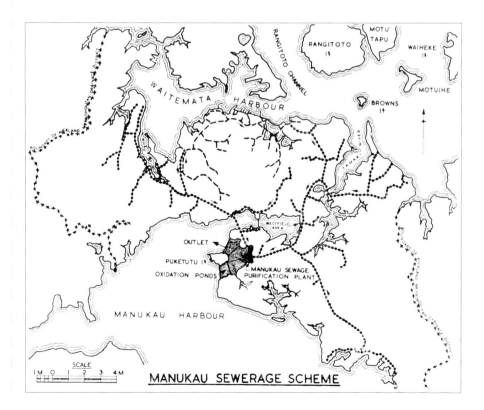

Brown and Caldwell, Consulting Civil and Sanitary Engineers of San Francisco, were appointed consultants for the treatment plant and pumping stations. Frank Kersner, one of the partners in the firm and well experienced in oxidation pond design, was later seconded from the firm as local resident design engineer and brought his family to Auckland.

Other parties caught the enthusiasm and, before the survey panel left in July 1954, Dr Caldwell visited Christchurch at the invitation of its Drainage Board and was later commissioned to design its new Bromley works.

At this time the writer had, at Rowntree's suggestion, applied for a Fulbright grant for post-graduate study in the USA and had been admitted to Harvard University to study for a Master of Science in Sanitary Engineering. Both Caldwell and Rawn from the overseas panel offered summer recess work in their organisations in San Francisco and Los Angeles respectively. Fellow students at Harvard insisted it be San Francisco and both the following summer and eight months subsequent to graduation were spent at Brown and Caldwell – the latter period working on the Bromley design with D. Leicester Steven FIPENZ, who had been seconded to the San Francisco office for this purpose by the Christchurch Drainage Board.

With adoption of its Manukau Scheme the board quickly employed extra staff and leased a pipe factory from Hume Industries Ltd so it could better control pipe production and costs for its interceptor sewer construction.

Charles Collom, then 47, whose quiet dignity had smoothed the pathways between board, staff and panel, was formally designated Chief Engineer, and things were reasonably harmonious throughout the junior level of board staff. However, there was some mistrust and prejudice at senior officer and board level between those who heartily endorsed the Manukau scheme and those who had expressed reservations or had openly favoured continuing with the Browns Island scheme. This atmosphere affected relations between some of the senior officers and board members and members of the panel, both Robbie and Caldwell being particularly dismissive of those who had expressed dissenting views or who had been intimately involved in the earlier scheme. This affected the career prospects of some senior officers, in particular Mynott being shunted to a largely nominal administrative position and Rowntree, while retaining the title of Designing Engineer, confined to being in charge of the design of the sewer system required for the adopted scheme while the more prestigious work of designing the treatment works and pumping stations was under the separate direction of Frank Kersner, the seconded American design engineer, designated Design Engineer (Special Works).

Collom ensured the scheme got off to a rapid start by prioritising design of sewer tunnel sections, which required less design but took longest to construct.

Work began in November 1955, the first contract for the Hillsborough section of the main western interceptor being awarded to Etude et Enterprises in compensation for the abandoned Browns Island works. The tunnel itself was the largest single local body project undertaken to that time. It was 3.2 kilometres in length at an average depth of 50 metres, large enough to accommodate a narrow-gauge railway with a battery-operated loco to haul the wagons of spoil loaded by the EMCO B12 rocker shovel at the tunnel heading. The tunnel face was broken down by manual drilling and explosives. The tunnel was progressively backfilled after the laying of the 1350 millimetres diameter concrete sewer pipe.

The oxidation pond method of treatment was lauded, and endorsed when, in March 1957, the North Shore Drainage Board chose oxidation ponds as the basis of its system.

On the downside were the rising costs of the scheme, running 40 per cent above estimate. Critics looked to Robbie, who looked to the panel, which gave the excuse that misjudgements were made in translating Californian costs to local work.

Meanwhile, on the political front, Robbie pushed for an elective board, more directly responsive to the public. On his badgering, the board sought but failed to obtain parliamentary approval, amid suggestions that he desired this to ensure he retain permanent chairmanship of the board. He resigned in protest on 8 November 1956 (one day prior to the writer's return from the United States – so little of the political shenanigans had changed!).

The local body elections which followed in March 1957 saw only one United Independent, Professor Cumberland, appointed to the board and the chairmanship pass to Clive Johns. The conduct of the political parties in making such appointments was manifestly unfair and the press decried that 'Robinson's unmatched knowledge has been brushed aside'. He was further humiliated at the November 1958 celebration unveiling the foundation tablet for the treatment plant when he was not invited to speak.

Robbie fought back politically, indeed winning election as mayor in 1959, even if only narrowly, as a candidate of the Civic Reform party. He wanted a seat on the Drainage Board and chairmanship, Johns having failed re-election as mayor of Mt Eden, but the new board accorded the honour to 78-year-old Thomas Bloodworth as a gesture to his four decades of local government service. Robbie failed even to get elected vice-chair.

The Manukau Wastewater Treatment Plant was switched on at dawn on 24 September 1960 by the Honourable Thomas Bloodworth. The writer, now having progressed to the position of Design Engineer (Special Works) indicated which button the Board Chairman should push to start the pumps at the Orakei Pumping Station to divert the flow to Mangere.

Problems soon arose – the smells that Calvert thought could arise from such large ponds had hardly begun to annoy local residents when the midge *Chironomus zealandicus* arrived en masse. The fact residents were assured, and indeed knew, that midges predated the construction of the plant did nothing to improve their Christmas of 1960.

A 700-strong meeting of Mangere residents threatened to withhold the area's levy to the board. Caldwell returned in March 1961 at the board's request (and Robbie's personal expense) and addressed a public meeting of some 500, assuring it that he retained confidence in the pond system once it settled down and that providing sludge lagoons would alleviate odours from temporarily malfunctioning sludge digesters. He departed – as did the summer conditions conducive to midge breeding, for a season.

Summer of 1961–62 was very trying for the board, with calls for a Ministry of Health inquiry from the Manukau County Council. The third summer, 1962–63, saw the problem lessen at Mangere, but midges struck in such swarms at the 43-hectare ponds of the North Shore Drainage Board's new plant at Rosedale Road that there were serious proposals to dispense with its ponds.

Dr Donald Spiller, an entomologist with Department of Scientific and Industrial Research, was employed to study the midge problem at Mangere. With the dredging of the ponds to a minimum depth of one metre, at which depth there is insufficient light to foster midge emergence, and with increase in biochemical loading to the ponds, both midge and smells abated. Nonetheless a commission of inquiry was set up, reporting in January 1965. By this time

John Fitzmaurice, Design Engineer (Special Works); Vince Taylor, Plant Engineer; Dr Dave Caldwell and Ron Hicks, Chief Chemist and Plant Superintendent, 18 April 1961.

NZ Herald

the Drainage Board had formally wound up (in March 1964), its functions transferred to the Auckland Regional Authority which came into being on 1 April 1964. To its credit, the board was one of the few ad hoc local bodies to willingly do so – perhaps in view of its past tribulations it was pleased as well as willing.

Mynott believed the consensus among staff employed by the board was in favour of the Manukau Scheme. Collom, who had ably carried out the task of translating the panel's proposals to reality, also supported this view, believing cost escalations would have applied equally to the Browns Island scheme. Hicks's continuing skill as Treatment Plant Superintendent, until he retired in 1972, was needed to keep the ponds functioning satisfactorily.

What have been the long-term outcomes of the Manukau Scheme and its proponents, the Drainage League? First, there were dramatic improvements in the water quality of both the Waitemata and Manukau harbours, even with loadings to the plant that greatly exceeded expectations.

The legacy of the Drainage League is that both the Auckland and North Shore systems are based on oxidation ponds, as are the Bromley works in Christchurch and many other community treatment systems. In fact, by 1986, 98 communities in New Zealand with populations greater than 1000 were being served by oxidation ponds.

A wonderful side benefit was bestowed on Auckland's scheme by the offer of past chairman, now Sir Ernest Davis, to purchase Browns Island from the Drainage Board and donate it as a gift to the citizens of Auckland.

Another gift to Auckland as a consequence of the drainage controversy was Robinson's six-term tenure as mayor, a total of 18 years' service to the city.

The scheme also enhanced the careers of many engineers who worked for the Drainage Board on the Manukau Scheme. These include the fiery ex-railways Construction Engineer, greatly feared by contractors, John Dow; R. (Bob) Gilmour MC MNZIE, his assistant; M. R. (Murray) Sargent, who became general manager of the Auckland Regional Authority; Vince Taylor, resident engineer during plant construction; J. D. (John) Moss, later of Brickell Moss Partners; Gordon Mills and Geoff Woodward, later to be Murray North Partners and Bill (Willie) Orr, later New Lynn Borough Engineer. The writer and Leicester Steven of Christchurch went on to form the consulting engineering practice of Steven, Fitzmaurice and Partners.

Notable among contractors involved with the scheme other than Etude et Enterprises, were Wilkins & Davies Construction Co. Ltd and mechanical sub-contractors Mason Bros Ltd on construction of the plant proper; New Zealand Earthmovers Ltd on oxidation pond embankment construction; and Green & McCahill Ltd on trunk sewer construction.

The plant operated satisfactorily over the next 20 years, although requiring close attention to both pond loading and midge control. These ponds were the largest in the world in full-time service, only some industrial ponds treating seasonal agricultural wastes being larger. Although a cheap and efficient treatment system – some four times cheaper in energy consumption alone, apart from economic construction, than orthodox land-based secondary treatment facilities – their very size made the need for close control critical.

With insufficient organic loading the ponds developed blooms of blue-green algae. These gave off offensive odours when die-off occurred in cooler autumn weather. Low loading also encouraged midge breeding, midges preferring a slightly polluted environment. On the other hand high organic loading could utilise all the oxygen produced by the photosynthesis of the algae, causing the ponds to go anaerobic, again causing odour. Apart from monitoring load, various stratagems were introduced to control algae: a jet-boat was used to break up algae mats, and later mechanical mixers were installed in the ponds to enhance circulation and so maintain oxygen levels.

However, progressive increased loading to the plant required a major increase in the land-based facilities. In 1974 the regional authority commissioned a report by Caldwell Connell (an Australian affiliate of Brown and Caldwell) which recommended replacement of the rock-filled trickling filters with nine large, high-capacity, plastic-media Fixed Growth Reactors.

A nation-wide depression in the mid-seventies meant money was scarce and industrial growth slowed down so that, in the event, only four reactors were built.

Chief and Principal Officers, Auckland Metropolitan Drainage Board, 1963. *Left to right*: R. Gilmour, L. G. Smith, J. R. P. Lee, M. R. Sargent, W. V. Clay, R. J. Franklin, H. S. Bunby, C. C. Blow Secretary, C. C. Collom Chief Engineer, J. Allen Treasurer, W. L. Mynott, R. Hicks, D. Spiller (DSIR), J. R. Fitzmaurice, E. H. M. Adams, K. Burke, R. M. Duckworth, Absent: J. B. Rowntree.

Sparrow Industrial

The Fixed Growth Reactors were cylindrical concrete structures, about the same diameter (53.3 metres) as the trickling filters but about five times their height. Each contained about 34 million small plastic media units. These polypropylene spoked rings, 97 millimetre diameter by 51 millimetre depth, were random-packed into each reactor. Provision was made for both natural and, if needed, forced ventilation of the reactors. With such aeration, primary effluent applied to the reactors would be purged of dissolved and colloidal impurities by the zoogeal growth that would build up on the media.

Overall design of the upgrade was undertaken by Caldwell Connell and local consultants Beca Carter Hollings and Ferner. The main contractors were Bitumix Ltd and McMillan and Lockwood. The latter firm was familiar with such undertakings, having built both the Palmerston North Sewage Treatment Plant designed by Brown and Caldwell and D. L. Steven, and the City of Hamilton Water Pollution Control Plant designed by Steven & Fitzmaurice. McMillan and Lockwood even persuaded the Auckland Regional Authority, now owner of the plant, to accept an alternative design for the reactors, utilising a free-standing post-tensioned prestressed cylinder on a sliding base in lieu of wall panels fixed to the base slab. Construction was complete by 1981 at a cost of $92.5 million.

A minor but interesting controversy arose regarding the media used in the Fixed Growth Reactors. The supply contract was awarded to AHI Chemical Engineering Services for Filterpak media, as marketed in the USA by Mass Transfer Inc. Because of the volume required, valued at $5.4 million, AHI set up a local manufacturing plant. Strict import control was in force at this time and so when similar Fixed Growth Reactors (FGR) were proposed for extensions to the Bromley Plant in Christchurch, AHI opposed the importation of Flocor. This was a modular crate-type plastic media favoured by the writer's practice, which had the design commission, because of its more open structure with less propensity to blockage. Only strenuous appeal at government ministerial level won the approval to import the media which was shipped in flat sheets and assembled into its crate form locally.

Gradual and progressive settlement and compaction of the random media in the Auckland reactors caused poor drainage and ponding of the applied primary effluent. Also unforeseen was the undesired efficiency of the tower-like structures in stripping out odours, which were inherent in the trade wastes that flowed into the plant from industrial sources as diverse as meat wastes to fertiliser manufacture. These odours were serious enough to require later covering of the FGR units. The direction of the forced ventilation was then reversed and extracted air passed through the original rock trickling filters for odour removal. Precedents for these types of plastic media fixed-growth reactors at Sacramento and San Pablo in California experienced more consistent wastes, predominantly from the cannery industry, than those locally; although the Sacramento plant eventually had to cover its reactors.

The Christchurch plant at Bromley experienced similar odour troubles, although without effluent ponding because of the more open media, and had to resort to a similar response.

Auckland's growth continued, as did the wastewater load to the treatment plant. By 1987 the plant was treating a tributary population of 630,000, with an industrial and commercial load equivalent to an additional 700,000. In 1987 the Works Committee of the Auckland Regional Authority commissioned an Auckland Area Sewerage Study to undertake a review of options for alternative discharges into the Kaipara Harbour, the Waikato River and the Hauraki Gulf, as well as forest irrigation and effluent reuse.

Manukau Sewage Purification Works after covering of fixed growth reactors.

Courtesy Watercare Services

The study recommended retaining the existing Mangere plant but adding a piped outfall to the Tasman Sea, with an initial discharge point in the Papakura Channel in the Manukau Harbour. The Tasman Sea outfall was formally adopted by the Authority in 1990, but not without the usual Auckland public controversy and, following the introduction of the Resource Management Act in 1991 with its heavy emphasis on consultation, the outfall scheme was abandoned.

Since local government reorganisation in 1989 the plant has been owned and operated by Watercare Services Ltd, a local council organisation, and renamed the Mangere Wastewater Treatment Plant. Watercare recognised that a major plant upgrade was going to be necessary as a consequence of poor pond performance and potential future loading to the plant. It embarked on an extensive public consultation programme in planning the upgrade of the treatment plant and took the approach that it would implement the most desired outcome the consultative process identified. Wastewater 2000, as the consultative process was styled, culminated in Project Manukau.

Project Manukau has seen the progressive removal of the oxidation ponds and their treatment capacity replaced by nine large BNR (biological nitrogen removal) activated-sludge reactor-clarifiers. Each 'doughnut-shaped'

Mangere Wastewater Treatment Plant before oxidation ponds decommissioning.

Courtesy Watercare Services

Mangere Reactor-Clarifiers.

Courtesy Watercare Services

reactor-clarifier comprises an inner 52 metres diameter circular clarifier surrounded by peripheral aerobic and anaerobic activated sludge compartments. Overall diameter is 78 metres and water depth 7.7 metres. Each sits on a concrete base of 1100 metres cubed volume, formed in one pour.

Other process changes and upgrades to effluent quality include influent milli-screening, sand filtration of effluent and ultraviolet disinfection. The effluent is held in a storage basin for discharge on the outgoing tide. Improved capture and treatment of solids includes primary-sludge gravity thickening, centrifuge sludge-dewatering and lime stabilisation. Sludge lysis (ultra-sonic vibration to release moisture) was also added for a time, but its use has been discontinued, as it was found to be ineffective.

Some residual midge problems remain with the open effluent channel and the effluent storage basin, but the upgrade has considerably reduced both midge and odour complaints. There has been a marked improvement in harbour water quality, particularly in bacteriological terms, and the foreshore area previously used by the ponds has been returned to recreational use.

The exposed nature of the effluent channel and, particularly, the effluent storage basin met the desire of Maori for 'contact with the earth' before discharge. However, these shallow, slightly polluted, fresh water areas are ideal for midge-breeding, necessitating control by chemical spraying. To eliminate the on-going cost of midge control, Watercare intends direct discharge to permanent harbour waters, so removing the midge habitat.

The Project Manukau upgrade to the Mangere Wastewater Treatment Plant became fully operational in terms of its resource consents in October 2003 at a cost of $460 million. It was a sign of the times that the community's environmental aspirations superseded concern over costs – a vastly different attitude to the frugality of the previous 150 years.

Project Manukau was executed under a 'design and build' contract by Manukau Wastewater Services, an alliance between CH2MBeca (design), Fletcher Construction and Civil & Civic (construction) and New Zealand Water Services (operations training). An interesting aspect of the project was the letting of the contract for construction on the basis of a 'Black Box', in other words, no design or construction plans were identified at the time of tendering. The effects-driven consents issued under the Resource Management Act required management plans alone portraying the detailed execution of the project to achieve the desired outcome.

Mangere Wastewater Treatment Plant after upgrade.

Courtesy Watercare Services

An outcome greatly valued by Tangata Whenua and the specific Maori interests of Tainui, the Huakina Development Trust and the local Makaurau Marae was the return of the area once occupied by the oxidation ponds to the sea, enabling restoration of fishing and foreshore use that had been denied them for the previous 44 years.

At the ceremony addressed by the Prime Minister, Helen Clark, to mark the completion of the project on 4 April 2003, the chairman of Watercare Services, Graeme Hawkins, alluded to the fact that the consents were issued without appeal and proclaimed it 'a triumph for the consultative process'. The Manukau mayor Sir Barry Curtis described it as 'a classic example of the much maligned Resource Management Act working very successfully to enable the community to achieve social and environmental goals'.

Also worthy of accolade are the dedicated treatment plant superintendents who, with one eye on the stability of the oxidation ponds, ensured the safe and efficient working of the plant through its operational history, especially when 'hot' refurbishments were under way. These were extensions being constructed while keeping the plant performing, as occurred in 1979–1981 and again in 2000–2003. It is not widely appreciated that a sewage plant is a 24-hour / 7-day operation, with no pause, even in the small hours of the morning or possibility of shut-down for maintenance. The chronological roll call of these men, some

Demolition commenced on the Hobson Bay sewer on 10 June 2010.

J. R. Fitzmaurice

engineers and some scientists, reads Ron Hicks, Theo Roland, Peter Welsby, Kevin McGiven, Ross Bauld, Les Jones, Peter Orr, Alan Harrison, Frank Lewis, Robin Lewis, Mike McCoy, Erle Robinson and Allan Twinch. Acting superintendents who ran the plant pending permanent appointments include David Blow, son of the earlier Secretary to the Drainage Board, Dave Woods, and Sanjay Kumarasingham.

An appropriate footnote to this historical survey of Auckland wastewater is the retirement of the Hobson Bay Sewer. Watercare's preference was for the sewer, in urgent need of repair, to be strengthened by encasement. Set as it was on piles above the high tide mark, this option would also provide a public walkway on top of the sewer. However, following public consultation a tunnel under the bay all the way to a deepened Orakei Pumping Station in Okahu Bay was chosen. It is 3.7 metres in diameter, concrete lined and three kilometres in length. Not for this tunnel the tedious and dangerous exposed-face drilling and blasting used in the original tunnels for the scheme, such as had been used for the Hillsborough section of the Western Interceptor. A purpose-built, completely enclosed, full-face tunnelling machine was imported for the project – named and blest *Te Kaha* ('The Strong One') by the local Ngati Whatua O Orakei in the presence of the Mayor of Auckland, the Hon. John Banks.

Te Kaha holed through successfully in February 2009 and when the old sewer was removed in 2010, at the completion of Project Hobson, it had served for 98 years. Would the Romans have demolished it?

References and further reading

Auckland Regional Authority, *Auckland Area Sewerage Study*, Summary Report, August 1987.

Brochure for Unveiling of the Foundation Tablet for the Manukau Sewage Purification Works, 1 November 1958.

Bush, G. W. A., *Decently and in Order: The Centennial of the Auckland City Council*, Collins, Auckland, 1971.

Bush, Graham, *Moving Against the Tide: the Browns Island Drainage Controversy*, Dunmore Press, Palmerston North, 1980.

Bush, Walter E., *The Main Drainage of Auckland, New Zealand Paper 4331*. Minutes of Proceedings ICE 1920/2, page 131 et seq.

Collom, C. C., *The Manukau Sewerage Scheme, Auckland*, New Zealand Engineering, Vol. 12, No. 2, 15 February 1957.

Collom, C. C., *Construction and Operation of the Manukau Sewerage Scheme, Auckland, New Zealand*. Proc Inst Civ Engrs Vol 27, 703–738, discussion Vol. 31, pp 94–114, 1964.

Commission of Inquiry: Report into Alleged Nuisances in Auckland Metropolitan Drainage District, R. E. Owen, Government Printer, 1965.

Fitzmaurice, J. R., *Municipal Wastewater Disposal in New Zealand*. IPENZ Transactions, Vol 14, No 1/CE, 1987.

Fitzmaurice, J. R., *Pumping Stations in the Manukau Scheme*, NZ Engineering, 18 (11): 405–17 (1963).

Harper, T. N., *Design of the Manukau Sewage Purification Works extensions*, IPENZ Transactions Vol. 10, No. 3/CE, 1983.

Sewerage and Drainage of the Auckland Metropolitan Drainage District New Zealand, Majority Report and Minority Report, AMDB, 30 June 1956.

Sewerage and Drainage of the Auckland Metropolitan Drainage District New Zealand, Summary report of Drainage Panel, AMDB, 1 July 1954.

The History of Wastewater Treatment in Auckland – Information Sheet, Watercare Services Limited (Undated – *circa* 2000).

Watercare Services Limited, *Project Hobson – Replacement of the Hobson Bay Sewer with a Wastewater Tunnel under Hobson Bay and Orakei Ridge, Project Description and Assessment of Environmental Effects*, March 2004.

2.3

North Shore Sewerage

by
John Fitzmaurice

Beginnings

Initial sewer construction in the North Shore area of Auckland was undertaken by the various local boroughs. Sewer reticulation began about 1908 in southern Devonport and shortly after in Northcote. The northern parts of Devonport and parts of Stanley Point were reticulated between 1920 and 1925. Reticulation of the southern areas of Takapuna commenced in 1928 and gradually extended northwards in the following years. Reticulation of Birkenhead started in 1936, in the Chelsea Bay catchment.

These local sewer systems discharged at the harbour foreshore with minimum, if any, treatment. The original sewers were 'combined' sewers conveying both sewage and stormwater. This was the norm at the time because of the need to flush away horse droppings on roadway surfaces and household yards. Discharge from the Devonport system occurred at North Head through a short outfall from holding tanks; from Northcote at Shoal Bay; from Birkenhead at Chelsea Bay through a 280 metre long outfall from a communal septic tank at the end of Brassey Road; from Takapuna through holding tanks at St Leonards Beach, and at Black Rock between Takapuna and Milford beaches.

There is evidence that the sewerage system local to Devonport was in fact designed as a 'separated' one, handling sanitary wastes only. Relatively good soakage in the volcanic soil areas of the borough meant that stormwater disposal at least through the piping network was not a priority. This is also borne out by the pipe sizes in the old system, which rarely exceeded 225 millimetres. Furthermore, with the flat gradients (there was virtually no pumping) sediment deposits would have quickly clogged the system.

Apart from Devonport, these communities were not intensively developed even as late as the forties and fifties; indeed some well-off Auckland families had summer holiday homes in Milford. This slow development is affirmed by the fact that, even as late as the year 2000, while 90 per cent of Devonport's sewers were over 60 years old, most of the sewers in other North Shore areas were less than 30 years old.

As time passed the boroughs of Devonport, Takapuna, Northcote and Birkenhead all developed separate but inadequate sewerage systems and separate administrations for wastewater services.

Escaping the Web

From the time of its creation in 1908 the Auckland and Suburban Drainage Board had nominal jurisdiction over all sewerage development in the area including the North Shore suburbs. However, on his return in 1931 from his extensive overseas tour of inspection of sewage treatment plants, H. H. Watkins, engineer to the board, proposed that the North Shore have separate treatment works, which he thought should be located north of Castor Bay.

This separation came to be the view of the North Shore boroughs, which objected to being included in the 1949 commission of inquiry hearings into the area of service of the Auckland and Suburban Drainage Board. Notwithstanding these views, the commission recommended inclusion of North Shore within the board's district. This led to the North Shore boroughs seeking control over their drainage affairs. In 1950 all of them, except Takapuna, which feared excessive rate rises, resolved to apply for their own drainage board.

However, by 1951 all four North Shore boroughs were unanimous in wanting their own separate drainage board and in the same year the North Shore Drainage Board was created. Mr E. J. Osborne, mayor of Birkenhead, was elected its inaugural chairman and R. P. Worley was appointed its first consulting engineer. The only condition the also newly formed Auckland Metropolitan Drainage Board required was that any North Shore scheme must not adversely affect the efficiency of its own proposed Browns Island Scheme (the controversial plan to build treatment works on Browns Island two and a half kilometres offshore, with discharge of screened and settled sewage to an outfall in the adjacent Motukorea Channel).

Designing the Scheme

The newly appointed consulting engineer, Ralph Worley, got to work and, in 1953, submitted two alternative schemes to the North Shore Drainage Board. No.1 scheme was an activated sludge plant in Wairau valley with an outfall to Hauraki Gulf; No.2 was four separate plants each serving different catchment areas of the North Shore. The first option was adopted. However, again Takapuna balked at the expense, and H. H. Vickerman, consulting engineer, and D. McDonald, an accountant, were employed to review costs.

Meanwhile the Wairau Valley treatment plant site zoning was changed, with the Northern Motorway centreline proclamation running through the proposed treatment plant. Alternative sites were investigated and, in 1957, the board finally adopted the Rosedale Road site.

Trickling filters and oxidation ponds were proposed for this site and Professor C. G. Hyde and Dr D. H. Caldwell, both of whom had been on the panel of overseas experts reporting on the Auckland scheme, endorsed this choice, recommending, however, that high-rate trickling filters be added at the outset rather than later.

The first contracts were let in 1958 and 1959. Initial construction was to serve only the Board's No.1 Area embracing the then urban zoning area of the Regional Planning Authority. Later extensions to the plant were to serve that part of Area No.2 which drained to the Albany Basin. A separate plant was intended for the Whangaparaoa Peninsula, to be sited in Okoromai Bay.

With the scheme underway, considerable development, to that time impeded by drainage restrictions, occurred on the North Shore – with the opening of the Harbour Bridge in 1959 greatly accelerating this development.

Scheme Description

Because of the plant being sited at quite a high elevation at Rosebank Road, inevitably the scheme involved considerable pumping; the two biggest pumping stations, PS No.5 in Wairau Road pumping to 52 metres above sea level and PS No.9 at Mairangi Bay having a 65 metre lift. This is a long-term disadvantage consequent on the compromised plant location.

Plant treatment processes, ably described in the paper by David Downey FIPENZ, by this time a principal in the engineering consultancy Worley Downey Muir and Associates, included primary sedimentation, biological oxidation with high-rate trickling filters and secondary sedimentation followed by 43-hectare oxidation ponds. Settled solids were digested in two-stage sludge digesters. The oxidation ponds were divided in two by the motorway, creating a primary pond and a smaller secondary pond, all in full motorists' view – and, incidentally, at motorists' expense, as the motorway embankment was constructed by the Ministry of Works, responsible for all highway construction at the time.

Effluent from the oxidation ponds discharged 600 metres offshore from Kennedy Park, between Campbells Bay and Castor Bay, at a water depth of 10 metres.

The sewage plant and motorway earthwork embankment dividing the oxidation ponds, early 1970s.

North Shore City photo, Courtesy Watercare Services

Plant development was intended in four stages, each for a design population of 40,000. The 1961 census population was 53,297, with future population predicted to rise to 185,000. Sewer reticulation involved over 43,000 metres of trunk sewers in trench and 7250 metres in tunnel, the largest sewer being 1330 millimetres in diameter.

The estimated cost of the scheme prior to construction was £2.6 million. The plant was officially opened in September 1962.

The sewage plant as it looked in 1962.

North Shore City photo, Courtesy Watercare Services

The scheme bore a strong resemblance to the Manukau Scheme of the board's southern neighbour – indeed, the treatment process train was identical. Another, annoying, similarity was the infestation of midges which, in the 1962–63 summer, struck in such swarms at the ponds of the North Shore Drainage Board's new plant that there were serious proposals to dispense with the ponds.

As plant loadings increased with time, the midge problem lessened – to be replaced by objectionable odours as loading to the plant began to exceed the capability of the ponds to oxidise the effluent from the land-based components of the plant. These odour problems became severe in 1977, hastening Stage 2 of the plant development, which duplicated the sedimentation tanks and trickling filter.

Stage 3, with a third primary sedimentation tank, filter and secondary sedimentation tank was added in the late 1970s. In the early 1980s the Stage 4 facilities, comprising the fourth primary and secondary sedimentation tanks, were installed. This stage completed the works originally envisaged for the ultimate development of the plant, except for the fourth trickling filter, intended for construction in the 1990–91 financial year.

All these developments were overseen by the North Shore Drainage Board, which operated from a fine, but now inconspicuous, brick building on the corner of Esmonde Road and Lake Road in Takapuna.

Mayor Paul Titchener presses the button for the official Stage 1 opening, September 1995.

North Shore City photo, Courtesy Watercare Services

1990 Appraisal and Project CARE

Local government reorganisation in 1989 saw the creation of the North Shore City Council and the demise of the North Shore Drainage Board. Michael Petricevich MIPENZ was the last manager and engineer to see service with the board in its old premises, all staff being transferred to the new City.

The City immediately commissioned consultants Beca Steven to undertake an appraisal of the performance of the sewerage collection and treatment system, and the needs of the system for the next 20 years. Their report highlighted the excessive organic load on the oxidation ponds as causing odour problems and the future need for a more appropriate discharge location than the near-offshore position off Kennedy Park. They were subsequently engaged to undertake an extensive oceanographic survey to determine an appropriate outfall length to avoid shoreline pollution. The consultant's reports form the basis for Project CARE, a $210 million, 20-year project to upgrade the treatment plant and achieve desired beach water standards.

Stage 1 of the Project CARE upgrade commenced in 1990 and was aimed primarily at taking the load off the oxidation ponds. Works comprised the construction of an activated sludge reactor with associated air blowers, together with a new secondary clarifier. Dissolved air flotation tanks to thicken collected sludge were also added. The works, designed by Woodward-Clyde and constructed by Downer Construction, were completed in 1995 at a cost of $11 million.

Project CARE Stage 2 provided additional sludge treatment capacity. The addition of two sludge digesters, and sludge dewatering and lime stabilisation of the de-watered sludge, enabled the retirement of the odorous on-site sludge lagoons used to that time. The works, designed by Beca Steven and constructed by Clearwater Construction, were completed in 1999 at a cost of $16.3 million.

Project CARE Stage 3 saw two further activated sludge reactors similar in size to the existing unit but with anoxic (no oxygen), aerobic and re-aeration zones configured as the Modified Ludzack Ettinger (MLE) process enabling reduction of effluent nitrates by direct removal of nitrogen. Two matching clarifiers were added. This extra treatment capacity enabled two-thirds of the organic load to be taken off the trickling filters, reducing smell and permitting them to be used as nitrifying filters and for the treatment of otherwise by-passed overflows in wet weather. The works, designed by URS and SKM and constructed by Downer Construction, were completed in 2001 at a cost of $25 million.

Stage 4 of Project CARE was started in 2002. Its main thrust was the provision of ultraviolet (UV) disinfection to inactivate any residual bacterial or viral contaminants in the discharge from the plant and remove hydraulic bottlenecks to increase the capacity of the MLE process. It also provided peak flow treatment capacity with the addition of a fourth clarifier and a chemically assisted sedimentation process. The UV unit is sited at the point of discharge from the secondary oxidation pond where pumped effluent is passed under powerful UV lamps before being discharged to the outfall pipeline. The four trickling filters, in service since the 1960s, have been removed, enabling construction of a bark-filled biofilter to remove odours ventilated from the sludge dewatering processes. The works, designed by SKM and constructed by Downers Construction and Fulton Hogan, were completed in 2004 at a cost of $34 million.

Stage 5 was officially opened by North Shore City Council Mayor Andrew Williams in May 2009, in conjunction with a public open day at the Rosedale Wastewater Treatment Plant. This upgrade provided improved inlet works

Official start to Stage 2 upgrade.
Left to right: Rob Lorden (Wastewater Manager, NSCC), Steve Singleton (Treatment Plant Manager, NSCC), Warwick Moulton (City Engineer, NSCC), North Shore Mayor George Gair, name unknown (Clearwater Construction), name unknown (Clearwater Construction), Councillor Bruce Lilley (Chairman Works and Environment Committee North Shore City (1996 or 1997).

North Shore City photo Courtesy Watercare Services

North Shore Treatment Plant as it looked in 2009.

North Shore City photo, Courtesy Watercare Services

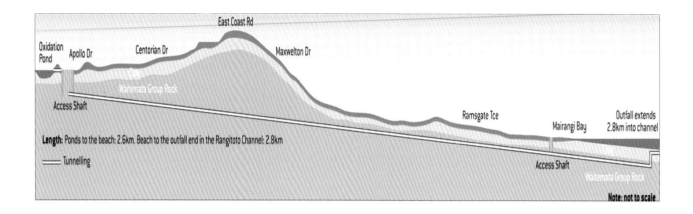

Oxidation Pond
Apollo Dr
Centorian Dr
East Coast Rd
Maxwelton Dr
Access Shaft
Clay
Waitemata Group Rock
Ramsgate Tce
Mairangi Bay
Outfall extends 2.8km into channel

Length: Ponds to the beach: 2.6km. Beach to the outfall end in the Rangitoto Channel: 2.8km

—— Tunnelling

Access Shaft
Waitemata Group Rock

Note: not to scale

Intended profile of outfall tunnel from plant.

North Shore City drawing, Courtesy Watercare Services

and primary sedimentation tank capacity. Added were a fourth 3 millimetre rotary screen, new vortex grit traps, improved screenings and grit handling facilities, two new primary sedimentation tanks and a new bark-filled odour biofilter. This upgrade was a 'design and build' contract costing $17 million, with CH2MBeca as the council's advising consultant and construction by contractor Fulton Hogan, whose design engineer was SKM Consultants.

In 2008 physical work started on a new $116 million tunnel and marine outfall for the Rosedale wastewater treatment plant discharge to replace the existing marine outfall, which was nearly 50 years old and had limited capacity. This consists of a tunnel, 2.8 metres in diameter, of 2600 metres length in the landward section and extending 600 metres seaward where it connects to a vertical shaft that, in turn, connects to a high density polyethylene pipe, 1.5

Full face tunnel boring machine for outfall construction, on display.

North Shore City photo Courtesy Watercare Services

metres internal diameter, trenched with one metre cover on the seabed to a point 2100 metres offshore. Here the plant effluent will discharge in a multi-pipe diffuser consisting of 'duck bill' valves on tees at six-metre spacing over the diffuser length of 300 metres.

     A public open day to demonstrate the full-face tunnelling machine used to drill the tunnel was held in November 2008. The tunnelling machine, stripped of working parts, remains at the seaward end of the tunnel, being used to form the connection to the vertical shaft leading to the seabed offshore pipe. Maunsell AECOM, into which Worley's firm had morphed, was the council consultant. The construction contractor was McConnell Dowell whose design engineer was Connell Wagner-DC Limited.

     In 2007 Steve Singleton MIPENZ, after many years of successfully guiding the treatment plant through numerous changes as the Rosedale treatment plant manager, became the group operation manager for water operations at North Shore City Council. Dr Paul Bickers, who had previously been the treatment plant process engineer, became the treatment plant manager.

North Shore City Mayor Andrew Williams with Plant Manager Bickers.

North Shore City photo, Courtesy Watercare Services

All these improvements represent considerable investment. The *New Zealand Herald* quoted Mayor Williams as saying, 'North Shore ratepayers have spent a fortune in the last decade to get the plant to a point where it has capacity for the next 50 years and the outfall pipe project to be completed in the next two years will give 100 years future-proofing for that plant.' At the time he was speaking, the government was proposing that North Shore City Council be assimilated into the then pending Auckland 'Super City'.

Auckland Council duly came into being in 2010, embracing North Shore City, and the Rosedale works came under the control of Watercare Services Ltd, a 'council organisation', within its North-western Wastewater Area.

References and further reading

Beca, Steven, *North Shore Sewerage Facilities. Engineering Review: Phase 1 – Preliminary Appraisal,* Report for North Shore City Council, 1990.
Downey, D. G., *North Shore Main Sewer Drainage System*, *Auckland,* New Zealand Engineering, Vol. 17, No. 2, February 1962, pp 49–56.
New Zealand Herald, 13 March and 20 May, 2009.

CHAPTER THREE

Harbour Development

The ports of Auckland and Onehunga were established in the early 1840s when the Auckland Harbour was becoming a busy scene. Shipping and commerce included not only the sailing ships of the Europeans but also canoes, even the great war canoes – laden not with weapons but with potatoes, onions, pumpkins, kumara and fresh fish. It had not taken Maori long to recognise the value of commerce. The need for a pier or wharf was manifest, as the existing foreshore was muddy, slippery and unsuited to the increasing volume of goods and cargo.

Auckland is situated on a narrow isthmus between two large harbours, the Waitemata on the east coast and the Manukau on the west. A port was constructed at each harbour, the distance between them being nine kilometres. The Port of Onehunga on the Manukau Harbour is 100 nautical miles closer to Sydney and over 200 nautical miles closer to Wellington and the eastern South Islands ports. However, it has a notorious bar at its entrance which allows ships only of shallow draft to enter safely. New Zealand's worst shipwreck occurred on this bar. HMS *Orpheus*, a 1,700 ton Royal Navy corvette, screw and sail propelled, was totally wrecked on striking the bar on 7 December 1863, losing 189 people. Notwithstanding its dangers, until there was a reliable road and rail link between Auckland and Wellington, the Onehunga Port was used extensively both for passengers and cargo. The passenger service through this port ceased in 1930 but it continues to be used by coastal ships for cargo.

In 1840 Governor Hobson moved the capital of New Zealand from the Bay of Islands to Auckland. Captain Rough was appointed Harbourmaster and Superintendent of Works. He was instructed by Governor Hobson, together with the Surveyor-General, Felton Mathew, to carry out a survey of the Waitemata Harbour in order to select the most suitable site for the port. Northcote Point (the northern abutment of the Auckland Harbour Bridge)

3.1

Development of Auckland Ports

by Les Jones

was originally called Rough Point after this harbourmaster, until in 1848 the name was changed to Stokes Point in honour of Captain Stokes of the survey vessel HMSV *Acheron*.

The first boatloads of immigrants to arrive at Auckland landed in October 1842 on board the *Duchess of Argyle* and the *Jane Gifford*.

The boat-building industry commenced in Freemans Bay about this time.

However, it was not until 1851 that the first public pier was constructed in Mechanics Bay. This was Wynyard Pier, a structure 150 metres in length; but not to be confused with the later Wynyard Wharf, well to the west. It was named after Lieutenant Colonel Robert H. Wynyard, who was the commander of the military forces in New Zealand from 1851 to 1858. From 1853 to 1855 he was the elected superintendent of Auckland Province.

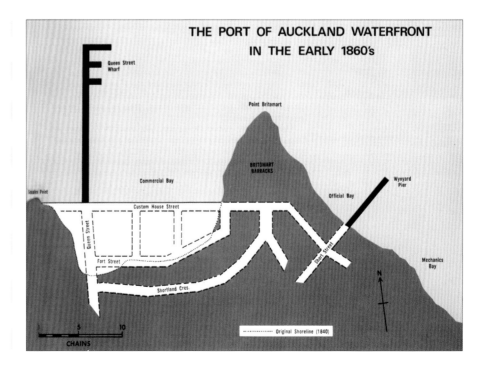

Following the construction of Wynyard Pier, in 1852, work commenced on Queen Street Wharf.

By early 1860, as can be seen in the adjacent diagram, reclamation of the mudflats in Commercial Bay had commenced, and Queen Street Wharf had become the main wharf. By 1864 it had been extended to 470 metres in length. By 1871, it was recognised that there was a need for formal management of the harbour. Consequently the Auckland Harbour Foreshore Act was passed by the Provincial Council, establishing the Auckland Harbour Board and granting the board 2,000 hectares of seabed for reclamation. At the board's first meeting, members were told that the Queen Street Wharf was very dilapidated, unsafe and the water too shallow at low tide for the new steamers. Accordingly a new timber wharf was built that was longer and wider.

Bean Rocks Lighthouse

The Bean Rocks Lighthouse is situated on the edge of the main shipping channel in the entrance to Auckland Harbour and is the only surviving wave-washed, wooden cottage-type lighthouse in New Zealand. Mr P. Bean was the master of the vessel carrying out the survey of the harbour in 1840. The Maori name for the rocks is Te Toka a Kapetaua after Kapetaua, who was marooned on the rocks by his brother-in-law.

The lighthouse was designed initially by James Balfour who was tragically drowned at Timaru in 1869. The work was completed by James Stewart and the lighthouse constructed in 1870. For the next 41 years the light was powered with kerosene and required a resident keeper. In 1912 the kerosene light was changed to an automatic acetylene light and consequently the resident keeper was no longer required. At this stage it was changed from a fixed light to a flashing light by using the pressure generated by the burning acetylene to revolve the reflector.

In 1936 a more powerful electric light was installed with an undersea power cable running from the Orakei wharf.

By the 1980s the lighthouse was in a very poor condition. The iron fittings had corroded and the kauri legs and beams were full of rot. The Auckland Harbour Board decided that it should be replaced with either a statue of religious significance or a worthwhile sculpture. After the board engineer pointed out the historical significance of the structure, the decision was reviewed and approval was granted to repair it. The house section was lifted off using the harbour board crane and taken ashore for renovation. New concrete foundations were constructed and the legs replaced with Australian hardwood.

The lighthouse is once again in service but is now powered by solar panels.

Bean Rocks Light House, 1909.

Auckland Graving Dock

By 1876 the Auckland Harbour Board had decided that a dry dock should be constructed. William Errington, the engineer who designed the Western Springs Water Supply Pumping Station, was contracted to design a graving dock just west of Queen Street. A graving dock (or dry dock) is a dock which, once a ship has entered, is then closed to the sea and pumped dry while the ship remains supported by timber bearers under the keel and props along the ship's sides. To 'grave' is to clean a ship's hull below the waterline. The dimensions of the dock were 90 metres long, 20 metres wide and 4 metres below Mean Low Water. Construction began in 1876. Initially the stone for the dock came from Melbourne but after criticism from the public local stone was tried. However, the local quarries couldn't match the required demand rate and so, once more, Melbourne stone was used. The dock was finally handed over to the Auckland Harbour Board in August 1878, two years and four months after construction began.

The entrance to the dock was closed using a sliding iron caisson, which could be floated into position and then sunk. The water below the low-water level was then pumped out using steam-driven pumps. Even during construction some members of the public were arguing that the dock was too short, too shallow and in the wrong position. This criticism proved to be correct and within a few years William Errington's services were again employed in designing a new dry dock on the North Shore.

Auckland Graving Dock with barque *Margaret Galbraith*, 1878.

Sir George Grey Special Collections, Auckland Libraries 4-945

Calliope Dock

After the graving dock west of Queen Street proved to be too small, work commenced on Calliope dock, on the North Shore, in December 1884. The length of this dock, after a couple of extensions, was 173 meters, making it the largest in the Southern Hemisphere. The entry width was 24 meters and the depth over the sill was 10 metres.

The project was very large for the relatively small Auckland town and took more than three years to build. Maori labourers could see that many years of work were involved and so whares for accommodation were built on the western abutment. Excavation for the dock was dug by hand and 300 labourers were employed. The structure required 1.5 million bricks and these were made locally. The cement used in the concrete came from England in barrels. The dock was officially opened in February 1888, with HMS *Calliope* and HMS *Diamond* both entering it with full pomp and ceremony.

The pumps for removing the water below the sea low-water level, like those of the previous dock, were steam driven, as were the winches and crane.

By 1899 the dock and associated wharf were in need of considerable maintenance and were under-used. The navy and shipping companies considered the workshop facilities to be inadequate and were going elsewhere. The Auckland Harbour Board negotiated a deal with the Royal Navy in which the navy would pay an annual subsidy on the condition that they had

Calliope Dock under construction, 1887.

Sir George Grey Special Collections, Auckland Libraries 4-3144

HMS *Calliope* and HMS *Diamond* in Calliope Dock for the opening ceremony, 16 February 1888.

Sir George Grey Special Collections, Auckland Libraries 4-2940

first call on the facilities. In return the board would upgrade and maintain the workshop facilities, upgrade the dock and associated wharf and provide 0.8 hectares (2 acres) of rent-free reclaimed land alongside the dock.

After the First World War the navy expanded its facilities in this area. By 1934 the Auckland Harbour Board had installed a mobile crane and workshops for engineers, carpenters, blacksmiths and painters. Garage, storage sheds, office and caretaker's house were also provided. In 1935 the dock was lengthened once again, to 185 metres, at the navy's request, to accommodate two large cruisers that had been ordered. The Royal New Zealand Navy paid for this extension. Eventually, on 26 February 1987, the navy bought the dock from the Harbour Board for $650,000.

Canal Proposals

Several canals were considered for the Auckland province from as early as the middle of the 19th century. Two were proposed to connect the Waitemata and the Manukau harbours. One followed the course of the Whau River south from the Waitemata to Karaka Bay on the Manukau Harbour, and the other from the headwaters of the Tamaki River through to the Manukau Harbour. Both routes were used for portaging canoes; hence the two existing 'Portage Roads' on these alignments.

A considerable amount of coal, grain and other agriculture products came to Auckland from the Waikato, and as the main trunk railway through the centre of the North Island was still to be completed, most of this cargo travelled down the Waikato River and was brought ashore several miles upstream of the river mouth, carried overland to Waiuku, and then transported by scow over to the Onehunga wharf. Accordingly, many businessmen also pushed for a canal to be dug between the Waikato River and Waiuku. When the main trunk railway was opened in 1908 the canals were placed much lower in public works priority lists, although the possibility of canals continued to be discussed until the latter part of the 20th century.

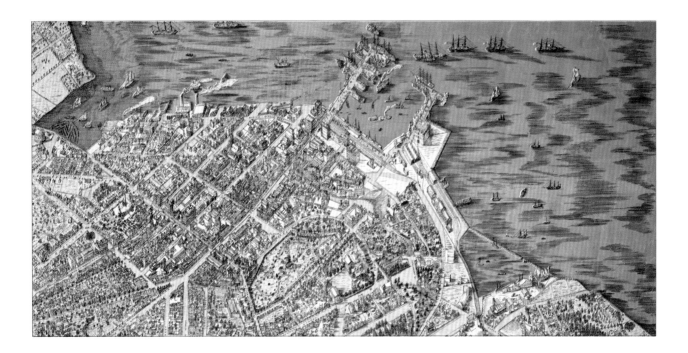

Further Wharf Development

In 1904, Mr. W.H. Hamer, the Auckland Harbour Board Engineer, formerly Resident Engineer of the London Dock Co., submitted a plan for the development of the Auckland Port which involved reclaiming large sections of Freemans Bay, Commercial Bay and Mechanics Bay. This proposal included eastern and western tide deflectors to minimise the currents around the wharves. Accordingly these structures had to be constructed out of solid fill. The three proposed new wharves were built at an angle to the foreshore and in the direction of the prevailing south-west wind to aid in the berthing of the ships.

His plan also included the replacement of the timber wharves with ones made of reinforced concrete. These would be strong enough to allow trains to go directly onto the wharves. Furthermore, the Auckland variety of the toredo worm was creating havoc with the timber piles. Even though Australian hardwoods were used, their life in New Zealand waters was very much shorter than in Australia. Accordingly, in 1903 the Harbour Board Engineer recommended that all future wharves be constructed in steel-reinforced concrete. As there was considerable opposition from some quarters to the use of steel in the marine environment, two small arches were constructed, one with steel reinforcing and one without. These arches were tested to destruction and proved beyond doubt that steel-reinforced concrete was the correct medium. The new Queens Wharf, built alongside the existing Queen Street Wharf, was constructed by Ferro Concrete Co. This was completed in 1913 and became

Perspective drawing of Auckland City in 1886, by George Tracy Stevens, who imagined he was 1,000 feet above Auckland Public Hospital.

Sir George Grey Special Collections, Auckland Libraries NZ Map 374

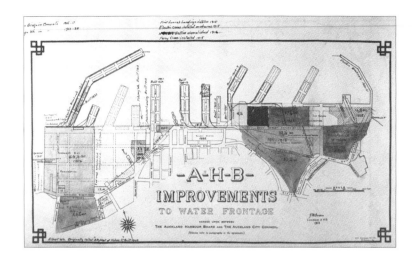

The Hamer 1913 plan for Auckland Harbour Board's improvements.

Sir George Grey Special Collections, Auckland Libraries 4-178

Freemans Bay reclamation in 1912.

Sir George Grey Special Collections, Auckland Libraries 1-W921

the main overseas passenger wharf for many years.

In 1913 the Federation of Labour was formed. Later in the year it declared a general strike that affected both the Wellington and Auckland wharves. This resulted in the government recruiting young farmers as special constables, known as Massey's Cossacks because they came to town riding their farm horses, to protect and work the wharves until the strike was called off.

During the period between 1904 and 1924, many new wharves were constructed. The growth in cargo and passengers was partly due to the fact that there was still no railway link north to Whangarei or east to Tauranga and the roads were often impassable.

Due to its high rainfall and a hilly terrain, New Zealand was very slow at constructing reliable roads between town centres. Consequently, most cargo, livestock and personnel were, for quite a period, carried around the coast by boat. The 'scow' type of vessel became very popular for this purpose, as it was flat bottomed and could enter tidal bays or rivers at high tide and then wait for low tide to load or unload. The increasing demand for wharf space created by these small boats arriving at Auckland Harbour resulted in a continuous programme of wharf construction.

It was also at this stage that Kings Wharf was built, although for a time it was known as Railway Wharf.

The installation of the five-tonne electric (direct current) cranes on the Auckland wharves commenced in 1910.

In 1913 it was decided to place both the ports of Onehunga and Auckland under the one controlling body. Accordingly the responsibility of the Port of Onehunga was transferred from the Marine Department to the Auckland Harbour Board.

In 1920 a new wharf at Auckland Port was designed by Harbour Board staff. This would be called Princes Wharf and would be positioned between

Hobson Wharf and the Ferry Tee. At this time BHP, the Australian mining and steel foundry company, was suffering from the effects of strikes, the high cost of coal and high wages, higher than in America or Europe. As a result, the company closed down several steel rolling mills. This caused long delays in the supply of reinforcing steel and, accordingly, the Board started ordering the steel for this project well in advance of letting a contract for construction.

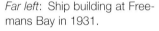

Auckland Harbour Board Offices, c. 1909, showing time ball on office roof.

Sir George Grey Special Collections, Auckland Libraries 35-R41

Construction eventually commenced in 1921. Whereas all previous wharves had single-story 'sheds' on them, Princes Wharf had a two-storey concrete structure. This was designed by board staff, using the column and flat slab technique. The structure was intended for 'break bulk' cargo (not in containers), with the weather-proof, light cargo being handled on the roof and heavier cargo being placed on the

Far left: Ship building at Freemans Bay in 1931.

Sir George Grey Special Collections, Auckland Libraries 4-4653

Left: Scow *Vixen* on Anniversary Day Regatta, 1907.

Sir George Grey Special Collections, Auckland Libraries 4-5541

lower floors. The wharf deck was designed to take a loading of 2.7 tonnes per square metre. The central road through the structure was lower than the deck level, providing a continuous 'cart dock' facility. The fifteen five-tonne electric direct-current cranes had one pair of legs sitting on a rail at the wharf edge, and the other pair placed on the roof.

During the Second World War, Princes Wharf was placed under the control of the American Armed Forces and used for provisioning the Pacific theatre. Records show that, in 1943, 104 warships and 284 transports used the wharf.

HMS *Hood* alongside Princes
Wharf in 1924.

Sir George Grey Special Collections,
Auckland Libraries 35-R38

Post War Developments

Deteriorating industrial relations led, in February 1951, to another strike by the
Waterside Workers Union. This resulted in a lockout. The government declared
a state of emergency and the army was used to unload ships. The dispute was
finally over on 15 July, with the waterfront union being de-registered and new,
separate unions being formed at each port.

   In the early 1950s, a new General Manager, Mr. A.C. Clarke, was appointed
to the Auckland Harbour Board from the Port of London. He sincerely believed
that the answer to ensuring the quick turn-around of ships lay in using 'lighters',
which would travel out to the ships anchored in the roadstead and ferry the
cargo ashore. At this stage most of the overseas cargo was in the form of wooden
cases, such as car cases or on pallets. Accordingly, 12 lighters were built at a
cost of $300,000. Each consisted of a dumb barge, i.e., a barge that is not able
to move by itself, with a hold that could contain approximately 200 tonnes. A
lighter basin was also constructed, which entailed excavating sandstone back
to Gaunt Street. The objective was to reduce the ongoing need for expensive
wharves, and instead deliver to points nearer industrial centres such as Te Atatu,
up the Tamaki River, and finally to Manukau Harbour, when and if a canal
was ever constructed to join the two harbours.

   This system proved to be very unpopular and was used only once: it was
inefficient due to high manpower requirements and slow speed and would be
acceptable only if, for some reason, no more wharves were to be built and ships
were lying at anchor awaiting berths. In Auckland's case wharves did continue
to be built and thus ships were unloaded on the wharves using the 5-tonne
electric cranes, which by this time numbered over 80.

Bucket Dredge working to deepen wharf berthage in 1904.

Sir George Grey Special Collections, Auckland Libraries 1-W1087

The depths beside the wharves had to be maintained as they tended gradually to silt up, and because ships with deeper draughts began arriving. This meant digging into sandstone, which was very slow work for the bucket dredge employed. The Harbour Board did most of the maintenance and some capital work with its own forces. For these purposes it had a large floating crane, a large bucket dredge and a cutter suction dredge. The cutter suction dredge was incapable of excavating in sandstone and was used only for removing accumulated silt.

The port Engineering Workshops (excluding container handling equipment) were housed at the eastern end of the viaduct basin. These included work areas for electrical needs, painters, a machine shop, boiler/blacksmiths and pattern shop. Castings were made on contract using the Harbour Board's patterns for everything from bollards to crane gear wheels. As at 2008, some of these buildings still exist but are now occupied by restaurants with offices above.

These workshops serviced the boats moored in the small marina at the eastern end of the viaduct basin. The marina housed the small tugs, towboats, workboats and 'transports' (floating platforms for such work as fender or wharf repairs, etc.). Most of the remaining area of the viaduct basin was quite shallow and used mainly by small fishing boats that unloaded their catch at Fisherman's Wharf, a small wharf running along the south side of the basin.

In the 1960s 'Roll on Roll off' ships [RoRo's] started visiting Auckland, both from other ports in New Zealand and from across the Tasman Sea. Because some had stern ramps, some of the wharves were modified to accept the ramps. Others had side ramps on their stern quarter and needed no modification of the wharves.

In 1960 the passenger facilities were transferred from Queens Wharf to

Princes Wharf. Later, in 1989, Princes Wharf was redeveloped into apartments, restaurants and a luxury hotel, the Hilton. This work, which revitalised one area of the waterfront, was carried out by Mace Development and included an upgrade of the facilities for the passenger terminal. Because of the magnitude of the new complex, holes were cut in the deck and new piles driven into the sandstone below in order to support the weight of the building.

In the early 1970s the British line P&O announced that it would start using shipping containers. In readiness for this, the Auckland Harbour Board undertook the construction of the Fergusson Container Terminal. Although this was completed in 1971, the first container vessel did not arrive until June 1973.

The container terminal operates 24 hours a day, 365 days a year.

Port Administration

In an effort to rationalise port development, the government had established the New Zealand Ports Authority in 1960. All major capital expenditure had to be vetted by this authority. However, other ports could present arguments to the authority as to why the application should be denied. This caused all sorts of problems and resulted in inappropriate expenditure. For example, in the mid 1980s the Auckland Harbour Board had two container cranes and wished to purchase a third. Because it could not gain approval for this, it hired a cheap crane that could handle containers, albeit slowly. This was poorly constructed, noisy and unreliable. As it was painted a very bright orange, it was known on site as the 'Orange Roughy'. When the Ports of Auckland was formed, the New Zealand Ports Authority was disbanded, and the Orange Roughy disappeared.

Ports of Auckland Ltd (POAL) was formed in 1988 with 80 per cent of the shares owned by the Auckland Regional Authority (later to become the Auckland Regional Council) and the remainder by the Waikato Regional Council. All assets of the Auckland Harbour Board were then transferred to POAL.

Up to this point most of the

First container crane.

Courtesy Ports of Auckland Ltd

maintenance had been carried out by the board's own staff. Under the new administration much of this work would be carried out by contract, and by 2008 the staff numbers reduced from approximately 1000 to 560 (full-time equivalents). The two dredges were sold off and most of the new dredging was contracted out. Contractors preferred to use powerful hydraulic diggers, with extension arms, mounted on barges. The land, buildings and wharves surrounding the viaduct basin had become dilapidated, and in 1996, POAL sold the land to Viaduct Holdings Ltd. This land was then made available to developers on long-term ground leases and has been developed into buildings with restaurants on the ground floor and offices and apartments above.

With the creation of the Auckland super city in 2010 the port company is now owned by Auckland Council Investments, an arm of the Auckland Council.

When the New Zealand yacht *Black Magic* won the America's Cup in 1995, it became obvious that the Viaduct Basin would have to be redeveloped to house all competitors in time for the defence of the Cup. This provided the much needed impetus to spend considerable sums and develop the whole area surrounding the basin, revitalising the waterfront and making it more of a 'people place'. A marina suitable for large yachts up to 50 metres in length was also developed, and the basin was deepened to accommodate the deep draught of the America's Cup yachts.

The Auckland Regional Council (the successor to the Auckland Regional Authority but with a different structure and responsibilities) had, by 2005, bought up all the remaining shares in POAL and these were then held by Auckland Regional Holdings, an Auckland Regional Council investment entity.

Recent Developments

By 2006 a total of five container cranes of the new generation were installed on Fergusson Wharf with sufficient reach, horizontally, to service 'Post Panamax' ships (ships too wide to pass through the Panama Canal). They were supplied by Zhenhua Port Machinery Company from China at a cost of NZ $9 million each. These cranes weigh 1,250 tonnes, are 103 metres high and have a boom length of 56 metres.

By 2008, POAL was dealing with 1,700 ship visits, handling four million tonnes of break bulk cargo (non-containerised) and 770,000 TEUs (20-foot equivalent unit) containers per year. This amounts to 50 per cent of the North Island trade and 37 per cent of New Zealand's trade. To increase efficiency, POAL also has two 'inland ports', at East Tamaki and Wiri, where containers are stored and sorted. The containers are shuttled to and from the seaport at night to avoid peak traffic.

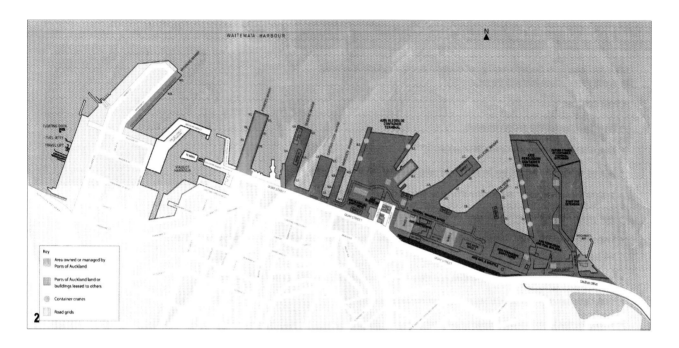

Above: Plan of waterfront in 2008.

Courtesy Ports of Auckland Ltd

Right: Container cranes working ships in 2007.

Courtesy Ports of Auckland Ltd

More than 70 cruise ships call each year.

By this time the shipping lane minimum depth had been increased to 12.5 metres and the radius on the curves had been increased to allow larger ships to use the port. The reclamation at Axis Fergusson Container Terminal is continuing, and when completed will add a further nine hectares to the terminal area.

Viaduct Rolling Lift Bridge

This interesting bridge was constructed for the Auckland Harbour Board in 1932 by the Cleveland Bridge and Engineering Co. at a cost of £23,000. It replaced a simple lifting pedestrian bridge and provided road and rail access to the Western Wharf (now the Wynyard Wharf) and to the board's tenants on the reclaimed land at Freemans Bay. A small 11 kilowatt electric motor provided all the power that was necessary to operate the bridge. The two-lane bridge had a waterway clearance of 15.25 metres and provided access for the fishing fleet and the board's plant.

There were vehicle barrier arms and large Stop / Go signs for the marine traffic. However, regardless of the signals, there were many accidents, including boats crashing into the bridge and cars into the barriers and trains into trucks. One small Morris car managed to climb up the ramp as it was opening and just made it to the other side, falling 2.5 metres as it did, badly damaging both the car and the driver.

In 1949 Australian termites were found in the bridge timbers and rapid action was taken. After the termites had been eradicated, the timbers were soaked in creosote.

The bridge was completely reconditioned in 1962 and was removed and overhauled once again in 1981. During the redevelopment of the viaduct basin a much wider entrance to the marina was developed further to the west. Since then the bridge has not operated and remains in the down position, being used for pedestrian and vehicular access to this section of the marina.

Auckland Ferry Building

In the early 20th century, ferry transport played a vital role in the social and commercial life of the city. Accordingly, the Harbour Board decided that a building to house the ferry companies

Rolling Lift Bridge.

Voyager New Zealand Maritime Museum, Q10

Alexander Wiseman design for
Auckland Ferry building
in 1909.

Auckland Council Archives ACC 015
Record No 3194/5

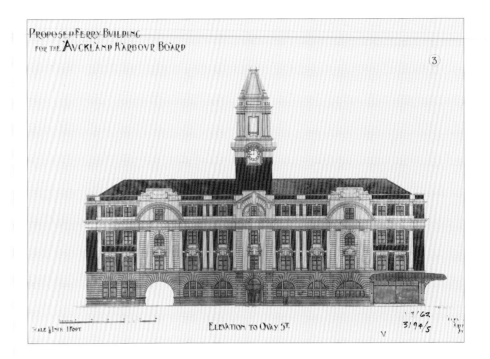

was required. This was one of the earliest Auckland buildings built entirely for lease. The original proposal was for a five-storey structure but this caused outrage, many Auckland citizens complaining that the view down Queen Street would be ruined. The press stated that it would 'seriously disfigure Queen Street'. Finally, agreement was reached on a building of four stories with a clock tower.

The base consisted of Coromandel granite and the building was faced with Pyrmont stone (a Sydney sandstone) and modelled on the Imperial Baroque style. It is said to be a scale model of the Port of San Francisco ferry building on the waterfront the Embarcadero. It was completed in 1912.

In 1982 a report stated that the building was substandard with regard to current seismic and fire codes. The estimated cost for the upgrading was $6.6 million. One prominent Harbour Board member was strongly of the opinion that if it could not be upgraded for less than $1 million, it should be pulled down. At this time the building did not have a heritage grading; but, even so, the public was strongly of the opinion that it should remain (it later received a B grading.)

As leases expired some board staff moved back into the premises. By 1982 the new Harbour Board building was complete and the staff withdrew from the Ferry Building. Proposals were called for redevelopment. Four were received and the one from Challenge Properties Ltd was accepted, with one of their conditions being that they had the leasing rights for 100 years. The proposal was based on installing an extra floor by utilising the original high stud and raising the roof a small amount above the existing parapet. The original roof trusses were to be used once again. The cost was estimated at $8 million.

The Governor General opened the upgraded building on 5 November 1988.

Wynyard Quarter (Tank Farm)

For many years Wynyard Wharf has serviced the area known as the 'Tank Farm', the main storage area in Auckland for liquids of all types prior to being exported, or after being imported. It was one of the main entry points for fuels until the fuel pipeline from Marsden Point to South Auckland was completed. Since then the oil companies have been gradually moving out as their mid- to long-term leases expire. The Auckland City Council is planning the staged re-development of this land to be a balance of public open space and private development.

Future Development

Over the next 15 to 20 years approximately 29 hectares of Auckland's waterfront within the Wynyard Quarter will be transformed, in stages, into a harbour-side community, with parks and plazas, apartments, shops and offices alongside the traditional marine and fishing industries. It is one of the largest waterfront urban renewal developments ever undertaken in New Zealand.

Proposed Wynyard development.

Courtesy Auckland Waterfront Development Agency, 3D artist's impression only, and subject to change over time.

North Wharf, which is a fishing-boat wharf immediately east of Wynyard Wharf and running parallel to the coast, has now been rebuilt as a working waterfront. The area will include a wide promenade, with seafood related eateries along its length.

There will be a public open space at the western end of Jellicoe Street with unobstructed views out to Westhaven and the Harbour Bridge. The 'six-pack' silos, as well as the single Golden Bay cement silo, are being retained in recognition of the area's industrial heritage, and people will be able to see elements of the marine industry at work from the water's edge. A large public plaza will be constructed at the eastern end of Jellicoe Street and a lifting bridge will connect this area with the viaduct basin. The Container Wharves and associated working wharves will continue to develop and present further engineering challenges to meet Auckland's future needs.

References and further reading

Blair, E. W., *Proposed Waitemata–Manukau Canal,* Auckland Harbour Board, 1908.
Rose, J., *Akarana: The Ports of Auckland,* Auckland Harbour Board, 1971.

CHAPTER FOUR

Roads and Motorways

Roads are important components of infrastructure, fundamental to civilisation and a reasonable standard of living. They are taken for granted and today we are accustomed to very smooth high-speed motorways and dust-free city streets. It has been aptly said that 'You pay for good roads and you pay more if you don't have them.'

Early Auckland roads were mud tracks on which scoria from the local volcanic cones was spread to improve wet weather access. Scoria was easily won by pick and shovel and transported by horse-drawn carts. The military method of 'corduroy' roads was also used, where muddy areas were covered with tree trunks and branches at right angles to the direction of the road.

Scoria roads gave rise to much complaint about dust, since the steel tyres of carts and steel shoes of the horses could crush the scoria to powder. Often shopkeepers watered the roads outside their shops to reduce this nuisance.

Roads

*by
Bryan Bartley*

Horse-drawn passenger coach in mud on Great South Road at Bombay in the 1870s.

Courtesy Howick Historical Society

Above: Horse and cart in Beach Road Parnell 1909.

Sir George Grey Special Collections, Auckland Libraries 1-W958

Right: Horses carting stone from Auckland City's Mt Eden quarry, 1907.

Sir George Grey Special Collections, Auckland Libraries 7-A1692

Below: Family outings could be difficult!

Courtesy Howick Historical Society

Loose metal (crushed rock) roads were used extensively throughout the country. They consisted first of a base layer of crushed rock of a depth appropriate to the loads to be carried. This layer was shaped and rolled (often by traffic) to high density and topped with a layer of smaller metal to form a wearing surface. Since these roads were prone to forming potholes and corrugations, regular maintenance from a grader to cut and reshape the surface was necessary. Such roads were common around Auckland until about the 1960s, when boroughs found that the capital costs of sealing roads was more economic than the continual costs of graders and road maintenance. Also, with increasing traffic from motorcars and trucks, the amount of dust was offensive as the standard of living was improving.

The earliest tar for sealing would have been imported, probably from Australia in barrels, which were opened by axes and upturned over heated tanks. Some tar or pitch was handled as lumps into the tanks. In the early 1860s the gas works was in production and tar was available as a by-product of gas production.

Road sealing required the use of harder stone than scoria, so quarries in the small basalt outcrops developed in many places, such as Mt Eden, Penrose and Mt Wellington. Hard-working Dalmatian immigrants from the gum fields up north were widely employed in this work and many sites carried their names even to the 1950s. Stone was blasted from a face, crushed by rock-crushing machinery and screened to sizes suitable for basecourse, concrete or road sealing chips.

Mt Eden Prison was involved in quarrying for road building; like many

gaols around the world prisoners cut kerbstones with heavy knapping hammers for city roads. Both the Auckland City Council and Mt Eden Borough had quarries near the gaol, as seen in the 2010 and 1920 photos showing the Auckland City Council quarry.

In the photo of a Rugby match above, the old quarry face on the left continued as the Colonial Ammunition Co. quarry, and is now an industrial site. The rest of the old quarry was converted to the playing field for Auckland Grammar School and separates the gaol from the school.

The first use of asphalt (a mixture of hot tar and stone chips that was spread on a road and rolled to a smooth surface) was in Queen Street at the time of building the tramway in 1902. Some roads were built with hardwood blocks used like cobblestones standing on end and bedded in tar with sand. Karanga-hape Road was built in this way.

Early roads followed English practice with a lot of hand placing of stones and Diagram 1 from a 1920s specification shows a section of such a road, and details the construction of the kerb and drainage channel along the side of a road. Note the use of scoria and the hand-placed stone or scoria rubble.

Above: Auckland City Council Mt Eden quarry in 1920.

Sir George Grey Special Collections, Auckland Libraries 7-A5701

Top left: Mt Eden quarry in 2010. The section has been converted into a sports field for Auckland Grammar.

B. Bartley photo

Above: Laying wooden block paving in Karangahape Road, c. 1909.

Sir George Grey Special Collections, Auckland Libraries 7-A119

Left: Diagram 1 showing 1920s kerb and channel detail.

B. Bartley

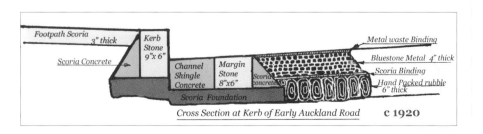

Many Auckland suburban roads started as loose metal roads as already described. As the standard of living rose tar-sealing would follow and later still, kerbs and channels and footpaths, often with grass verges, were added. Sealing started with the basecourse cleaned, shaped and rolled all true to line and level. Then followed a sprayed coat of tar or bitumen, on which was spread 30 to 20 millimetre stones from a moving truck. This layer was lightly rolled to bed the chips into the tar. A second coat was sprayed and covered by a layer of smaller chips, 19 to 12 millimetre grade, which were lightly rolled into the soft tar. In the city a finer layer of tar and chips or sand might be added to reduce noise and give a smoother surface.

Auckland basalt aggregates have special properties that are prized by the road-building contractors. First, the rock is hard enough to be strong and durable, but soft enough to crush under the steel wheels of a 10-tonne roller and lock into place quickly and easily. Secondly, basecourse from a crushing and screening plant has an abundance of fine particles, so locks in place easily. The sealing chips have good skid resistance properties.

Greywacke stone from the Hunua ranges is much harder to crush, having a particle strength up to twice that of the local basalt. It therefore requires more fine particles from the crushing machinery and breaks less under a roller. It has a lower skid resistance. This writer shared in the patents of a successful

Barmac Crusher.

B. Bartley

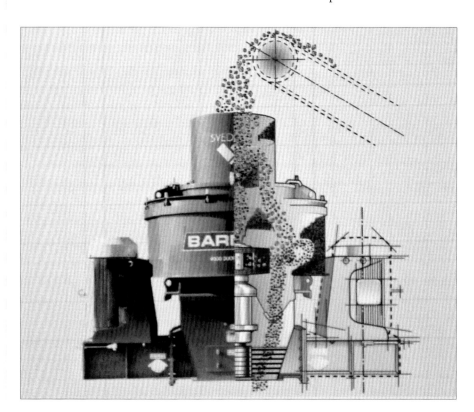

rock-crushing machine that breaks stone against stone, instead of stone against steel, and easily produces the sandy fines needed in a good greywacke base-course. It is called a Barmac Crusher.

Since 1950, machine-placed asphaltic concrete has progressively come to dominate the sealing of city main roads and motorways. Although more expensive than the traditional chip seals it is quick, accurate and with factory mixing has a high level of quality control. It is thus more convenient for traffic and neighbourhoods, so the extra cost is justified.

Tar was used extensively, but over the years bitumen use from the oil industry has increased. Since the closure of the gas works in early 1970s it is used exclusively. Bitumen is a by-product of fuel oil refining at Marsden Point Refinery, so oil companies have competed to get rid of their share. Such companies have bought a significant shareholding into the road contracting companies for this reason.

There was an interesting problem to solve with bitumen and basalt sealing chips. Basalt soaks up water like blotting paper and on a motorway chips were being thrown off the road after rain where previously they were well embedded in the hot bitumen. The problem was identified that basalt had a stronger bond with water than with bitumen. The water, passing through the stone by very fine capillary action, broke the bond with bitumen and the stones showed no sign of the previous bonding. This was proved, for example, where chips sheltered from the rain under bridges were perfectly in place and well bonded. Tar did not have this problem, nor did greywacke chips. One solution was to spray the chips with tar oil (or creosote) or pre-coat them with light bitumen. The problem is now solved with an additive to the bitumen.

As the suburbs developed, many as tram routes, new roads provided access to all houses as a planned part of the developments and surveyed sub-divisions. A driving force was minimum-cost road building to enable the projects to go ahead. Sources of funds were in the price of sections, rates from ratepayers and government funds from taxation.

The huge importance to a developing community of roads and road building methods is underlined by the fact that the first local government was in the form of road boards. Communities would band together to solve their problems, in this case road access. In order to build the proposed roads they would agree to levy their land-owning residents. An example was the Mt Roskill Road Board, which quarried away one of the Three Kings cones and built strong roads through the area that are still in use today. At the time of the 1930s Depression some road boards were bankrupt and they all became borough councils through legislation. This ontinued on until their demise with the 1989 local government reforms.

4.2

Auckland Motorways

by
Mike Lancaster
and
John La Roche

Germany's autobahns, Italy's autostrada and America's freeways set the scene for our motorways. The growing popularity of cars in New Zealand made motorways a good alternative to crowded urban streets. Right from its beginnings in 1840, Auckland has continued to grow and still keeps growing, needing more and better transport infrastructure. After World War II, and the construction of new housing developments in many parts of the region, Auckland needed better roading links. The Honourable Robert Semple, Minister of Works, announced plans for Auckland in 1946 that would cost an estimated £5,000,000. The proposals described in the editorial of *New Zealand Engineering* of 10 June 1946 (well before the Harbour Bridge and Mangere International Airport) included:

• A Southern Outlet – an improved four-lane motorway from the tram terminus in Great South Road to Drury, involving deviations to avoid Otahuhu, Manurewa and Papatoetoe.

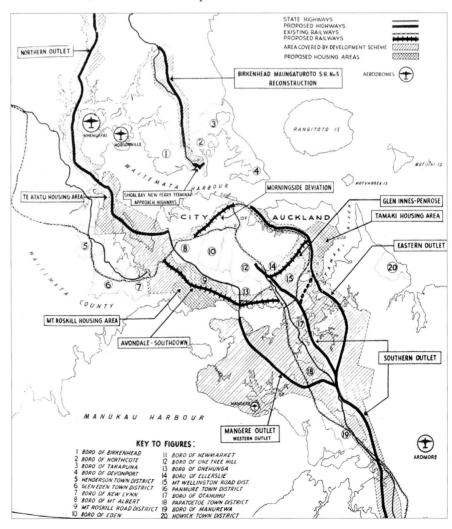

1946 proposal for Auckland Motorways.

NZ Engineering, 10 June 1946

- An Eastern Outlet – a modern highway branching from the waterfront road, passing east through the Tamaki housing area over the Tamaki River, and curving round through the undeveloped country to join the great southern outlet north of Manurewa.
- A Northern Outlet – originating at the city boundary at Avondale, the highway would cross shoal water near Pollen Island, traverse the Te Atatu Peninsula and run northward past Hobsonville and Whenuapai to Dairy Flat.
- A Mangere or Western District Outlet – another proposed route connecting Onehunga with the new southern outlet, swinging across Mangere Bridge and round to the south of Papatoetoe. This would enable through-traffic to bypass the heart of Auckland City.
- A Northern Improvement – reconstruction of the Birkenhead–Maungaturoto State Highway on a better alignment as far as Albany.

Good transport links are vital to the country's well being. As cities have grown and streets have become congested with vehicles, motorway connections have become an essential part of life in our major cities. Motorways involve much sophisticated engineering analysis, from detailed soil investigations to the design of alignments and curves that will allow for safe speeds of up to 100 kilometres per hour. There are no intersections or traffic lights. Many bridges are necessary to cross over or under urban roadways and other natural features. Specially designed on- and off-ramps allow traffic to leave or re-enter the urban roading network at convenient intervals. Motorways require significant land and the reshaping of land forms. Maintenance and the aesthetic enhancement of these areas and structures is a vital part of our urban landscape.

The first motorway in New Zealand was from Johnsonville to Tawa Flat north of Wellington, in 1952, followed in July 1953 by 3.2 kilometres between Ellerslie and Mt Wellington in Auckland. Then in 1954 the National Roads Board (NRB) was formed. Under Ministry of Works and Minister, the Honourable Stanley Goosman (later Sir Stanley Goosman) great progress was made. At that stage all the money derived from roading taxes was given to the NRB. The only restriction on progress was the capacity to design and construct the roads.

A master transport plan for the Auckland metropolitan area was prepared by the Auckland Regional

Reshaping the Central Motorway Junction, 2006.

Auckland Motorways P17, NZ Transport Agency

De Leuw Cather plan for
Auckland motorways, 1955.

Master Transportation Plan for
Metropolitan Auckland, P51,
courtesy Auckland Council

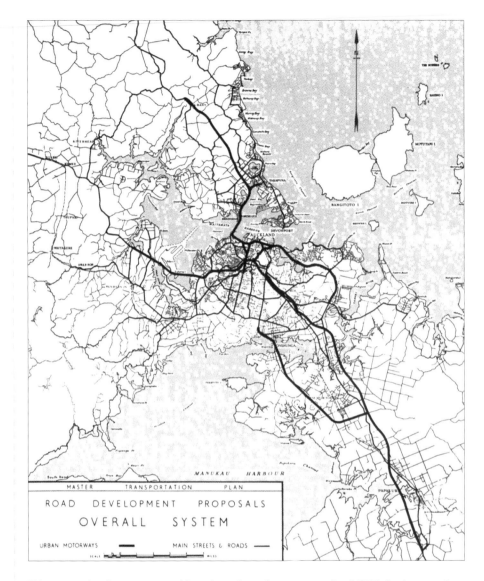

Planning Authority in 1955 and within three years the NRB had agreed to meet the full cost of certain designated motorways. The American consulting firm De Leuw Cather and Company was engaged by Auckland Regional Planning Authority in 1962 to prepare a comprehensive transport proposal for Auckland's transport needs up to 1986. The plan, delivered in 1965, recommended continuing motorway construction and the upgrading of important arterial routes. Many aspects of this plan were the basis of the present motorway system now enjoyed by Aucklanders.

The Southern Motorway was progressively extended: 9.4 kilometres to Wiri in 1955, 5.4 kilometres to Takanini in May 1963, 2.1 kilometres to Greenlane by December 1963 and 1.3 kilometres to Market Road by April 1965. The North-Western Motorway commenced with the opening of 11.5 kilometres between Point Chevalier and Hobsonville Road in 1961, significantly reducing the distance and travel times for people in the western suburbs served by this link. It also provided easy access for domestic and international air travellers to Whenuapai Airport, before Mangere International Airport was opened.

With the opening of the Auckland Harbour Bridge in 1959, a further 7.7 kilometres of Northern Motorway was available from Fanshawe Street to Northcote Road, with exits to Northcote, Takapuna and Wairau Valley. The Victoria Park Viaduct extending the motorway to Cook and Wellington Streets was completed in 1962. At the northern end, the motorway was extended from Northcote Road to Tristram Avenue in 1969 and on to Sunset Road by 1979.

The popularity of the bridge was so great that by 1965 it was obvious that its capacity had to be increased. In 1969 the 'Nippon clip-ons' were added to each side of the bridge, doubling its capacity.

Joining up these motorways through the central city was a major engineering achievement. The Southern Motorway was extended northwards when the Newmarket Viaduct was opened in 1965. This left the central city section connecting the North, South and Western motorways yet to be built. At this stage, in 1967, Mike Lancaster was given the responsibility as Resident Engineer, Ministry of Works and Development (MWD) to construct this vital link. It was fortunate that this section was left until then as motorway design had changed markedly since the early 1950s and the design was significantly different from the earlier plans. Construction of the earthworks was carried out by MWD's own staff, using surplus machinery from the hydro-electricity works on the Waikato River and hired plant. The concrete structures were designed in the main by MWD, but some bridges were designed by consulting engineers as MWD could not design all of them fast enough. Structures and final paving were done by contract, with overall supervision and control by MWD.

Before opening the link joining the Southern Motorway to the Harbour Bridge, the route was opened for a greatly appreciated public walk-through. By 1975 the Northern and Southern motorways were connected and by 1979 the North-Western Motorway had been extended from Point Chevalier to Nelson Street. However, at this time there was no connection to either the Northern or Southern motorways. Access to the port from the Southern Motorway via Grafton Gully was completed in 1988 and the Southern Motorway linked with the North-Western in 1989. This central section, with its tangle of concrete viaducts and bridges, was nicknamed 'Spaghetti Junction'. It had been intended to provide a motorway connection to another new motorway parallel to Dominion Road, but this was abandoned after residents objected.

The MWD was made into a State Owned Enterprise (SOE) in 1988 and Works and Development Services established as a commercial organisation.

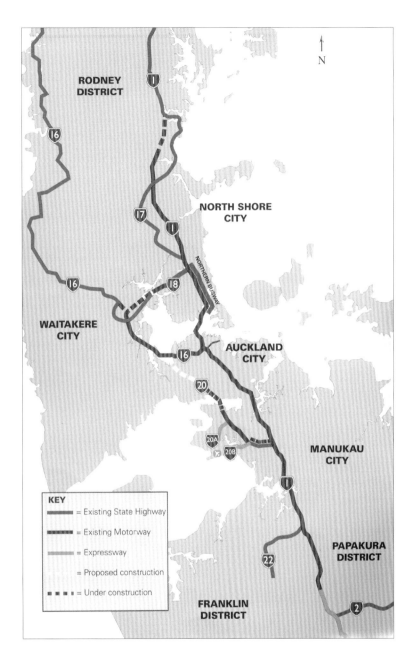

Plan of Auckland motorways,
2008.

Courtesy NZ Transport Agency

This led to the establishment of Works Consultancy Services and Works Civil Construction. These two organisations were sold in 1996, becoming Opus International Consultants and Works Infrastructure.

Transit New Zealand was formed in 1989 as the New Zealand crown entity responsible for operating and planning the New Zealand state highway network. This organisation changed its name in 2009 to the New Zealand Transport Agency.

In 2002 the major Central Motorway Junction Project was commenced to provide links in any direction between all the motorways, Southern, Northern, North-Western and Grafton Gully. Widening to increase the capacity of these links was carried out at the same time. These were major works, all done while keeping the traffic moving. The Grafton Gully project commenced in 2001 provided direct access to the port, Auckland Hospital and the Domain. A new railway bridge was required to make a direct link between Stanley Street and The Strand, and new bridges were built for Grafton Road and Wellesley Streets. Much innovative design work was required to link all the other motorways into the Grafton Gully link, giving heavy traffic a direct route to and from the port, and reducing the need for large vehicles in the central business district. One particularly impressive feature is the twin 'T Rex' pylons supporting the widened south-bound lane of the Southern Motorway where it crosses over lanes to Grafton Gully.

The Central Motorway Junction Project was finally completed in December 2006. It included the use of decorative features in concrete structures like bridges and retaining walls. Two kilometres of retaining walls have motifs of karaka leaves and berries, kowhai flowers and pohutukawa flowers and leaves.

Special stormwater holding tanks and treatment facilities were included. Planting of embankments with 143,000 plants in 1300 cubic metres of imported topsoil softened the visual impact. Work is now proceeding to ease the traffic congestion at the Victoria Park Viaduct by constructing a tunnel for northbound traffic.

The Northern Motorway has now been extended from Albany to Puhoi. Having taken the tolls off the Harbour Bridge in 1984, the section from Orewa to Puhoi has now become a toll highway bypassing a particularly winding and difficult part of the highway around Waiwera. This extension incorporates impressive engineering structures,

Above: Central Motorway Junction 2010.

J. La Roche

Left: T Rex Pylons, Central Motorway Junction.

J. La Roche

including twin tunnels through Johnstone's Hill, the 520 metre long Waiwera Viaduct crossing 30 metres above the tidal estuary, two eco-viaducts over bush-clad valleys, and a 55 metre deep cut at China Hill. Extensive environmental

Waiwera Viaduct and John-
stone's Hill twin tunnels.

J. La Roche

investigations and impact reporting were required along the route. Coping with difficult geological conditions was a challenge for the designers. At the time of writing Auckland has 327 kilometres of motorways and state highways providing huge benefits to the daily lives of Aucklanders.

References and further reading

Ministry of Works and Development, *Auckland Motorways*, Ministry of Works and Development, Auckland, 1984.

NZ Transport Agency, *Auckland Motorways*, NZ Transport Agency, Auckland, 2008.

Regional Plans (editorial), *NZ Engineering*, Vol. 1, No. 3, 10 June 1946, pp 200–202.

Technical Advisory Committee of the Auckland Regional Planning Authority, *Master Transportation Plan for Metropolitan Auckland Report & Survey*, Auckland Regional Planning Authority, July 1955.

CHAPTER FIVE

Ferries and Trams

From the earliest days of European settlement, ferry services were essential to meet the needs of Devonport. By 1841 this first settlement on the North Shore had become home to the navy, as well as to the sailors who survived the 1840 wreck of HMS *Buffalo* in Whitianga – including my great-grandfather Thomas Duder.

Initially, ferry passengers travelled between Devonport and the bottom of Queen Street in whaleboats, which were highly manoeuvrable, open rowing or sailing boats. As early as 1851 the first steam ferry with the first locally made boiler, the *Governor Wynyard*, was introduced. It ran a short-lived, unprofitable service to Otahuhu via the Tamaki River, before being sold to Melbourne in 1852. The service then went back to whaleboats under a provincial government contract to several locations on the North Shore. It was not until 1860 that the *Emu* set up a regular service to the Shore, before being wrecked on Emu Rock, Motutapu, in October of the same year.

Once again it was back to whaleboats until the Waitemata Steam Ferry Company inaugurated its service in March 1865 with the paddle steamer *Waitemata*. After various short-lived ventures by rival factions, its successor the Devonport Steam Ferry Company was formed in 1881, running a service that was free of disasters during the 78 years of its history.

A succession of around 10 handsome, if smoky, paddle steamers was superseded after 1886 by screw steamers and, finally, diesel vessels, both passenger

5.1

Auckland Ferries

by
John Duder

Paddle wheel steam ferry, Birkenhead.

Sir George Grey Special Collections, Auckland Libraries 4-2691

Passengers disembarking at Devonport, 1895.

Sir George Grey Special Collections, Auckland Libraries 4-3044

Ferries departing Auckland ferry terminal, 1936.

Sir George Grey Special Collections, Auckland Libraries 4-2935

and vehicular. The passenger ferries were distinctive double-ended, two-decked screw ferries, running to Devonport, Bayswater, Northcote and Birkenhead. Well-known names included the *Albatross*, the first of these vessels which operated from the early 1900s until the advent of the modern catamaran vessels. The last was the diesel *Kestrel*, now back home after being 'retired' to Tauranga in 2005. Two others, *Toroa* and *Ngairo*, are in various stages of preservation.

The vehicular ferries, six in number – of which the two most modern recognised the family who managed the company, *E. W. Alison* and his brother, *Alex Alison* – ceased operation abruptly when the harbour bridge opened in 1959. Several were buried in the Westhaven reclamation.

The early-established Waiheke Island ferry services have also had a long and often troubled history. Although the island's nearest port is but 11 nautical miles from the city, and the voyage largely inside Hauraki Gulf islands, sea conditions can be unpleasant for all but the larger and more modern craft, particularly those used in the lean years after the Second World War.

Starting in 1868 with the paddle steamer *Novelty* on passage to Coromandel, services were good by the standards of the Victorian era and the first half of the 20th century. Fine paddle steamers and then screw steamers provided suitable accommodation for ladies in long skirts and gentlemen in hats.

Matters deteriorated, however, after the Second World War and by the 1950s there was a motley fleet of ex-Navy submarine-hunting Fairmile launches (*Ngaroma, Motonui, Iris Moana*), various launches and a couple of scows for cargo – *Esme* and *Jane Gifford*, the latter now restored. Probably the most famous was the *Baroona*, if only for her long career and distinctive shape. Finally ending up as a restaurant, of all things, in Manukau City, she was built in 1904 in Newcastle of Australian hardwood, to service a river sheep station. After spells on the Kaipara Harbour, in the Pacific Islands, on the New Zealand east coast and as a trawler, she was on the Waiheke and Waitemata runs for 54 years until 1989, still with her original Australian boulder ballast in the bilges.

In total there were over 100 vessels of all types servicing Waiheke for 120 years until the advent of the modern high speed and so much more comfortable Quickcats which now service the island and Great Barrier Island.

References and further reading

Balderson, David, *The Waiheke Ferries of Auckland*, Grantham House, Auckland, 1991.

Stewart, W. W., *Steam on the Waitemata*, A. W. & A. H. Reed, Wellington, 1972.

Walsh, T., *From Wherry to Steam Ferry on the Waitemata: A History of the Romantic Conquest of the Silvery Waterway*, Walsh Printing Co., Auckland, 1932.

Above: Vehicular ferry, Mollyhawk arriving at Mechanics Bay in the 1930s.

NZ Herald, E/H 200807 GSPT 1PG 19G

Above: Ferries during construction of the Auckland Harbour Bridge, 1958.

Sir George Grey Special Collections, Auckland Libraries 998-2

5.2

Auckland Trams

by
Colin Zeff

The first known passenger railway or tramway was the 'Mumbles Train' on the south coast of Wales in 1807. This consisted of a carriage body mounted on mineral wagon wheels and drawn by a horse. It provided a much smoother ride than the roads of the day but, unknown though it was then, this tramway was to be the forerunner of a new era in transportation.

Horse-drawn tramways became common throughout the world and New Zealand was no exception. The first passenger service vehicle to run on rails was on the 13 mile Dun Mountain railway, built to service the copper mine and to bring the ore to the port of Nelson. It ran through the town, so the town section of about a mile was opened for passenger traffic in May 1862.

The passing of the Tramways Act in 1872 allowed municipal authorities to grant licences to tramway operators, and this resulted in horse-drawn tram services starting throughout the main towns of the fast-developing colony.

In Auckland the tracks were laid and a service started in 1874 which ran from the bottom of Queen Street to Ponsonby Road via Karangahape Road. Compared with the horse-drawn omnibuses running on the rutted and pot-holed roads of the time, this was a magic-carpet ride. Not only was the ride smoother but, because of the steel wheels running on steel track, the horses could manage much larger vehicles of greater capacity.

The tramway was built and operated by the City of Auckland Tramways and Suburban Land Company Limited and this set the scene for tramway development. It was land subdivision for housing that led to the need for public transport to serve the resulting suburban sprawl.

A horse-drawn tramway was also built and operated for a short time in 1886–7 serving Devonport and Cheltenham.

The application of electric traction to street tramways is generally credited to the Siemens Company, who in 1881 opened the world's first electric street tramway in Lichterfelde, Germany.

Horse tram at Ponsonby terminus in the 1890s.

Sir George Grey Special Collections, Auckland Libraries 7-A11099

Dunedin was the first city in New Zealand to adopt electric trams and The Roslyn Tramway Company Limited opened its first line in October of 1900.

The British Electric Traction Company was a land development company and they bought land areas around many cities in the world. In Auckland they purchased the City of Auckland Tramways and Suburban Land Company and renamed it The Auckland Electric Tramway Company (AETC) with a view to replacing the horse trams with electric trams and substantially expanding the network.

The tracks were all built to the 'standard' gauge of 4 feet 8½ inches (1,435 millimetres) and the power to the trams was supplied through overhead conductor wires at 600 volts, direct current (DC). The population of Auckland at this time was only 68,000.

On 17 November 1902 the mayor of Auckland, Mr Alfred Kidd, switched on the power at the purpose-built coal-fired steam power station located at the foot of Hobson Street and Sir John Logan Campbell then drove the first of a convoy of trams up Queen Street. The trams immediately became very popular and the whole venture was a huge success.

Initially the tram routes went to Herne Bay, Ponsonby, Grey Lynn, Kingsland, Newmarket and Onehunga. Gradually, over the next 30 years or so, the network expanded to include Westmere, Point Chevalier, Avondale, Owairaka, Mt Roskill, Three Kings, Great South Road as far as the 'Harp of Erin' and

Mayor Alfred Kidd switching on the tramways power supply in 1902.

Sir George Grey Special Collections, Auckland Libraries 7-A15208

Sir John Logan Campbell starting the first tram, 17 November 1902.

Sir George Grey Special Collections, Auckland Libraries 7-A7641

No. 49, the first tram
built in Auckland.

Sir George Grey Special Collections,
Auckland Libraries 4-1013

Ellerslie Racecourse, and Meadowbank via Remuera Road, with a branch down Victoria Avenue as far as Shore Road. This made a total of 72 route kilometres.

The services were started in 1902 using 43 trams that had been imported in knocked-down form from The Brush Electrical Engineering Company Ltd of Loughborough, England and assembled at the Ponsonby Depot of the AETC. Eventually there were three depots located at Gaunt Street, in the city, and at Herne Bay and Epsom, with workshops located at Herne Bay and Royal Oak.

The demand for more services and extended routes meant that the initial fleet of tram cars was inadequate, so more were imported from the Brush Company in 1905 and 1907. However, from then on AETC designed and built their own trams using imported mechanical and electrical components with some of the body construction being contracted out to the coach-building company Cousins and Aitken Limited, and later DSC and Cousins & Cousins, Auckland.

Eventually the fleet comprised 269 trams, although some were withdrawn

Plan of Auckland tram system.

Courtesy MOTAT and Erik G. Holst

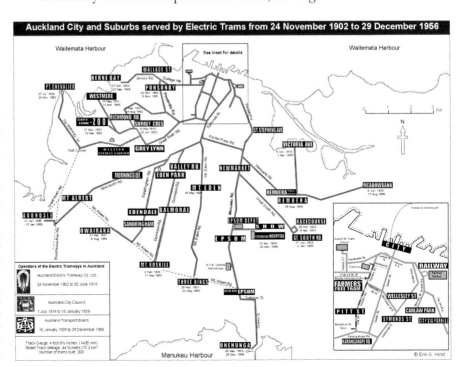

over the years and many trams were either rebuilt or their working parts recycled into new trams.

From an engineering viewpoint, this was a very substantial operation. With over 200 trams to operate and maintain at any one time, and over 80 kilometres of rail and overhead wires, and a power station to operate, there was employment for as many as 700 men and, later during the Second World War and thereafter, women. In 1919 the whole operation was bought by the Auckland City Council and renamed Auckland City Corporation Tramways. In 1929 it was re-formed as the Auckland Transport Board.

Queen Street trams, 1919.

Sir George Grey Special Collections, Auckland Libraries 7-A7833

The tramway was the principal form of public transport, along with sub-urban rail services, and was the life blood of the expanding city in a manner that is hard to visualise in the present motorcar-dominated city. At its peak in the early 1940s the tramway carried 99 million passengers per annum at a time when the population of Auckland was 182,000.

The ravages of the 1930s Depression, followed by labour and material shortages throughout the Second World War, resulted in the whole system being in a worn-out state by the late 1940s. Despite many protests it was decided not to renew it but to replace the trams with trolleybuses and diesel-powered buses. Routes were progressively converted, starting in 1949. The last tram in public service, number 242, ran on the city to Onehunga line on 29 December 1956.

Trams and buses in Upper Symonds Street, c. 1929.

Sir George Grey Special Collections, Auckland Libraries 589-58

A number of trams have survived and some are restored to working condition and can be seen running at Auckland's Museum of Transport and Technology. These include: No.11, one of the first batch of Brush-built trams and the very first electric tram to be erected and run in Auckland, No. 248, a 1936 streamliner, one of the last trams to run in Auckland, and No. 44, a Brush-designed four-wheel car and one of the first to be built in Auckland.

No. 44, the second tram built
in Auckland, now at MOTAT.

Courtesy MOTAT

Other Auckland trams at MOTAT awaiting restoration are No. 17, a Brush-built double-decker, No. 253, another streamliner, No. 89 and No. 147, both M-class cars, and No. 204 a so-called semi-steel. There are also trams in the hands of private collectors.

The story of trams in Auckland would not be complete without including the Takapuna steam tramway. In 1907 Takapuna business interests tried to persuade the Auckland Electric Tramways Company to build an electric tramway to open up the fast-developing suburbs on the North Shore. The AETC decided against such an investment but the people of Takapuna were not easily discouraged. They raised the capital and proceeded to form the Takapuna Tramways and Ferry Company Limited. The tramway was initially steam-hauled to reduce the investment required and the tram cars were built as

Tram 248 Streamliner.

Sir George Grey Special Collections,
Auckland Libraries 1021-0353

trailers, with a view to conversion to electric cars at a later date. The Company also built a new ferry, the *Pupuke,* which was launched in 1909 to be ready for the opening of the tramway in 1910.

The tramway started at the Bayswater wharf, climbed up a substantial grade into King Edward Avenue and on to Belmont. From there it went north to Hall's Corner, Takapuna and thence clockwise around Lake Pupuke to Milford, returning to Hall's Corner down Hurstmere Road, thus completing the loop. The tramway was powered by seven steam tram motors, which were in effect small steam locomotives. Four were imported from the Kerr Stuart Company Limited, Stoke-on-Trent, England. Later, three more came from the Baldwin Locomotive Works, Philadelphia, USA.

A total of 14 steam-tram trailers were built in Auckland by DSC and

Steam tram at Halls
Corner, Takapuna.

North Shore Library T1505

Cousins & Cousins with later conversion to electric trams in mind. They operated in 'trains' of two to four cars in conjunction with the ferry service. Certainly
land development was the motivation for the operation of the company, and
there were people who benefited financially from the tramway's existence, but
it failed to gain enough traffic and the company failed in 1927. The tracks were
torn up; the locomotives sold. The tram-trailers were also sold – to Wanganui
(9) and Dunedin (4), where they were finally converted to electric power and
went on to serve until the demise of those systems.

References and further reading

Stewart, Graham, *The End of the Penny Section: A History of Urban Transport in
    New Zealand*, A. W. & A. H. Reed, Wellington, 1973.
Stewart, Graham, *Always a Tram in Sight: The Electric Trams of New Zealand
    1900 to 1964*, Grantham House, Wellington, 1996.
Stewart, Graham, *Fares Please! The Horse, Steam & Cable Trams of New Zealand*,
    Wellington, Grantham House, 1997.

CHAPTER SIX

Railways

The Auckland to Drury Rail Project

Large coal deposits were discovered in 1858 just east of Drury and Opaheke, some 22 miles (35 kilometres) from Auckland, with the mining operation undertaken by the Waihoihoi Coal Company. This was the second railway in the country, built some three months after the Nelson railway. The line was surveyed and plans drawn by engineer James Stewart in 1860 and estimated to cost £4,176. Substantial engineering problems occurred, with horses having to drag wagons over a difficult gradient across many bridges and viaducts to the Manukau Harbour for shipping across to Onehunga and then by drays across to Auckland. It increased the cost from 18 shillings a ton at the mine to 33 shillings ($1.80 to $3.30) at Auckland. An alternative was considered requiring more capital expenditure, for a tramway out to the Wairoa River and shipping through the Tamaki Strait direct to Auckland.

Coal was the major source of energy for Auckland and was being imported from New South Wales, and it was hoped that the Drury coal might replace some of this. The concept of a railway was considered by the Provincial Council as a more economic method of transporting the coal and other produce to the Port of Auckland.

There was a conflict of opinion as to whether the cost of a railway should be the responsibility of the Provincial Council. However, the railway became of strategic importance when, in July 1863, war broke out in earnest with Maori tribes in the Waikato. The main transportation was by an inadequate roading system to shipping on the Waikato River.

At the same time it was considered a necessity, for both passenger transport and shipping freight, to link the two harbours by constructing a branch line from Penrose to Onehunga. Surveys, plans and estimates were undertaken

6.1

A Brief History of Auckland's Railways

by Rhys Thomas

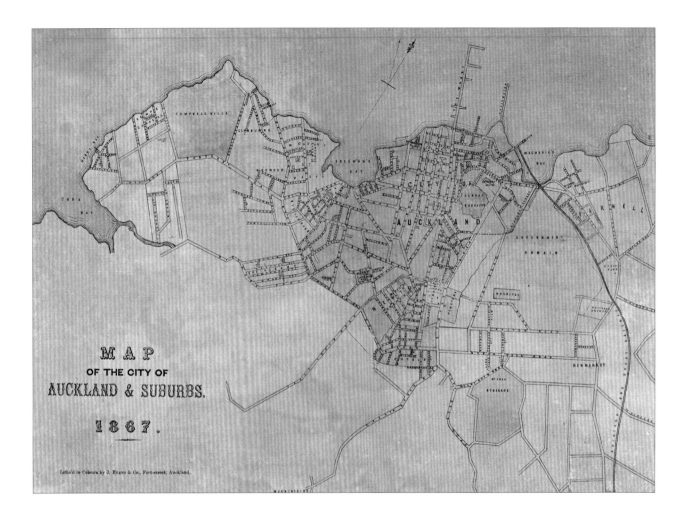

MAP
OF THE CITY OF
AUCKLAND & SUBURBS.
1867.

Litho'd in Colours by J. Evans & Co., Fort-street, Auckland.

1867 Map of Auckland
showing the first section
of the Auckland to
Drury Railway.

Sir George Grey Special Collections,
Auckland Libraries NZ Map 4610

by civil engineers James Stewart and Samuel Harding and presented to the
Provincial Council in 1863.

The council then passed an act empowering the appointment of a Railways
Commission for the purpose of constructing a £100,000 railway from Auckland
to Drury, with a branch line to Onehunga. The money was raised under the
Loans Act 1863, and it was also resolved that a further £50,000 be raised by
debentures on the security of the work.

The Provincial Council had recently appointed as Engineer-in-Chief an
English professional engineer, William Weaver, who was at the time working
in New South Wales. He was to play a prominent part in the development of
Auckland for the remainder of his professional life. Some of his early work
involved reports on the proposed railway. There were a number of routes considered for the first section from downtown Auckland to Newmarket. After
detailed investigations Weaver recommended the central route, beginning on
the sea beach near the eastern end of Custom House Street (now Customs

Street), through Mechanics Bay with a tunnel under the Parnell ridge, with the preferred location for the terminal station near the central business area.

Construction Commences

The Auckland to Drury railway was to start and tenders were called on 20 September 1865, attracting a good deal of interest (18 tendering). The contract was let to a Melbourne firm, even though it was some £13,000 higher than the council's estimate. The contractor was then permitted to sublet it in four separate smaller contracts to minimise the risk. This, as it eventually turned out, was financially advantageous for the lead contractor.

First contract: 100 men were working on the section through Parnell to Newmarket in March 1865, but problems soon arose.

Second contract: On from Newmarket for two miles to the junction of Great South Road and Panmure Road, again with problems.

Third contract: For two miles on to the Onehunga branch line just beyond Penrose.

Fourth contract: The remainder of the line on to Onehunga.

There was no contract as yet for the line on to the terminus at Drury.

Commission of Enquiry

Over that year so much money was expended that it was obvious the railway to Drury was not going to proceed without a great deal of additional funding. A Commission of Enquiry was set up, Weaver being a member, and reported to the Provincial Council. The report, dated 10 March 1866, showed that the initial investigations were sub-standard. To quote from parts of it:

Contract No.1: 'regret to report that the whole of the works are in a very unsatisfactory state…the brickwork and masonry is rough and of inferior character and not of a standard acceptable in important public works…brickwork in the tunnel, although more substantial, is rough due to the various sizes and quality used… the tunnel is defective in design and strength…the Engineer considers the cuttings will take 10 months to excavate and with the winter

approaching and the disorganised state of the works, it may take up to 12 months to complete the contract.'

Contract No.2: 'the works are in a much better state than No. 1 but the long culvert under the Newmarket embankment is objectionable and may cause problems hereafter…owing to improper ground examination and no trial borings, no provision was made for rock excavation in Mr Dilworth's paddock where it was estimated that it will cost a sum equivalent to the amount of the whole of the other works in the contract. This will give the contractor an excessive profit on the extra works, upward of £5,000 more than the lowest and upwards of £2,000 more than the highest tender. The works in this section are in a forward state and soon to be completed.'

Contract No.3: 'the scoria embankments are finished in an inferior manner and should be hand packed. The rigidity of the road bed over the embankments requires more ballast – it will work down into the interstices of the stone work and must be increased.'

Contract No.4: This was apparently in much better state than the other contracts and it appears that a few rails were laid.

The report goes on to say:

We cannot conclude our remarks under this head of enquiry, without expressing our opinion that the plans, sections, contracts and other documents necessary for the proper carrying out of the works, have not been prepared in a desirable manner, and requisite for the satisfactory conduct of important engineering works. The documents do not appear to have been maturely considered before contracts were let and works commenced, even now they are not in a satisfactory condition. There does not appear to be the desirable unity of action between the two Chief Engineers who were not thoroughly conversant with the preliminary arrangements. Their terms of engagement tend to divest either of them for the responsibility of the works.

It is thus lamented that this, the most important work carried out by the Province, should in design and execution, be so unsatisfactory that the resultant cost is so disproportionate to the outlay. The cost per mile will be at least £11,000, exceeding some of the most expensive lines constructed in Europe, and if such a large outlay had been foreseen, we doubt whether the work should have been commenced.

The act passed by the General Assembly and the Provincial Council contemplated a railway from Auckland to Drury, hence its title, but it achieved only a short line to Onehunga, little less than one third of that designed, with the result that it would have a probable cost nearly equal to the estimate for the whole main line plus the branch to Onehunga. The Commission of Enquiry considered it difficult to estimate what the final cost could be until a decision was made on the intended site of the terminus and the cost of the filling around Mechanics Bay.

This report considered that with the increasing cost, the coming winter weather, the indeterminate final cost and the province being in the grip of a severe financial depression, it was evident that the works could not proceed further at that time.

The Railway to Nowhere

The Provincial Council took over the project from the Railways Commission and stopped as much of the work as possible. A few piers had been built in Mechanics Bay, the Parnell bridge was built, the tunnel started, and the formation to Onehunga completed with a few rails laid. Some further work was done on the first section and on the tunnel until slips occurred. The Council had no money for more work, so the Auckland to Drury Railway Act 1867 was passed in October, authorising the disposal of salvageable plant. Some reclaimed land was sold and the Act gave authority to transfer its powers to anybody who would undertake to complete the railway. Nobody came forward, but some 15 wagons, together with some rails, were sent to the Bay of Islands for the tramway at the Kawakawa coal mines.

The Auckland to Drury Railway came to a sad end, with uncompleted work and two engines. It was 'The Railway to Nowhere': a prime example of insufficient investigations and inadequate control of the contract. The local newspaper in its leader described the railway as a monument to folly, conceit, incapacity and the want of principle of all and sundry. The general feeling of the public was summed up in an 'obituary' written in the newspaper concluding that, '… my proposal is that £2,000 to £3,000 should be voted to put the railway out of sight, fill in the cuttings, and remove the fences etc. If we could manage to bury the commissioners, engineers and contractors in the same cutting all the better!'

The locomotives

During the construction of the works a ship arrived from England with the first locomotive, which was received with great ceremony and celebration. The 18 ton engine was considered too heavy for the primitive wharf of those days, so a lighter brought it ashore and then the engine and its components were transferred to Newmarket. It was like a triumphal march up Queen Street via

Auckland's first railway locomotive being used to construct the Parnell Railway Tunnel, c.1873.

Sir George Grey Special Collections, Auckland Libraries 4-1071

Khyber Pass, with everything in tow. An account was presented to the council for a trumpeter to clear the way for the procession and for some 120 quarts of beer for the workmen (whether the latter was paid for is not recorded). It was indeed a celebration, as it seemed at that time that the railway was now on the move.

On 5 February 1866 the engine had been assembled, and afterwards the Chairman of the Railways Commission mounted the engine and blew the whistle which was heard for the first time in Auckland. The engine was mounted on chocks and the wheels were allowed to turn to show everything was in order. It was then lowered on to the rails and run back and forth over a short length – this was the most it ran! A second locomotive arrived later in the year and both were put into storage at Newmarket. They were never used as intended, but only for construction purposes when work eventually recommenced.

Parnell Railway Bridge

The Parnell Railway Bridge was included in the first contract for the Auckland Provincial Council's ill-fated Auckland to Drury Railway.

It was a significant part of the landscape from the early days of Auckland. It was constructed between 1865 and 1866, and is believed to be the oldest railway bridge remaining and still in use in the North Island. It has technological interest as it retains elements of major engineering achievement from our early colonial history and reveals information about construction, quarrying and other techniques of construction. The initial structure involved a bowstring truss bridge with a viaduct over Parnell Rise, all supported on large basalt piers. These were built in a monumental style typical for the time, with mortar-bonded ashlar masonry concealing rubble backing. It was unusual for early railway bridges to feature basalt as a construction material. It is still in good condition today, except for some mortar cracking because of vibration at the top of a south-western pier.

It remained a costly 'white elephant' when work stopped on the railway in 1866. It is interesting to note the public frustration with the ill-fated project.

One correspondent wrote: 'the solitary piers built would, in future ages, rank equally in interest with the ruins of Pompeii and Herculaneum.'

It was not until the early 1870s when the government public works policies, which are explained in further detail later, came into operation that the new rail system progressed south from Auckland. It became the first part of the nation's railways to be operated by the government.

Partially completed Parnell multi-span bow string truss railway bridge, 1868.

Sir George Grey Special Collections, Auckland Libraries 4-836

The rail gradient through the Parnell bridge section was always considered to be too steep and improvements made in the 1890s required raising and altering the masonry piers. Then in 1908 and 1909 substantial modifications were made as two piers were removed to provide a wider road carriageway. The entire superstructure was replaced with a 128 foot (39 metre) span double intersection Warren truss with overhead ties. The remaining piers were widened for a double-track rail.

The construction was of identical style to the original. This work was completed soon after the main trunk railway between Auckland and Wellington was opened.

The original track complied with the Provincial Council's standard which was to be 4 feet 8½ inches (1,435 millimetres). But when the New Zealand

Parnell railway bridge soon after completion of the railway in 1873.

Sir George Grey Special Collections, Auckland Libraries 4-237

Parnell railway bridge,
c. 1870s.

Sir George Grey Special Collections,
Auckland Libraries 4-947

Government's narrower 3 feet 6 inches (1,067 millimetres) gauge was standardised for the whole of the country, the tracks had to be narrowed.

The Parnell Railway Bridge remained part of the main trunk line until the Auckland to Westfield deviation came into operation in 1930, but it has remained in daily use for suburban trains on the Southern and Western lines passing through Newmarket, with only some rail replacement. In 1974 overhead ties were added to the truss. The aesthetic value of the monumental appearance is largely concealed today by advertising hoardings.

Railway Construction Resumes

There was little interest in recommencing work on the railway until 1869/70 when Julius Vogel, a minister in the Fox administration, proposed an ambitious immigration and public works policy, which brought a ray of hope. In the past, provincial administrations had looked after only themselves with little regard to a regional network, resulting in non-standard construction methods, including rail gauge. Refreshingly, Vogel took a country-wide broad view of the situation and changed this parochial outlook with his policy on colonial public works.

With the whole country's resources behind him, he was able to have greater access to finance and manpower and, without the provincial government's permission, obtain crown land for national roading and railway construction. This resulted in the Immigration and Public Works Act 1870, which was followed by the Railways Act 1870 that dealt with aspects more related to railways. The latter act established the national rail gauge as 3 feet 6 inches, a recommendation by a London firm of consulting engineers who outlined the advantages, quoting experience with railways of this gauge in Canada, Norway and elsewhere.

The Auckland Military Reserves Act 1871 was enacted to dispose of military reserves and other crown land,

Warren truss being installed as the intermediate piers were being removed, 1909.

Sir George Grey Special Collections,
Auckland Libraries 4-902

as the Waikato wars were now over and land could be vested in other public utilities. Land could be set aside for the Auckland and Waikato Railway and the Auckland terminus. Fill from the Point Britomart excavations was used for the Mechanics Bay reclamation and rail embankment.

The first railway station was now able to be built by Fort Britomart reclaimed land, as described in further detail later. This was not the site nearer the central business area, as earlier recommended, that area still being non-reclaimed waterfront.

The first rail project to be approved was the Auckland to Tuakau and Waikato River line with a branch to Onehunga, commencing and terminating at points to be determined. The cost was to be no more than £4,000 per mile, compared with the ill-fated original contract at some £11,000 per mile. The old Auckland to Drury railway was to be on the move at last.

Julius Vogel's national scheme did much to accelerate the interior development of the country. He became premier in 1873, and then again for a short period in 1876 as Sir Julius Vogel. The honour bestowed on him was justified as his policies instigated the beginning of modern road and rail transport in New Zealand.

Before contracts were let there remained doubt as to whether the Parnell tunnel, which had caused so much trouble earlier, was the best alternative. A decade before, Weaver had recommended this route. Alternatives to the east and west were again surveyed and it was confirmed that the central Parnell line was best, because land and slip problems were not as difficult as had been feared.

Vogel entered into negotiations with an English firm to undertake a contract to build the line from Newmarket to Mercer for £168,924 and Auckland to Newmarket and Penrose to Onehunga for £59,049, the entire work to be completed by 1875. These figures are somewhat higher than the estimates seven or eight years before. But that was for a line only as far as Drury, and it was now a much longer length – to Mercer. Time and inflation had crept in, and higher standards of construction were now required. But work was on the way at last.

When the eight-mile Auckland to Onehunga section was completed in 1873, this became the first of the so-called 'Vogel railways' to be brought into use. It was also the first government railway opened for traffic in the North Island, and was the first in New Zealand to be worked directly under the auspices of the central government.

The first timetabled train from Auckland was an eight-mile trip to Onehunga on 24 December 1873. There was little public excitement about this trip, as the line had been officially opened on 20 December, with provincial and central government and other dignitaries present. Speeches and celebrations

were made acknowledging Sir Julius Vogel and others for providing the first working railway in Auckland.

The two locomotives originally purchased some eight years earlier were unfortunately built for the 4 feet 8½ inch gauge. Now the standard gauge was 3 feet 6 inches and they were only able to be used for construction purposes. New engines and rolling stock were purchased.

Further Extensions

(a) Southward

Railway construction continued at a fast rate throughout the country, but here we restrict comment to those lines commencing from the Auckland terminal. In 1872 there were less than 100 miles of railway open for traffic and 960 miles under construction in the whole country, whereas by 1930 it had reached a length of 3,287 miles. The population of the entire country was 316,000 (including 280,000 Europeans) with about 20 per cent living in Auckland and its environs.

In 1874 Parliament approved the abolition of the North Island provinces, but the act did not come into effect until December 1876, when central government took control. Works were then carried out by the Public Works Department, with the Railways Department formed to operate the system. However, it was not until 1896 that the Railways Department took over both construction and operation.

Meantime construction continued southward from Penrose towards Mercer and by October 1874 the line was complete as far as Drury – good progress, but some eight years after the date once expected. The contractors were able to run a special train from this point to the Ellerslie races. Then on 20 May

1875 Mercer was reached, four months ahead of the contract date, and 43 miles (70 kilometres) from Auckland.

A route was agreed on across the Whangamarino swamp and onwards to Hamilton. A bridge was built over the Waikato River at Newcastle (Ngaruawahia) and opened amid great celebration on 17 November 1876 and then on to Hamilton by 19 December 1877. A special train with 16 cars and two engines left Auckland and was welcomed on a fine summer's day by over 1,000 people with much festivity – it was a red letter day for the Waikato. A good part of this line was built by the Armed Constabulary, as the government feared a renewal of hostilities by Maori retaining bitter memories of the recent war.

Railway terminus on Waikato River at Ngaruawahia, 1867.

Sir George Grey Special Collections, Auckland Libraries 4-3801

The main line progressed southwards. There was a hold-up in the Rukuhia swamp, where special attention was given to the soft foundations in the wet peat bog areas. Alternatives for a route via Alexandria (Pirongia) were proposed, but rejected, and the line through the swamp continued. This concern remained for years on the important main trunk line. A railway directive gave warning that no engine was to remain stationary at the Rukuhia siding for any length of time. A close watch must be kept, and if any indication of subsidence, the engine must be kept moving every few minutes!

Te Awamutu was reached and the official opening was on 1 July 1880. The railhead remained here for another seven years as the King Country was only a few miles on, where Maori had retreated after their last battle. It was the area included in the final settlement of the land wars called Te Rohe Potae, an area where few Europeans ventured. Finally, the rail moved south from Te Awamutu to complete the North Island main trunk line in 1908.

Extensions further afield from Auckland were steadily progressing. The interior of the productive Waikato area was served by a line eastward from Hamilton. Later other important lengths of line were constructed from Hamilton, where the junction was now called Frankton. The line to Rotorua was completed in December 1894; Paeroa was reached from Morrinsville and Hamilton in December 1895 and Thames in 1898.

Later the Kaimai tunnel to Tauranga was a major improvement with the subsequent closing of the Paeroa to Waihi section. Earthworks formation on a proposed line from Pokeno to Paeroa was undertaken (some of it can be seen today) but it was never completed.

Another line that has since been taken out, but was important in its day, is one in central Auckland. Up to 1985 there were connections from the Auckland Freight Yard down the centre of Quay Street to the wharves for the placement of wagons to serve pre-container shipping. These lines continued over the Bascule Bridge at what is now the Viaduct Basin and ran through to the Tank Farm. For many years a daily petroleum train ran from here to supply Hamilton. By the mid 70s the supply point was switched to Mt Maunganui and the tracks became redundant as cargo handling methods and wharf usage changed. The line had also continued up Beaumont Street to the gasworks for delivery of coal. These tracks were removed about 1977.

(b) Northward

On 29 October 1875 a 16 mile length of rail was opened from Riverhead to Helensville. This isolated line had to be linked to the main line by construction of a 22 mile railway westward from Newmarket. It was opened in sections as they were completed, joining up with the Helensville line at Kumeu. The line back from Kumeu to Riverhead was then closed.

The line progressed north to Whangarei, and then on again through the Bay of Islands to the northern terminus of Okaihau. Further formation, still visible today, was constructed towards Kaitaia, but it was abandoned when it was decided the financial return could not be justified from this sparsely populated area. In 1987 the whole of the line from Otiria to Okaihau was closed.

The Auckland Railway Stations

There have now been four sites where the Auckland Railway Station has been located.

No. 1 Site: Fort Britomart Area, 1873 to 1884

It was considered desirable to have the terminus within the business centre of the town but the land adjacent to Queen Street was waterfront at that time,

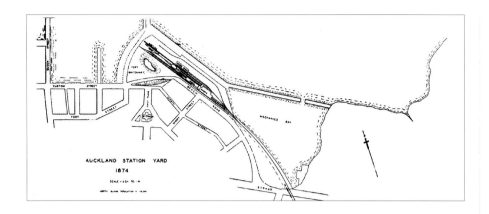

The first Auckland railway station, 1874.

Sir George Grey Special Collections, Auckland Libraries 4-1416

and it was expedient to locate it on the reclaimed land of Fort Britomart – on the northern side of the junction of the present Anzac Avenue and Beach Road.

The station was named 'Britomart Station'.

An experimental train trip on the newly constructed line started from this point to Onehunga on 25 October 1873, taking 24 minutes at 30 mph. The locomotive, an F class numbered 242, had just arrived from England. The six-wheeled carriages were made by A & G Price at Thames. It was the first railway in New Zealand to be constructed as part of the 1870 Public Works Act, although there had been some passenger train activity at Thames and Kawakawa for a couple of years.

The construction of the first railway station was now complete. Although it was soon to be considered a 'fourth-rate temporary station', it was to remain here for another 11 years. Excavation of Point Britomart slowly continued and the station became more isolated and difficult to access for the public. It had to be relocated.

Consideration was given to a site near Wellesley or Victoria streets, but the majority view was that it should be sited at the end of Queen Street wharf.

No. 2 Site: East side of Queen Street, 1884 to 1930

The Auckland Railway Station Act 1882 vested further areas of land in the Crown to provide land for a bigger and better site near the central business area and handy for passengers working in the city. Problems were encountered in obtaining sufficient filling until the Harbour Board provided it from the Point Britomart excavations. Timber (totara) piling was driven through the reclamation, down to bedrock.

The station was built on Customs Street and completed within the contract time on 27 November 1885. The passenger station was opened for use ahead of that date on 26 October 1885. Its main pedestrian entrance was from Queen Street with a side entrance from Customs Street opposite Commerce

Street. A new engine shed was built at the site and the railway workshops were shifted to a much larger building at Newmarket.

At this time surveys were carried out to explore a route from the new station via Freemans Bay to Kingsland. This was one of the many attempts to extend rail on from downtown – all without success. The July 1908 completion of the North Island main trunk railway added to the station rail traffic. Duplication of the Auckland to Penrose section was undertaken between 1905 and 1910, and in 1909 the Parnell tunnel was duplicated and the Parnell railway bridge was enlarged for the double track. There were now a total of six platforms at the station.

Conflict with the Post Office

The Chief Post Office had been located at several sites at different times in Auckland. The existing one in Shortland Street became too small and investigations in the late 1890s were undertaken for a new site.

Above: 1886 perspective view of Auckland waterfront with the first station site clearly shown and the second station fronting Queen Street not so clearly shown.

Sir George Grey Special Collections, Auckland Libraries NZ Map 374

Right: Auckland station yards, 1917.

Sir George Grey Special Collections, Auckland Libraries 4-1416

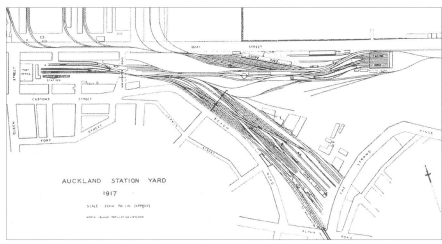

AUCKLAND STATION YARD
1917
SCALE - 3CHN TO 1IN (APPROX)

The railway frontage on to Queen Street was covered with hoardings and looked under-utilised. In 1901 approaches were made for this land to be used for a new Chief Post Office. Strong objections were voiced from the Railways Department, saying that the length of the yard and platforms were already insufficient for expansion. It was hoped that a new station would be built facing Queen Street, similar to that of Wellington.

The Minister of Railways reported that the government could not incur more expenditure added to the cost of the duplication of the Auckland to Southdown line. This argument went on for the next few years, but in December 1907 the Prime Minister made the announcement that he had approved the construction of a Post Office building with a 212 foot (65 metre) frontage on Queen Street occupying the whole frontage of the railway property.

This was devastating news for the Railways Department. It was the single most damaging decision for rail passenger traffic in the city. At the time the *New Zealand Herald* objected to the decision in their editorial, stating that the building *will later be transformed into a Railway Station* – an amazing prediction, fulfilled a hundred years on!

Above: Second railway station facing Queen Street, 1908.

Sir George Grey Special Collections, Auckland Libraries 7-A1729

Below: Reclamation for new railway across Hobson Bay.

Sir George Grey Special Collections, Auckland Libraries 1-W778

Increase of Rail Traffic

There was remarkable growth over the previous decade: it had doubled over ten years in the late 1890s and doubled again from 1900 to 1910. The Post Office was to take up valuable space, and as Auckland was expected to be a large city, there was intense planning for further reclamation and a possible move to another site.

Although the main trunk line to Wellington had been opened in 1908, there were limitations imposed on loads

and station operations by the steep gradient before the Parnell tunnel. This could be avoided by a new outlet from Auckland by way of an almost level deviation across Hobson Bay and through Panmure to join the main line at Westfield. It would also open up more land for development.

Reports and negotiations took place over the years between 1911 and 1914, when a new site for the station was decided on, and it was not until 1916 that all arrangements for the land were finalised.

No. 3 Site: East of Beach Road opposite Eden Street, 1930 to 2003

World War I had taken a toll on manpower and finances. Planning was slow. Although in the early 1920s the country was passing through a period of depression, the project proceeded. Gummer and Ford were chosen as the architects and a contract for the new grand station was let in April 1928. The official opening by the Minister of Railways took place on 26 November 1930 with 250 people invited. The architects won the NZ Institute of Architects Gold Medal for the most outstanding work of the year. Aucklanders and the Railways department were proud of their new, modern station building. A little earlier, on 16 November, the station opened for traffic along with the Auckland to Westfield deviation. Changeover of staff took place on the new station yard between 15 and 17 November, but both lines had been open to goods traffic earlier, from 11 May 1930.

Changing Attitudes

Over time there was much criticism of the passenger station location. It had originally been considered by planners that it was to be a through station and

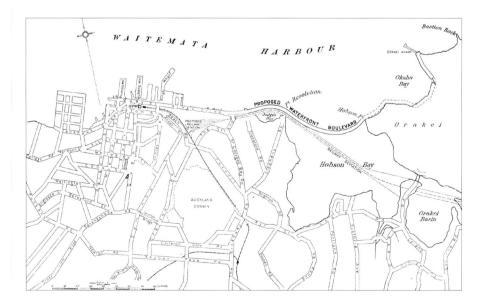

1925 plan of proposed railway station in Beach Road showing the new railway deviation across Hobson Bay and proposed Waterfront Boulevard.

Auckland City Council Municipal Record

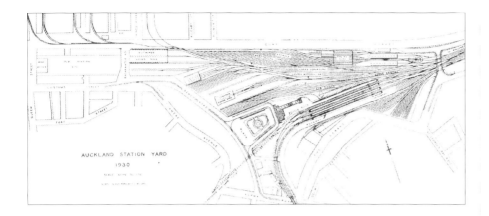

Plan of Auckland Railway
Station and yards, 1930.

Sir George Grey Special Collections,
Auckland Libraries 4-1416

not a terminal. Financial and political considerations doomed the long hoped for Auckland to Morningside deviation through the city, although a number of investigations were made. Political power at the time had the majority of representatives nearer Auckland who were promoting it, but with a change of government this representation lessened and the scheme was removed from the schedule. A much greater use would have been made of Auckland's suburban rail system if the deviation had been implemented.

For most of the past, Railways had been the major recipient of public works funds. For example prior to World War I, railways accounted for 35.9 per cent; roading 14.5 per cent, and post and telegraph 16.4 per cent of the public purse. This was to change, under the influence of the costs of World War II and more emphasis on roads and other means of transport. Government policy until then had always favoured railways as they had a vital influence on the development of the country since the first lines were opened in the 1860s, perhaps more so than in many other countries.

Auckland Railway Station,
31 October 1940.

Sir George Grey Special Collections,
Auckland Libraries 4-2728

Attitudes were changing post-war. Railways were losing money and it was difficult to justify new projects. Some lines were being disbanded and work on others curtailed. The earlier criticism that transferring the station away from Queen Street would cause inconvenience was confirmed. Places of entertainment were being located nearer the Town Hall and even lower Queen Street became less fashionable. The phasing out of trams in the mid 50s and the decreasing reliance on ferries with the opening of the harbour bridge in 1959 added further to the demise of the railway station.

However, some progress was made in Auckland with loading stations and a diesel depot at Parnell and extensive marshalling yards at Westfield and Southdown. This was the major cause of the decline of the Auckland freight yard with the gradual transfer and consolidation of freight handling activities at the new site.

The industrial centre of the city was also moving to the suburbs and surplus railway land was being made available for other purposes, with a large area sold to the local Maori Trust Board. Government's deregulation policies also contributed to the decline. A Railways Commission was set up to ensure the railways were run efficiently, but was later disbanded and the railways were again controlled by the minister. Major state spending on motorways was taking place, as proposed by the Master Transportation Plan.

By 2000 traces of rail activities in the city had all but disappeared apart from the existing passenger platforms and that serving the port. The old station, once the pride of Auckland, now became almost forgotten and attracted some vandalism.

There was still the need to maintain the small amount of suburban traffic that existed. A light rail system was investigated but not proceeded with. Diesel Multiple Units (DMUs), 19 of them, had been purchased from the newly electrified Perth system in 1993. Although five to ten years old, these DMUs, each carrying 128 passengers, were cleaner, more comfortable and more convenient than the older loco-hauled trains. Patronage on the suburban lines increased from 1,100,000 in 1993 to over 2,000,000 in 1996, showing that train travel would increase if travelling conditions were improved.

Proposals for a return of rail to the Britomart area were again being investigated. In November 1984 the District Engineer's team submitted to the Urban Transport Committee a relatively low-cost scheme for a surface station costing around $1.3 million. This did not develop much traction until about 1995. At that time the Perth units started to lift patronage when a proposal for an underground station costing $17 million was considered.

It was now confirmed that there would be a return of rail to the Britomart area.

No. 4 Site: The Britomart Transport Centre – Downtown, 2003 to today

The Council reluctantly committed $125 million for a grander scheme, but this was revoked by a change of council which went through a series of public consultations and came up with a set of principles to be incorporated in the design. This was a controversial, bolder, part-underground scheme that was to cost considerably more.

They then embarked on a two-stage design competition from which seven design finalists were selected. The winner was announced early in December 2000, the choice being Mario Madajag, a Californian living in Auckland, and Auckland's Jasmax Architects. The estimated cost was now considerably greater at $204 million and funding was agreed as follows:

Auckland City Council $135.7 m
Infrastructure Auckland $45 m
Transfund New Zealand $20 m
Auckland Regional Council $1.9 m
Land Information NZ $1.8 m

Britomart, the largest infrastructure project undertaken by a local authority in New Zealand, is located on 5.2 hectares of reclaimed land in Auckland's central business area. It links train, bus and ferry services and is part of the city's developing passenger transport network. It is also an urban renewal project that preserves adjoining heritage buildings and creates a low-level heritage precinct with new public spaces.

It was the country's first underground railway station and was planned to handle 10,500 passengers per peak hour. It occupies a floor area of 30,626 square metres and required the excavation of 190,000 cubic metres of soil with the pouring of 40,000 cubic metres of concrete, including a basement slab in places up to 1.5 metres thick and 13,000 square metres in area.

The station box is 300 metres long, 45 metres wide and 12.5 metres deep and is designed to support an eight-storey lightweight structure, with the east end designed to support a twelve-storey structure. The grand entry on the ground floor leads down to the station and by way of a 'glasshouse' out to the adjacent bus terminals and open space.

Meeting demanding seismic specifications, the close proximity to the sea and the need for existing buildings within the station footprint to remain operational during construction, together with severe cost restraints, required much innovation in the engineering and architectural design. It is unique in that it is the only underground rail station in the world that services diesel-powered rolling stock. This imposed significant design challenges for fire engineering, acoustics and air quality.

Special construction techniques included excavation by 'bottom up'

Britomart Railway Station,
2011.

J. La Roche

Original hinged foundation of a
column inside a case.

J. La Roche

construction in better ground and 'top down' in poorer ground, construction of the main beams at ground level prior to excavation and the use of shotcrete in upper shear walls of the old Central Post Office (CPO), saving time and formwork.

The new floor level was the floor of a 'crawl in' basement for the old CPO, which had its general ground floor at a higher level reached by several steps up from the street. Lowering the ground floor exposed the large hinged foundations of the columns that sat on the basement floor and were supported on a piled raft foundation. These substantial column bases can be seen displayed in glassed-in boxes as one enters the building from Queen Street.

Over time contracts were let for the demolition of the existing car park, the bus terminal and several buildings. The major contract for the underground station was let to Downer Construction on 8 October 2001. This was a return to the original site of the second station, which was started some 119 years before and departed from 27 years later. It now involved something much greater and was part of a centre connecting trains with buses and ferries.

After completion of Downer's contract the Britomart Transport Centre was taken over by the Auckland City Council. Britomart was handed over to the Auckland Regional Transport Network Limited (ARTNL) on 4 July 2003 to manage the centre on behalf of the city.

The first unofficial train arrived at the station in May 2003 to test the tracks and signalling systems. At 5.40 am on 23 June 2003 the first official train called at Platform 5 of the underground station. This was a historic occasion as almost 73 years had passed since a train had arrived in downtown Auckland. A large crowd assembled and a lone piper marched down the platform welcoming the first train to the station. The official opening was held on 25 July 2003 with 400 invited guests attending. It followed similar procedures of the past, but this time was the grandest of them all.

The public response was to use the suburban rail system in ever increasing numbers, a salute to those involved in the planning process. The Auckland Rail Transport Authority and others provided the following suburban patronage figures:

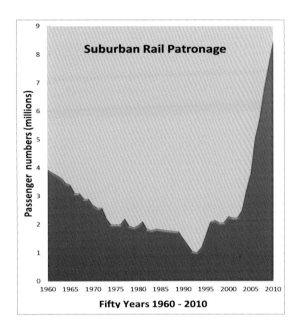

In the 1960s the total annual passenger patronage was 3.93 million, and it fell to 1.88 million by 1981 and 1.1 million by 1993. With the advent of the Perth units passenger numbers climbed back to 2.0 million in 1996 and at the opening of Britomart was 2.5 million. It then immediately climbed to 5 million in 2006 and 6.8 million in 2008, continuing to increase rapidly. By 2011 9.42 million passengers were being carried.

It has averaged an annual increase of 14 per cent over the last four years. It should be noted that these figures are for the total passenger network and not just for those passing through Britomart, although naturally it has by far the greater patronage.

It was justification for those who, a century before, were critical of the government decision to surrender railway land to the post office and eventually force the railways to move out of the business district. The *Herald*'s prediction in 1907 that the post office building would someday be transformed into a railway station came true. Resembling a modern European or Asian metro station, Auckland's gleaming transport centre has helped boost rail commuter patronage in this car-dominated city. The planned electrification of the network, due to be completed by 2013, will see peak-hour trains running every 10 minutes. Commuter patronage is expected to rise from the present nine million passenger trips a year to 30 million by 2030. Redevelopment as a through-station with an underground loop through the central business district would be required to meet growth on this scale.

It is to be hoped that government and local politicians do not procrastinate as they did in the past, and that they will enable these predictions to be fulfilled. If Auckland rail becomes a significant means of commuter transport in this city, the endeavours of those early engineers, surveyors and planners will be justified. Although often frustrated by political decisions, they are the people who laid the groundwork for rail traffic in Auckland.

References and further reading

Auckland Provincial Council Minutes, Auckland Council Libraries.

Ball, Anne Stewart, *Beginning Days of a Railway: The North Island Main Trunk Line. The Auckland End*, unpublished manuscript, July 2008.

Fletcher, R. S., *Single Track: The construction of the Main Trunk Railway*, Collins, Auckland, 1978.

'Is this New Zealand's second oldest railway?', *Rails*, July 1990.

Low, David, *Track Across the Isthmus*, The Lodestar Press, Auckland, 1972.

McGavin, T. A., *A Century of Railways at Auckland*, New Zealand Railway and Locomotive Society, Wellington, 1974.

Maylin, Melvyn and Shanmuganathan, Sulo, *Britomart Underground Railway Station*, Sesoc (Structural Engineering Society of New Zealand), Journal Vol. 16, No. 1, p. 200.

Walker, G. W., *The Auckland Railway Stations: A History*, unpublished, edited by J. F. Webley.

CHAPTER SEVEN

Bridges

As far back as 1860 plans were made to bridge Auckland Harbour. Yet it was not until 1 December 1950, with an act of Parliament forming the Auckland Harbour Bridge Authority, that it finally got going. The new Authority, chaired by Sir John Allum, quickly moved on and appointed the English firm of Freeman Fox and Partners to design and supervise a bridge. Early plans were for five lanes and two footpaths. After much discussion between the Authority, Auckland local bodies and central government, and a delay of many years, a bridge of four lanes with no footpaths was finally approved. A contract was let to a partnership of Dorman Long Ltd and Cleveland Bridge & Engineering Ltd in October 1954. Dorman Long had built the Sydney Harbour Bridge.

7.1

Auckland Harbour Bridge

by
Mike Lancaster

Building the Bridge

Construction of the reclamation at Westhaven was completed by September 1955 and work started in October on the bridge caissons (watertight structures within which construction is carried on underwater). It was fortunate that the pier construction method was by caisson as they were very large. At a later date when the bridge was running at capacity it was found that it would be possible to utilise the bridge piers for the two additional 'clip-ons'. Maybe the designers had an inkling that this would be necessary.

Erecting the steel superstructure began in December 1956, though fabrication of the structural sections in the contractor's workshops in England had started about a year previously. Erection began at the south end of the bridge, where the first two spans were built on temporary timber trestles. From pier No. 5 the spans were cantilevered northward to be landed successively on piers No. 4 and No. 3. At about the same time a start was made at the north

Early bridge proposals.

Reproduced from *1951–1961 The Auckland Harbour Bridge Authority*, booklet printed to commemorate the opening

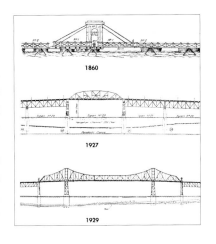

end, where the steelwork was erected on timber trestles over Northcote Point and then extended to pier No. 1. From there it was cantilevered southwards for 122 metres to form the northern half of the 244 metre navigation span.

Constructing the 146 metre span between pier Nos 3 and 2 presented the most difficult problem. It could not be cantilevered northward from the preceding span, partly because of its shape

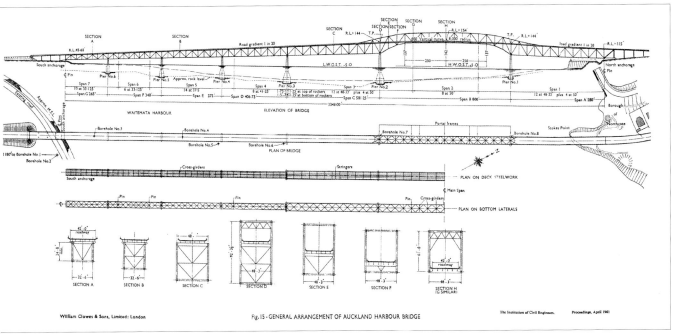

Fig. 15 - GENERAL ARRANGEMENT OF AUCKLAND HARBOUR BRIDGE

Harbour Bridge elevation.

From 'Auckland Harbour Bridge: Design', Roberts and Kerenski, Proceedings of the Institution of Civil Engineers (London), Vol. 18, 1961

and partly because the main expansion joint in the bridge is above pier No 3. It could not be cantilevered southwards from pier No. 2 because the adjacent navigation span was at that time only half completed and it would have been difficult and expensive to build this span first. Temporary trestles were out of the question because of the deep water in the centre of the harbour.

The Greatest Challenge

The bridge contractors therefore devised one of the largest and most unusual 'floating-in' operations ever undertaken in bridge construction of this nature. The span was initially built on the top of a smaller span near the south

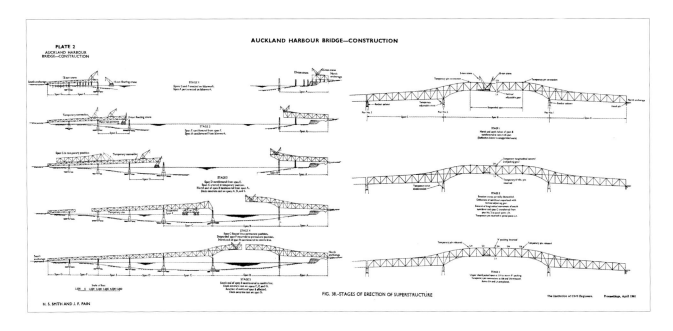

anchorage. Four pontoons were floated under the structure. One of the smaller supporting spans was disconnected from its neighbours and with the help of the rising tide, the large span, supported on the smaller one, was lifted off its supports. It was then towed out to mid-harbour and moored until weather and tide enabled it to be floated into position and lowered on a falling tide to its supports on pier Nos 2 and 3.

This was the famous 'pick-a-back' operation of 29 November 1958. The whole floating outfit, consisting of pontoons and a 61 metre long span supporting the 146 metre 'pick-a-back' span, weighed nearly 2,000 tonnes. It towered

Construction sequence.

"Auckland Harbour Bridge: Construction", Smith and Pain, Proceedings of the Institution of Civil Engineers (London), Vol. 18, 1961

Floating out Span C on 29 November 1958.

Sir George Grey Special Collections, Auckland Libraries 998-28

50 metres above the water. Control was not made any easier by a wind, gusting up to 30 knots, which sprang up while it was moored.

From that stage onward, construction was straightforward, though a considerable amount of work remained. The southern half of the navigation span was cantilevered out from No. 2 span and was joined to the northern half in March 1959. The bridge was finally opened on 30 May 1959 as a toll bridge. Enormous crowds of Aucklanders disdained boisterous weather to enjoy a walk-over prior to its opening.

Clip-ons

The traffic on the new bridge was far greater than expected. In 1967 a contract was let to a Japanese firm, Ishikawajiama-Harima Heavy Industries, for two steel box girder bridges. These bridges were to be built on each side of the Harbour Bridge, with the only connection at the existing piers using steel structures, colloquially called the 'Nippon clip-ons'. Freeman Fox and Partners were designers and the new bridges were state of the art structures using high tensile steel.

Most of the steelwork was prefabricated in Japan and transported to New Zealand on a converted oil tanker. Two massive floating cranes were used to place the units. The eastern bridge was completed in January 1969, and the western one in time for the official opening of the new bridges on 23 September 1969. Auckland now had eight lanes crossing the harbour. With 'tidal flow' on the lanes, using lights to designate direction, the bridge could now take far more traffic, more than fed into it from the northern motorway.

An Expert Commentary

In his book *You can't win 'em all: Confessions of a Public Works Engineer*, Bob Norman, a former Commissioner of Works for the New Zealand Government, writes the following:

> Now I would like to turn to one of the unsung sagas of post-war engineering in New Zealand. The first Auckland Harbour Bridge was designed by an eminent British firm of consulting engineers. The overhead steel truss was a sound economical solution, and the bridge was a great success. The time came very quickly to extend it, and the Harbour Bridge Authority decided to double its capacity by adding two more traffic lanes on each side, making eight lanes in all. The Authority retained the same British consultants who by this time had achieved worldwide recognition in

their designs of three bridges among the world's longest: the suspension bridges across the Severn, the Bosphorus and the Humber.

By this time the state of the art had advanced, and the consultants elected to use a hollow girder system instead of steel trusses. This had the advantage of using less steel and it kept all the supporting system below the roadway instead of above it. Having steelwork above the roadway exposes the bridge to some risk from being hit by vehicles and it is also harder to cope with oversized loads.

The consultants submitted their design to the Bridge Authority. It so happened that the Auckland Harbour Bridge Act required the plans to be approved by the Minister of Works on the grounds of public safety. This in turn involved the commissioner of works advising the minister, and as the department's chief designing engineer at the time I had to certify the design as sound.

So I received a bundle of plans and ran the rule over them. It did not take more than a few minutes to grasp the fact that we were dealing with a completely new animal, right at the forefront of technology. The main span of 800 feet (244 metres) was only 9½ feet (2.9 metres) deep in the middle which made it by far the most slender bridge of its type in the world. It fell right outside any codes of practice or design rules available.

I had many talks on the phone to the London consultants who were perhaps somewhat piqued that little men in the colonies would dare question their design. They were confident that no problems would arise. I even phoned up some of my old colleagues in the California Bridge Department, who were as concerned as I at such a slender structure. I suggested to the British consultants that they seek a second opinion, but in their prestigious position they were reluctant to do this.

I returned to one of those fundamental things we were taught in engineering: 'If something seems wrong, go back and have a look at the basic assumptions'. So I went back to find out why the consultants had used 9½ feet (2.9 metres). The answer turned out to be simple. The Harbour Bridge Authority had to meet the needs of two public agencies: the National Roads Board whose state highway went over the top of the bridge, and the Auckland Harbour Board whose waters flowed underneath. Since road levels at the ends of the bridge were fixed this limited the height in the middle. The Harbour Board required a clear opening of 43.5 metres above high water. This fixed the lowest height of the underside of the bridge in the middle. Thus the consultants were stuck with the bit in between and this was 2.9 metres and so they designed accordingly.

So I went to the Roads Board and asked 'would it really matter in these circumstances if the road were a wee bit steeper, say 1 in 19.5 instead of 1 in 20 – because this would make all the difference in the centre?' I also went to the chairman if the Harbour Board and asked why he wanted the 143 foot (43.6 metre) clearance. 'I don't know' said the chairman, 'but I'll find out'. It turned out the measurement related to the mast height of the Canberra, the largest ship trading in NZ waters. Since all the port facilities are down-harbour from the bridge crossing this seemed to me to be a bit unrealistic. I asked the chairman if he could envisage the Canberra sailing under the bridge and anchoring up-harbour, or perhaps tied to the Chelsea Sugar wharf. So we squeezed 4 feet (1.2 metres) out of the Harbour Board, the consultants re-designed the bridge with a 13½ foot (4.12 metre) deep centre span, and I signed the plans.

But that was not the whole story. Some years later a series of failures occurred to similarly designed box girder bridges all round the world, culminating in the disaster at West Gate Bridge in Melbourne. There were various contributing factors, but one thing stood out. Structures designed right up to the limit are the ones that are more likely to get

Auckland Harbour Bridge with 'clip-ons' viewed from Northcote.

into trouble if anything goes wrong – in the design, the construction, or when in use.

The same firm of British consultants had designed the Westgate Bridge and one day we had a call from one of the partners, who was in Melbourne. He wanted to come over and have a look inside the hollow box girder of the main span at Auckland. So he went up with our chief civil engineer, and with the Harbour Board staff they entered the box in the main span. They made their way along the cat-walk inside the box beam and came to the third vertical stiffener from the end. 'Yes there it is', said the consultant, 'just as I predicted'. The 9.7m high stiffening member was buckled 61 millimetres out of line. By this time I was back in the ministry's top management group, and the next few months saw a flurry of activity. It was decided to strengthen the girder system. Following some delicate negotiations with the consultants, an eminent German engineer was retained by the Authority to work out what had to be done, in cooperation with the British firm. Our chief civil engineer was directed to draw up terms of reference for this new consultancy, and one upshot of his involvement was a hurried trip to Berlin to arbitrate on some areas of disagreement between the two consultants. The bridge was quietly and successfully strengthened at minimal cost.

What would have happened if the old Works Department, in advising the minister on the consultant's first proposals, had simply been prepared to accept without question a design produced by one of the world's top consulting engineering firms? At the least would the Auckland Harbour Bridge Authority have had a major facility out of service for a long time for extensive reconstruction? Or at the worst would a row of Auckland Regional Authority buses filled with the bones of passengers now be rusting on the bottom of the Waitemata Harbour?

There are two morals of this tale. The first is that a major public work was limited to some quite unrealistic restraints in the design, and that neither the client (the bridge authority) nor its overseas consultant was aware that these constraints were negotiable. It took an independent adviser, the ministry, to look back at the reasons, and to find a solution which, until then, had never been explored.

The other lesson is a bit more subtle. After a rash of bridge failures, came the witch hunt. In Britain a committee of inquiry was set up to develop a new set of rules for box girder designs. The resulting report made it so tough for designers that box girders virtually disappeared from the scene, and for years a new technology languished with little sponsorship.

Cracking Problems

Some 15 years after the 'clip-ons' were finished, it was noticed during a routine inspection inside the box girders that there was a small problem with some fillet welds on strengthening channels of the deck. While it was not a major problem it had to be fixed by replacing the fillet welded sleeves with 100 per cent welds. It was basically a metal fatigue problem, not previously encountered, which meant the clip-on section of the bridge concerned had to be closed overnight while re-welding was done. The heavy traffic was confined to the centre bridge while the repairs were being made and the whole process took about a year, as several thousand welds were needed.

Removal of Tolls

With vast increases in traffic, the revenue from tolls was great and tolls were first reduced and then made one way. The bridge having been financed with low interest loans, high interest on excess revenue from tolls meant that the loans could be paid off. Also the cost of collecting the tolls with inflation was becoming more than the toll revenue, so the Harbour Bridge Authority asked the National Roads Board (NRB) if it would like to take over the bridge, provided it would be made toll free. After an inspection of the bridge and operations this was agreed by the NRB and it then became the responsibility of the Ministry of Works and Development (MWD). Most of the Auckland Harbour Bridge Authority staff were taken over and operations were carried on without any problems.

Moveable Barriers

While the 'tidal flow' on the bridge was easily controlled by the light signals, the increased amount of traffic was making it potentially more dangerous, so when an enterprising civil engineer suggested the possibility of a moveable concrete barrier this option was investigated. It was a novel concept invented in France and considered in Australia, but never used on a bridge like ours with a 1 in 20 gradient. Although there were some initial teething problems, the barrier was installed in 1990 and worked very well for nearly 20 years.

Light Rail

In the first discussions on a harbour crossing, putting rail tracks on the bridge was considered, but rejected mainly because of cost. However, decades later, with a big resurgence of interest in public transport and particularly light rail, the Auckland Regional Authority asked the MWD to check the possibility of putting a light rail track on the 'clip-ons'. This was shown to be feasible provided the residual 5.5 metres wide roadway was used only by light road traffic. As the heavy road traffic had been confined to the centre bridge for over a year without any problems this would be perfectly reasonable. Recently, for other reasons, this has now been required.

While a tunnel to the North Shore would be preferable because present motorways are approaching capacity, an extension of the railway from the Britomart station would thus make it feasible to put light rail over the Harbour Bridge.

Acknowledgement

Grateful thanks are due to Bob Norman for permission to quote his book at length.

References and further reading

Auckland Harbour Bridge Authority, *1951 1961 The Auckland Harbour Bridge Authority*, booklet to commemorate the opening of the bridge on 30 May 1959.

IPENZ Heritage Website, www.ipenz.org.nz/heritage.

Lang, Renée, *Auckland Harbour Bridge: 50 Years of a City Icon*, Random House, Auckland, 2009.

Norman, Bob, *You can't win 'em all: Confessions of a Public Works Engineer*, Slide Rule Press, Porirua, 1997.

Roberts, Gilbert & Kerensky, Oleg Alexander, 'Auckland Harbour Bridge: Design', Proceedings of the Institution of Civil Engineers (London), Vol. 18, pp 423–458, 1961.

Smith, Hubert Shirley & Pain, John Freeman, 'Auckland Harbour Bridge: Construction', Proceedings of the Institution of Civil Engineers (London), Vol. 18, pp 459–478, 1961.

7.2

Grafton Bridge

*by
Bryan Bartley*

There is a link between engineering heritage in Australia and that in New Zealand, in the form of Auckland's Grafton Bridge, which has a special pride of place in New Zealand but was designed and built by the Australian company Ferro-Concrete of Australasia Ltd.

It took two and a half years to build, being opened in April 1910. At that time it was claimed to be the biggest-span, concrete-arch bridge in the world. The three-pinned arch spans 97.6 metres, rising 25.6 metres above the abutments and 43.3 metres above the valley floor. The arch is actually two reinforced concrete arches side by side and connected by short beams.

It was certainly a pioneering structure, being very early in reinforced concrete, showing great engineering enterprise and brilliance of design. The American Concrete Institute recognises it as one of the 100 most significant concrete structures in the world.

The Auckland City Council received two tenders in 1907. The first was from the Messrs J. McLean & Son for a steel bridge to be manufactured by the American Bridge Building Company for £28,730. The second tender was for the reinforced concrete bridge, for the sum of £31,918. The new city engineer, Mr W. E. Bush, recommended that the concrete design be accepted, because the maintenance costs would be much lower.

For the Ferro-Concrete Company Mr R. F. Moore was chief engineer, and Mr Rosseger the chief assistant engineer who made the calculations. The timber falsework (temporary structures used to support spanning or arched structures to hold the component in place until its construction is sufficiently advanced to support itself) was massive and consisted of 943 cubic metres of West Australian jarrah and Oregon pine. According to *Cassier's Magazine* in August 1910, 'The height of the moulds was accurately adjusted by 160 bottle jacks which performed their work more effectively than the sand boxes more generally employed.'

Concrete was made from beach shingle, a six to one mix using local cement. Preliminary tests of the concrete were made by Professor Warren of Sydney and the design strength fixed at 3.4 mPa (megapascals, a unit of pressure).

All did not go well for the Ferro-Concrete Company. The site was difficult, being in a steep-sided bush-clad valley, and there was trouble with the complexity of the formwork and getting it in place. Late in the contract the company could not continue and was declared bankrupt. The job was finished by council labour. The arch design had been submitted to Professor Moersch of Germany and a clause in the contract stipulated that 'no progress payments should be made on the arch span till it was completed and tested.' This no doubt caused the downfall of the company. The final cost was £35,000, an overrun of only 9.5 per cent.

Loading test on the newly completed Grafton Bridge, 14 March 1910.

Load tests were carried out on the newly completed bridge. First, one half of the arch span was loaded with 297 tonnes of roading aggregate giving, in technical terms, 5.4 kPa (kilopascals) and the deflection was 3.17 millimetres. However, temperature movement was also significant. When the road metal load was removed, two steam rollers, of combined weight 31.5 tonnes, were run over the bridge. The deflection was 2.12 millimetres. 'In all cases the results were very satisfactory,', according to the test report.

The claim by Mr Bush that the maintenance would be very low was borne out by experience: 'the record of maintenance on the structure over a quarter of a century was excellent being almost nil' according to City Engineer James Tyler in a report to the Auckland City Council in 1936.

However, in 1936 cracks, which had been observed for some time, became worse and 'a considerable piece of concrete became detached and fell away from the bottom chord of the span adjacent to the main arch at the Grafton Road end'. (A. J. Dickson report.) The spans away from the main arch were made up as Vierendeel girders (an open truss form of bridge support) with a top and bottom chord and vertical posts being 2.7 metres deep. The appearance was of a number of square openings with big chamfers in the corners and with the end openings adjacent to the supports filled in. The shear stresses in these Vierendeel frames were excessive, as the detailed study that followed demonstrated, and it was considered surprising that the structural performance had been so good. The remedy was to fill in the square openings with concrete, with special emphasis on the shear reinforcement, thus turning the frames into large I-section beams.

Since that time the maintenance has been of a minor nature, associated

The completed Grafton Bridge in 1913, showing Vierindeel girders with openings under the bridge deck that were later encased.

Sir George Grey Special Collections, Auckland Libraries 1-W1400

with the ravages of time, such as cover to the reinforcing steel inside the concrete on the beam edges. Repair details are given in a paper by A. J. Dickson, later to become city engineer, who at 36 became the youngest president of the New Zealand Institution of Engineers (now IPENZ). After the repairs, however, the bridge loading was reduced to cars and pedestrians only. No trucks were allowed and even fire engines attending the Auckland Hospital were required to take the long journey round.

When the bridge was 99 years old in 2009, it was decided to upgrade it to carry the heaviest traffic, Class 1 loading, which would enable it to become part of a main transport route acting as a bus lane on weekdays between the city and Newmarket. The maximum load was to rise from seven to 44 tonnes. This upgrade was a major test of professional engineering skills and use of new materials and techniques.

The design work and supervision for the latest upgrade was done by Auckland consultant engineers Beca Carter Hollings & Ferner Ltd. The main contractor was Brian Perry Civil, with specialist contractor BBR Contech (Construction Techniques Ltd). It was reported in the *New Zealand Herald* of 28 July 2009 that the bridge was 'being bolstered with carbon fibre' in a strengthening project which included 'injecting epoxy resin into 805 metres of cracks in the 99-year-old structure's concrete beams and columns.'

Carbon fibre-reinforced polymer plates were used for the first time in New Zealand as part of the strengthening. These have been inserted into slots in the existing bridge and coated over so as to be invisible after completion. Other strengthening techniques include coring into piers beneath ground and inserting reinforcement to increase strength to resist modern earthquake loading.

It is a remarkable story of a pioneer structure with low maintenance for 100 years being upgraded to a new life carrying much heavier loads. Grafton Bridge was reopened ahead of schedule in October 2009 at a cost of $6.9 million, ready to celebrate its centenary with no significant change in its heritage appearance.

References and further reading

Bush, G. W. A., *Decently and in Order: The Centennial History of Auckland City Council*, Collins, Auckland, 1971.
Dickson, A. J., *Reconstruction of Approach Spans Grafton Bridge*, Proceedings NZ Institution of Engineers, Vol. 26, p. 32.
NZ Historic Places Trust, *Grafton Bridge*, Register Number 16.
Thornton, Geoffrey, *Cast in Concrete: Concrete Construction in New Zealand 1850–1939*, Reed Publishing, Auckland, 1996.
Thornton, Geoffrey, *Bridging the Gap: Early Bridges in New Zealand 1830–1939*, Reed Publishing, Auckland, 2001.

A harbour crossing between Onehunga and Mangere has always been important, but until 1875 it was necessary to use a row boat or the ferry. The *Taranaki Herald* reported in June 1866, 'A company is being formed for the purpose of connecting Onehunga and Mangere by means of a bridge across the Manukau. The proposed capital is £10,000. The Provincial Government have granted the company a right to erect a bridge, and to collect tolls thereon for the period of fifty years, and have further agreed to contribute £1 per acre for all the confiscated lands in the district.'

A design competition was called and civil engineer James Stewart was announced the winner on 7 August 1866. A meeting of shareholders a month later was adjourned until the Provincial Government could advise how much money it could contribute. After continuing discussion and debate a public meeting held in June 1872 called on Provincial Council member Captain

7.3

Mangere Bridge

*by
Mike Lancaster
and
John La Roche*

Drawing of the first Mangere
Bridge, 1875.

Ministry of Works brochure, 1983,
South Western Motorway Mangere
Motorway Bridge, courtesy Opus Inter-
national Consultants

Lundon to explain what had happened to the bridge proposal. He said that the government would consider granting 300 acres of land at Mangere as an endowment, but this could not proceed because the land was required for 'native' purposes. The Colonial Secretary had promised £15,000 under the Public Works Act subject to conditions. The Minister of Public Works, Mr J. D. Ormond, promised that the work would start, but nothing had been done. Another public meeting in July 1872 resolved:

> That this meeting is of the opinion that as the General Government have intimated that they are prepared to appropriate (on certain terms) £15,000 for the erection and formation of a bridge or causeway across the Manukau to connect Onehunga with Mangere and the up-country districts, it becomes imperatively necessary to urge the Government and Public Works Department to a speedy commencement of such a desirable and reproductive public work.

By 1874 the government authorised the Public Works Department to call tenders for a bridge across the harbour to Mangere. The narrow timber truss bridge, a common design at the time, had 20 spans each of 12.2 metres, and cost £14,997 to build. In stormy weather it was hazardous for pedestrians, but no doubt less hazardous than a boat crossing in strong tidal currents. The bridge was supported by jarrah timber piles imported from Western Australia. Within two years these piles were being vigorously attacked underwater by teredo worm, *Teredo navalis,* often called shipworms. These are a salt water clams that bore into wooden structures immersed in seawater. Samples were sent to Western Australia for testing when it was suggested that the worms would only attack the outer sap wood. Similar problems were being experienced with Auckland's Queen Street Wharf piles. Continual replacement of piles was necessary, and in 1910 more than 30 piles were replaced. A replacement bridge was obviously needed. A petition from the ratepayers to the Mangere Road Board was presented to the House of Representatives on behalf of the Manukau-Tamaki Canal Project on 30 September 1911 by Mr J. E. Taylor, a member of Auckland Harbour Board. The petition requested that the canal connecting the Tamaki River with the Manukau Harbour be constructed with a lock at Mangere Bridge and another across the Tamaki River, which would

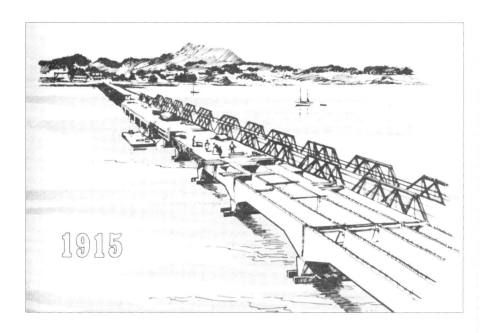

Drawing showing the second
Mangere Bridge being
constructed in Ferro-concrete
in 1915.

Ministry of Works brochure, 1983,
South Western Motorway Mangere
Motorway Bridge, courtesy Opus Inter-
national Consultants

create two salt-water lakes to provide a navigable waterway. A connection to the
Waikato River at Waiuku was also proposed. At the time, the Marine Depart-
ment were advocating an opening span in the new ferro-concrete Mangere
Bridge.

Mr R. F. Moore of Ferro-Concrete Company of Australasia, who designed
Grafton Bridge and Queens Wharf, was awarded the design contract in 1914.
This low-level bridge with 17 spans was built for the Onehunga Borough
Council between 1912 and 1916 at a cost of £22,000. It is 246 metres in length
with multiple span reinforced concrete beams resting on four reinforced con-

Ferro-concrete, low-level
Mangere Bridge, now used
only for foot traffic, 2010.

J. La Roche

crete piles. An alternative design with
one span opening was presented but
this was not accepted. A vehicle count
spread over four days in February 1922
showed the importance of this bridge.
There were 1,565 motorcars, 231 lorries,
68 motorbikes, 61 horses, 427 horse and
traps, 177 horse and carts, 36 wagons,
713 bikes and 735 pedestrians using
the new bridge. But by 1927 there was
significant deterioration of the concrete
surface, the handrail posts, the supporting beams and approach embankments.
The cost of repairs was estimated in
1938 to be £4,500 to be shared between

Temporary Bailey bridge on the
old Mangere Bridge, 1980.

MWD photo, A. W. Aitken collection,
courtesy Opus International Consultants

the Main Highway Board, Manukau County Council, Onehunga Borough and Auckland City.

Increased traffic after the opening of Mangere International Airport 1966, the need for a by-pass for Onehunga and the deteriorating condition of this bridge made a new bridge necessary. By 1980 the Ministry of Works had to erect a temporary Bailey bridge over the most deteriorated section to carry the 33,000 vehicles per day using the bridge. After the opening of the new bridge in 1983, the old bridge was closed to traffic, leaving it for use by fishermen, pedestrians and cyclists.

The following report was presented to the December 1982 meeting of the then National Roads Board by the chief highways engineer Mr E. J. Burt.

The transportation study carried out in Auckland in 1965 by De Leuw Cather proposed construction of a network of motorways to service the long term traffic needs of the metropolitan area. Amongst these motorways was to be a major connection running south eastwards from Pt Chevalier and the possible site for the second Auckland Harbour Bridge, through Onehunga and thence on via a new bridge across the Manukau Harbour at Mangere through to the Southern Motorway at Wiri. Motorway connections were envisaged from this new motorway on the north side of the Manukau Harbour heading to Mount Wellington and south of Mangere heading to the airport.

To cater for the total traffic demand this system would generate, eight traffic lanes were seen as necessary across the Manukau Harbour.

By the late 1960s replacement of the existing Mangere Bridge taking SH 20 across Manukau Harbour was becoming a priority need due to the very poor structural condition of the bridge and the high levels of traffic congestion being experienced daily on the approaches to it. As budgetary restraints were beginning to affect the progress on many major roading projects throughout the country, design work and tender documents for the new motorway bridge and its approaches were produced to enable a single four lane structure to be built. The possibility of it having to be duplicated at some later stage was taken into account. The approaches were planned to extend to Queenstown Road across Onehunga Bay and Gloucester Park on the north side of Manukau Harbour, and from the bridge, via a bypass to the east of Mangere Bridge settlement and its commercial area, to rejoin SH 20 near Walmsley Road on the south side of the harbour.

Requirements from the harbour board for possible development of industrial areas in the upper part of the harbour to be serviced by barges resulted in a minimum clearance of 40 ft (12.2 metres) having to be provided over this navigational channel. The possibility of shipping using a canal link to the Tamaki River was considered a future possibility. The bridge length was minimised by use of a substantial filling across the tidal mudflats at the southern approach to the bridge.

The Ministry of Works who were responsible for design, undertook model testing for earthquake shocks to ensure flexibility of the pier substructure. The bridge is divided into four sections, each able to move independently during an earthquake. Hinged joints connecting each section will absorb earthquake vibrations and up to 430 millimetres of temperature movement. With an overall length of 650 metres there are fifteen spans of lengths between 30 metres and 86 metres. At the time of construction, the 86 metre span over the proposed shipping lane was the longest concrete bridge span in New Zealand. The superstructure is formed from twin 4.4 metre wide prestressed concrete box girders with a cantilevered deck giving a total width of 21.9 metres. There is a 4 metre wide pedestrian and cycleway under the traffic deck on the west side and, in between the two box girders, there is a service walkway for electricity cables, gas pipes and telegraph cables.

Work commenced in 1972/73 with earthworks in the Gloucester Park area at the northern end of the new bridge and on the construction of an embankment of the southern abutment, in the readiness for the foundation piling contract. At that stage it was intended to construct the bridge in two contracts with foundations assessed to cost $1.334 million and the superstructure $6.944 million giving a total $8.278 million for the complete work.

The contract for the construction of the foundations was let on 25 January 1973 to Gilberd Hadfield Pile Co Ltd for $1,042,010.

On 24 July 1974 a contract for completion of the bridge structure was let to Wilkins and Davies Construction Co. Ltd with a contract price of $6,841,053. This contract was due for completion in three years, that is, by July 1978. Initial progress was satisfactory but by 1975 and 1976 industrial problems seriously affected the project, reaching a peak in September 1976 when no work occurred.

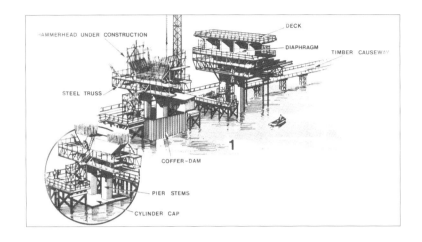

Above: Mangere Bridge construction sequence, stage 1.

MWD Brochure, South Western Motorway Mangere Motorway Bridge, courtesy Opus International Consultants

Below: Mangere Bridge construction sequence, stages 2 and 3.

MWD Brochure, South Western Motorway Mangere Motorway Bridge, courtesy Opus International Consultants

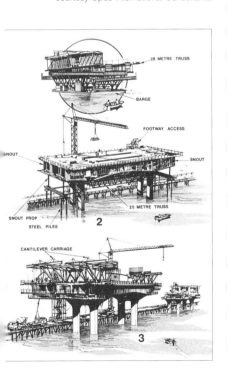

Regrettably, the industrial situation failed to improve and, by July 1978, the position was reached where the Board accepted that suspension of the contract was necessary. The contract work was finally terminated in May 1979 by which stage contract payments totalled $8,510,726 with 80% of the work completed. Industrial problems had resulted in the loss of some 47,000 man hours during the first three years of this contract.

After a further period, in which it was hoped that the industrial problems could be solved satisfactorily, tenders for completion of the remaining structural works were invited in December 1979 from four selected contractors. A contract was eventually let in November 1980 to Fletcher Construction Co. Ltd with a contract period of 15 months plus an assessed site establishment time of three months, which was expected to see work completed by May 1982. The contract price was $5,257,391. The contract did not proceed as rapidly as had been hoped, while tidying up and repair works resulting from the break between the two contracts was more extensive than had been anticipated. Contract extensions were approved up to October 1982, but completion of all works was not expected until February 1983, with the final contract payments likely to be $7,637,000.

In summary then, the bridge which was expected in 1973 to be completed over a four and a half year period at a cost of $8.3 million in 1972/3 values has taken 10 years to complete at a total construction cost of $18.4 million in dollars of the day, or $7.85 million when reduced back to 1972/3 values.

Taking account of the costs of approach works between Neilson Street, Onehunga and Walmsley Road at Mangere, together with ancillary works arranged by the Ministry of Works and Development, plus the cost of providing Bailey bridge strengthening to maintain the existing bridge in an adequate operational condition for the past two years, the cost of this project has been almost $25 million [$74,750,000 in today's terms].

State Highway 20 will soon provide a motorway to bypass the central city linking the North-Western Motorway at Waterview to the Southern Motorway at Manukau City. This motorway has been progressively extended since the building of the third Mangere Bridge in 1983. With each extension, this route becomes more popular and traffic volumes have increased to the stage that a second four-lane Mangere Bridge became necessary, with 89,000 vehicles crossing the bridge by 2007. It was completed by Fletcher Construction Ltd at a cost of $230 million, and opened to traffic seven months ahead of schedule on 27 July 2010. The majority of visitors for the 2011 Rugby World Cup arrived by air and travelled to the city across Mangere Bridge. This new bridge and the motorway widening on either side was designed to provide for 160,000 vehicles per day crossing the bridge by 2021.

References and further reading

Auckland Motorways, Ministry of Works, 1984.

Auckland Motorways, NZ Transport Agency, 2008.

Ball, Anne Stewart, *Mangere Bridge*, unpublished information, Auckland Council Archives letter files.

Mangere Motorway Bridge, Ministry of Works and Development, 1983.

Papers Past, *Taranaki Herald*, 9 June 1866, p. 5.

Papers Past, *Daily Southern Cross*, 27 August 1866, p. 6.

Papers Past, *Daily Southern Cross*, 13 June 1872, p. 3.

Papers Past, *Daily Southern Cross*, 11 July 1872, p. 3.

Papers Past, *Daily Southern Cross*, 20 May 1876, p. 3.

Ringer, Bruce, *Manukau's Journey,* an on-line history of the Manukau region, first published in 2004 by Manukau City Council.

Thornton, Geoffrey, *Bridging the Gap: Early Bridges in New Zealand 1830–1939*, Reed Publishing, Auckland, 2001.

Top: First Mangere Bridge motorway under construction.

MWD photo, A. W. Aitken collection, courtesy Opus International Consultants

Above: Duplicated Mangere Bridge viaducts on open day, 25 July 2010 .

J. La Roche

7.4

Newmarket Viaduct

by
Mike Lancaster
and
John La Roche

The Newmarket Viaduct near the start of the Southern Motorway is a massive structure towering over 45 metres above the old borough of Newmarket. It was described by the *New Zealand Herald* in June 2007 as 'one of the most distinctive engineering features of New Zealand'. It is 689 metres long, 27 metres wide and built of prestressed concrete. At the time of its construction, from 1962 to 1966, it was the largest prestressed concrete bridge in New Zealand and very much 'state of the art design'.

Newmarket viaduct.

Ministry of Works Auckland Motorways 1984, courtesy Opus International

Designed by the Ministry of Works for the National Roads Board at a cost of $2.26 million, the Newmarket Viaduct is a vital connection in Auckland's motorway system. Initially a steel girder structure was considered, but after consideration of the imported steel content and maintenance costs, a concrete structure was proposed. The need to cross a busy urban area, major roadways and a dual track railway led to the design of a prestressed concrete box girder structure. The twin parallel structures that form the viaduct have a longitudinal 'S' curvature and super elevation (cross slope to allow for high speeds). It was a very complex structure for its time. There are 16 spans varying in length between 33.5 metres and 50 metres. It was designed to be constructed from each supporting column as balanced cantilevers, progressively moving out from each side until the cantilevers from adjacent columns met in the middle.

As each new 3.2 metre long section was added, it was tied back to previously erected units by prestressing cables. This process continued until finally the cantilevering spans from adjacent piers were closed at mid span. Further prestressing cables were then threaded into the units to tie the whole structure

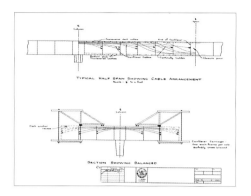

together. Very precise calculations of the loads in each prestressing cable were necessary. The design included dynamic analysis for the loads to withstand an earthquake that might occur only once in 500 years.

Of particular interest in the engineering world was a problem which occurred early in its life due to a temperature differential between the deck, which had a black bitumen wear coat, and the bottom of the beams, which were light-coloured concrete. This caused some unacceptable cracking that had not previously been known as a design problem. The solution, which was of interest to engineers around the world, was to put in additional prestressed cables and place a light-coloured stone chip on the black bitumen road surface. This solved the cracking problem, but now that traffic has increased significantly, the existing six traffic lanes are not adequate.

In 2007, the viaduct carried an average of 163,500 vehicles per day, making it one of the busiest sections of the Auckland motorway system. Because it is a vital link in the motorway system more lanes are needed. A new structure is being built now, designed to withstand an earthquake that might occur only once in 2500 years. There will be four stages in the construction of the new replacement viaduct. The first stage, completed in 2010, has built four new south-bound lanes alongside the original viaduct. Stage two will be the dismantling of the original south-bound lanes. Stage three will build three new northbound lanes in place of the present southbound lanes. The

Above: Newmarket viaduct construction, 1964.

Sir George Grey Special Collections, Auckland Libraries 7-A1032

Top left: Balanced cantilever construction, from a John Built technical paper,

Courtesy Opus International Consultants

Below: Perspective view showing balanced cantilever construction, from a John Built paper.

Courtesy Opus International Consultants

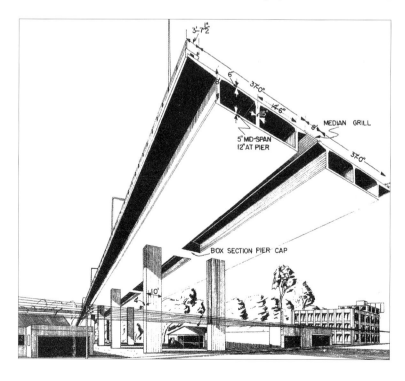

Top: Newmarket viaduct replacement, 2010.

B. Bartley

Above: Removal of north side of original viaduct, February 2011.

B. Bartley

final phase will be the demolition of the original northbound viaduct. A fourth lane could be added to the northbound side at a later date but because of other capacity restrictions around Spaghetti Junction (the junction of the motorway systems at Newton) it has been decided not to add the extra lane at this time. The reasons for dismantling the old viaduct are given in an article in the e.nz magazine referred to below. The public of Auckland turned out in their thousands on a blustery and rainy day for a walk-over prior to the opening of the new southbound viaduct in 2010 just as they had done for the original viaduct 44 years previously. It is clear that Aucklanders relish celebrating their iconic engineering motorways and bridges.

References and further reading

Auckland Motorways, NZ Transport Agency, 2008.

Built, John W., *Newmarket Viaduct*, New Zealand Engineering, Vol. 20, No. 12, December 1965.

From Viaduct to Viaduct, e.nz Magazine, Vol. 10/6, November/December, 2009.

IPENZ, *Engineering to 1990*, Engineering Publications Co. Ltd, p. 10.

Newmarket Viaduct, http://en.wikipedia.org/wiki/Newmarket_Viaduct

Noonan, Rosslyn J., *By Design,* Ministry of Works & Development, Wellington, 1975.

A very early example of a swing span bridge was the bridge across the Tamaki River at Panmure connecting the important outpost of Howick to Panmure and Auckland. Fencible settlements had been established by the New Zealand Government in 1847 at Howick, Panmure, Otahuhu and Onehunga as outposts to protect Auckland from a possible Maori attack from the south. The Fencibles were retired soldiers from Britain and Ireland who were given land and a cottage in return for being available to defend Auckland. The bridge was built in 1864–65 and had a 12.2 metre swing span.

In 1857 local residents had petitioned the Auckland Provincial Council for a bridge. The bridge was designed by Mr W. R. Collett under direction of William Weaver, Engineer-in-Chief to the Auckland Provincial Government from 1864 to 1868. Work began in October 1864 to construct the bridge, 576 feet (175.6 metres) long and 21 feet (6.4 metres) wide. The wrought iron swing span and associated ironwork was fabricated by P. N. Russell & Co. in Sydney before being shipped to Auckland. The abutments were made from bluestone blocks, each weighing one and a half to two tons, which were brought from Melbourne. The bridge had 18 fixed spans and the opening span that provided 40 feet (12.2 metres) of clear waterway opening for ships to pass.

7.5

Tamaki River Bridge, Panmure

by
John La Roche

Tamaki River Bridge, 1910.

Sir George Grey Special Collections, Auckland Libraries 7-A10001

Tamaki River Bridge showing on the left the hand winch, swing span and rotating platform.

Courtesy Alan La Roche, Udy Collection

Scow *Pukapuka* passing through the Panmure Bridge 1912.

Courtesy Howick Historical Society

There was considerable difficulty in obtaining totara timber piles of up to the necessary 65 feet (19.8 metres) in length. These in turn had to be sheathed in Muntz metal (brass, 60 per cent copper and 40 per cent zinc) to prevent the attack of teredo worms. Foundations for the bridge at the eastern abutment under the swinging span were also difficult, requiring excavation to 14 feet (4.3 metres) below the bed of the river using a cofferdam (a temporary watertight enclosure used for construction below water level). The ground conditions were particularly difficult, changing from silt to hard blue clay and rock within a short depth. The total cost of the bridge was £15,189 14s 7d plus £1,835 5s 5d for the approach roads, toll house and mooring dolphins.

The bridge was opened by Mr Robert Graham, Superintendent of the Auckland Province, on 20 October 1865, with long-winded speeches and toasts followed by dancing on the kauri deck of the bridge. After the official opening there were delays while the approach roads were finished and the swing bridge loaded with ballast, before traffic was finally admitted in the first week in March 1866.

Winch and turntable of
original bridge under the ship
chandlery store.

J. La Roche photo

The swinging span is mounted on a circular rail that was turned by a hand-operated winch. There were many complaints about the time taken to open the swinging section and sometimes boats were held up for days when difficulties with the swinging section were experienced, angering many farmers along the river who relied on ships to take their wheat and chaff to markets.

Like the Auckland Harbour Bridge, initially tolls were charged for crossing the bridge, but later phased out. Today part of the swinging steelwork, the circular rail and hand winch on top of the massive bluestone pier remain under a ships' chandlery store built over the old swing span. Although the chandlery store and jetty are privately owned, the public are permitted to visit the remains of this historic bridge under the store.

This first bridge lasted 51 years until 1916 when it was replaced by a higher-level ferro-concrete bridge, which deteriorated and was demolished after the present bridge was opened in December 1959. This latter bridge is a three-lane reinforced high-level bridge, with the centre lane being used for

View to the ship chandlery
store with the 1959 Pakuranga
Bridge underneath and the
Waipuna Road bridge behind,
2011.

J. La Roche

traffic flow westwards in the morning and eastwards in the afternoon. It was designed by A. O. Barrowclough of Andrew Murray Partners for the Manukau County Council. While still in use, it is dwarfed by the soaring upstream Pakuranga Highway Bridge, known locally as the Waipuna Bridge. This bridge was designed by Gavin Cormack of Beca Carter Hollings and Ferner, built by Etude et Enterprises and opened on 10 May 1974.

References and further reading

Baker, R. A., *From Bush to Borough: An Illustrated History of the Mount Wellington Area*, Published by Tamaki City Council, 1987.

Illustrated London News, 12 October 1867.

Journals of the Auckland Provincial Council 1865, 1866.

La Roche, Alan, *The History of Howick and Pakuranga*, Howick and Districts Historical Society, Auckland, 1991.

Ringer, Bruce, *Manukau's Journey,* an on-line history of the Manukau region, first published in 2004 by Manukau City Council.

CHAPTER EIGHT

Telecommunications

Introduction

Right from the very first days of the Auckland settlement there was a need for better communications. A feature of the response to this need was the quick uptake of new technology as it became available, a feature which continues to the present day.

Telegraph

In the early 1860s there was a strong stimulus for establishment of telegraph lines in Auckland, arising from the perceived threat of attack from the Waikato Maori in response to invasion and land-grabbing by European settlers.

Corporal Alexander Brodie had arrived in Auckland aged 21, having attended the UK Telegraph School of the Royal Engineers at Chatham in Kent. Along with a detachment of Royal Engineers surveyors and telegraphists, he was sent to New Zealand in October 1862 to open up electrical communication for the military forces in the Waikato. Commencing in February 1863, Brodie worked south from the Albert Barracks in Auckland through Otahuhu to connect the line to the Drury military base by 17 June. The line was a single wire, mounted on kauri poles of which some 300 were needed for this work.

By April 1864 Brodie had reached Rangiriri, crossing many Waikato swamps. Te Awamutu and Cambridge were connected by October of that year. Brodie came under fire on several occasions and received the New Zealand War Medal. He was commended by the British Commander, General Cameron, and the Provincial Government for his services. Brodie was appointed Inspector of the Military Electric Telegraph in New Zealand from 1863 to 1867. He instructed the first telegraph operators in the country, many of whom went on to hold senior positions in the telegraph department. Telegraph offices were

8.1

Telecommunications in Auckland

by
Neil Mander
and
John La Roche

British troops on the Devil's
Nest road through the bush
near Drury.

Sir George Grey Special Collections,
Auckland Libraries 1-W474

small huts where operators tapped out messages in Morse code. Official messages were sent free, but the public paid one shilling for a 20-word message from Auckland to Otahuhu and one shilling and sixpence for a 20-word message to Drury. Military officers were allowed to send personal messages at half price. By September 1866 the line was very profitable, with an annual return of nearly £7,000 on a capital expenditure of £1,400.

A line was connected through to Wellington in April 1872, going via Thames, Tauranga, Taupo, Napier, Castlepoint and Masterton. Telegraph links were completed to Hokianga, Dargaville and Kaitaia in the north by 1881.

Later developments saw paper tape punched from keyboards and the introduction of a five-unit code. The tape was fed into a tape reader which converted the pattern of holes in the tape into the online signals which were decoded into printed, gummed paper strips which were glued onto yellow telegram forms.

This public point-to-point service was eventually phased out in the late 1980s, taking with it the well-established tradition of 'wedding telegrams'.

Working examples of some of this equipment, including Morse equipment and a pole-head with cross-arms and insulators, etc., can be seen in the telecommunications section of the Ferrymead Museum, Christchurch.

Telex

A development in the early 1960s was that of 'telegraph exchange' or telex. This service, used mainly by business and government departments, utilised page-printing teleprinters in customers' premises, connected to a central exchange using automatic switching technology similar to that in the, by then, widespread telephone exchanges.

This service was eventually replaced by email.

Telephone

The telephone patent was granted to Alexander Graham Bell in 1876. There was a demonstration of Professor Bell's 'speaking telephone' in Dunedin on 2 February 1878 followed soon after by other trials in Tauranga and

Blenheim. Private lines were established for the new telephones, often with inadequate physical construction. The government curtailed this activity by the 1884 Electric Lines Act that placed the construction of all electric lines for lighting and communication under government control. Switching of telephone lines through exchanges became a priority and an exchange was officially opened at Auckland Central Post Office in Shortland Street on 24 October 1881.

By March 1891 Auckland had 507 telephone subscribers. Suburban telephone bureaux and offices were established, the first in Newton, where people not connected to the service could go to make calls in a degree of privacy between the hours of 9 am and 5 pm. By 1884 manual exchanges at the main centres were operating 24 hours per day.

Multi-pair underground cabling for telephones became necessary by 1910, partly because of utterly congested pole-head space, and also because of electrical interference to overhead wires after the introduction of electric trams (November 1902) and power reticulation. Most cables were pulled into underground ducts while smaller cables were laid in trenches which were then backfilled. Some cables were laid on the bottom of streams or rivers, or across the harbour in prohibited anchorages.

The first automatic telephone exchange in Auckland used Strowger equipment and was in service by May 1913. Western Electric 7A Rotary switching equipment was installed from 1925 with exchanges at Wellesley St and several suburbs. By the 1960s Step by Step switching equipment was replacing the WE Rotary and the remaining manual exchanges in rural areas. Working examples of some of this equipment can be found in the telecommunications section at the Museum of Transport and Technology (MOTAT), Auckland. Still later developments included crossbar during the 1980s and were followed soon after by electronic (digital) exchanges.

Auckland telephone directory, 1883.

Courtesy Hesketh Henry Lawyers

New telephone switchboard for Auckland, 1898.

In parallel with the increasing demand for telephone service there was the need for large increases in the number of circuits to interconnect the exchanges. In suburban areas this need was met largely by underground, multi-pair cables in ducts. To minimise the loss of signal strength and to equalise the sloping loss across the audio frequency bandwidth, inductive 88 milli-Henry (mH) loading coils were installed at 6,000 foot spacing. Later, during the 1960s and 1970s, specialised negative-impedance repeaters (amplifiers) known as Negistors, were installed on many routes. A few studio to broadcast trans-mitter site cable links were installed with 22 mH coils at 1500 foot spacing to provide a programme-grade band-width. Over greater distances, such as those to other cities or provincial towns, open-wire carrier systems were installed. These systems provided 1, 3, 12 or 24 audio channels on a single pair of wires on pole-mounted overhead lines.

By 1960 the open-wire lines were being replaced by broadband under-ground coaxial cable and microwave radio systems, each typically providing

Telegraph pole, Queen Street, 1907.

Laying underground telephone cables in Shortland Street, 1909.

Sir George Grey Special Collections, Auckland Libraries 7-A5512

up to 960 circuits. The Auckland-Hamilton coaxial cable was completed in December 1956. The cable was pulled into ducts underneath suburban streets, and in rural areas was laid in trenches dug alongside the main road. Repeater (amplifier) stations were installed at 6-mile spacing. The amplifier equipment was fed with no-break power over the coaxial cable from the terminal stations (Auckland and Hamilton), with the capability to drop back to local mains at each repeater station in emergency. The link to Wellington was completed in September 1960 via the Hamilton-Palmerston North microwave system and the Palmerston North-Wellington coaxial cable.

Since the early 1980s, digital technology has progressively taken over in both telephone exchanges and transmission equipment, with 24-channel and then 36-channel pulse-coded-multiplex (PCM) equipment providing inter-exchange circuits over the multi-pair cables. These required intermediate repeaters which were installed in manholes in the place of the previous loading coil housings. From the late 1980s, fibre-optic cables were installed to provide a huge increase in circuit capacity without needing additional ducts to be laid in the ground. These cables utilised digital technology and interfaced directly with the newest generation of digital telephone exchanges. They also enabled the provision of broadband, high-speed internet access.

A further driver for the installation of new crossbar exchange and transmission equipment was the introduction of subscriber toll dialling (STD) in November 1976. This required the installation of four dedicated new exchanges

Telephone at NZ Army
recruiting station in
Victoria Street,
1917.

Sir George Grey Special Collections,
Auckland Libraries 1-W1599

at the main centres, the extension of free-calling areas and the replacement of most of the few remaining manual exchanges and multi-party lines.

VHF Land Mobile Radio-Telephone Service

From 1948 the NZPO provided a very high frequency (VHF) radio-telephone service for vehicles such as those used by commercial concerns, police, taxi, ambulance and fire brigades. Base stations were installed on sites with good line-of-sight coverage to the surrounding area, such as at Mt Eden, Mt Victoria and Waiatarua. Subscribers usually bought or rented their own equipment from one of the commercial suppliers, but rented a (generally shared) radio channel through one or other of the base stations.

International

International telecommunications are described in later sections 8.3 and 8.4.

References and further reading

Wilson, A.C., *Wire and Wireless: A History of Telecommunications in New Zealand 1860–1987*, Dunmore Press Ltd, Palmerston North, 1994.

The Institution of Professional Engineers New Zealand (IPENZ) has an engineering heritage programme, one of the key activities being to identify significant heritage places, structures and artefacts and list them on a national register. Where appropriate, and with the owner's approval, IPENZ heritage plaques may be awarded and affixed to the sites to acknowledge and recognise them as part of the engineering and technological history of New Zealand. Musick Point Radio Station was a site that was selected and the unveiling of the plaque took place on 12 January 2002. The ceremony is described later.

Musick Point, located on the eastern side of the Tamaki Strait, has outstanding natural and cultural heritage value, with the headland offering panoramic views of the Waitemata Harbour. It was also an ideal site for radio transmission and reception.

When the 1903 New Zealand Wireless and Telegraphy Act gave the government the sole right to transmit, receive and administer wireless communication, it constructed a number of marine coastal radio stations, as shipping was the main user requiring radio communication. New regulations were promulgated in 1923 aimed at promoting broadcasting, and private radio stations flourished. In 1936 the new government purchased most of these stations and the Post Office administered all national and international radio links until the1980s.

The first coastal station in Auckland, VLD, had the important function of serving the busy port. It was linked by landline with the Awanui station which served ships further afield. Auckland Radio operated a month before the opening of the Central Post Office (CPO), located in a small structure on the top of the building with masts above. In 1923 it moved to a space on the first floor.

Transmission was satisfactory but interference from telegraph equipment housed nearby, tram cars, factories and Auckland's direct current electric power supply affected reception. Other areas were tried and found somewhat better than the CPO but no permanent decision was made until the late 1930s.

During this time, governments around the world were providing for aviation, which resulted in airmail and defence responsibilities. The New Zealand Government elected in 1935 wanted to nationalise commercial

8.2

Musick Point Radio Station

*by
Rhys Thomas*

Aerial view of Musick Point Headland.

Courtesy Alexander Turnbull Library, Whites Aviation Collection

Samoan Clipper landing on
Auckland Harbour,
30 March 1937.

Courtesy Archives New Zealand
Auckland Regional Office BBGZ
A1060/19

Pan American Airways and
Imperial Airways flying boats
at Mechanics Bay,
19 January 1938.

Sir George Grey Special Collections,
Auckland Libraries AWN

aviation in a similar way to rail and other services.

In 1937 Tasman Empire Airways (TEAL) was established by New Zealand, Australian and British governments to provide a trans-Tasman link. At the same time Pan American Airlines was investigating a trans-Pacific route.

On 30 March 1937 Captain Edwin Musick and his crew landed the large four-engined Sikorsky S42B flying boat *Samoan Clipper* off Mechanics Bay during a route survey flight from the United States to New Zealand. This was an exciting event for thousands of New Zealanders watching, with its promise of a commercial passenger and airmail service reducing our isolation. Captain Musick was accorded a hero's welcome.

Later the same year on Boxing Day, Aucklanders were treated to the sight of two large float planes moored side by side when an Imperial Airways flying boat and Captain Musick arrived at Mechanics Bay on his second Pan Am survey flight. The fact that the Prime Minister himself welcomed crews shows how important international aviation was thought to be for New Zealand's economy and technology. Captain Musick was not to visit Auckland again: the *Samoan Clipper*, with Captain Musick and his six crew aboard, crashed into the sea near Pago Pago on 11 January 1938. This was to have been the first official commercial flight from the United States to New Zealand. There are differing reasons given for the crash, but it appeared there was a problem when the crew were discharging fuel prior to an emergency landing.

With the added impetus of international air communication and the unsatisfactory radio reception difficulties at the CPO site, the government carried out investigations for the type of facility needed for a permanent trans-Tasman air service, which required a large area of flat land near the terminal base but far enough away from electrical interference. The choice was soon narrowed down to the head of the Tamaki Estuary where the transmitting site was available with flat land. Forty-nine hectares of land was purchased for the receiving station and a further eight hectares for the transmitting site five kilometres away at Oliver Road.

The natural beauty of the receiving station was such that part of the initial planning provided for a public reserve. Since the tragic loss of Captain Musick and the interruption of the new Pacific air service were strongly felt by New Zealanders, the government had decided that a suitable memorial would be erected. The proposed radio station intended for Tamaki Head was considered appropriate, with the radio station being the memorial and the headland renamed Musick Point.

Tablet at Musick Point placed by the government, commemorating the loss of the Samoan clipper and crew on 11 January 1938.

J. La Roche photo

The building was designed by the government architect with initial approval dated 21 April 1939. The station was intended to house equipment to communicate with off-shore aviation and to operate as a coastal radio station which had been the function of the CPO for some 30 years. Besides two-way communication with aircraft and ships it was to receive meteorological information. It was to have contact with Awarua Radio to the extreme south of New Zealand and with New Plymouth, where direction-finding observations were made across the Tasman.

Musick Point Building.

Archives New Zealand AAQT 6401 A78330

Tenders were called in 1940 by the Public Works Department and construction was undertaken by the DC Street Construction Company, at a cost of £51,453. It was built in the Art Deco style with the shape representing the form of an aeroplane.

The entrance to the landward side was by a long driveway flanked by lawns and native shrubs. The main entrance to the building opened onto a memorial hall, with relief panels on the side walls depicting an American eagle.

Plaque commemorating Captain Musick, presented by Mrs Musick.

J. La Roche

Coast Radio Service notice.

J. La Roche

COAST RADIO SERVICE
AUCKLAND RADIO

THIS STATION IS OPERATED BY THE NEW ZEALAND POST OFFICE AND PROVIDES COMMUNICATION WITH SHIPS PRINCIPALLY FOR THE PURPOSE OF SAFETY OF LIFE AT SEA.
THE BUILDING AND GROUNDS CONSTITUTE A MEMORIAL TO CAPT EDWIN MUSICK PIONEER AVIATOR WITH PANAM AIRWAYS CAPTAIN OF THE FLYING BOAT "SAMOAN CLIPPER" LOST WITH ITS CREW ON A SURVEY - FLIGHT OFF PAGO PAGO ON THE 11ᵗᴴ JANUARY 1938

Large operating rooms faced the sea. The roofs of the two wings served as a 'survey promenade' and the tower as a lookout point. A staff of 20 maintained the essential services and housing was built to accommodate both single and married personnel.

Because of the start of the Second World War, access to the site was strictly controlled by the army and it was not until January 1942 that it was officially opened by the Prime Minister. The station provided 24-hour regional maritime and emergency services on medium and high frequencies, and was significant in fostering a close relationship between New Zealand and America by providing an important military and diplomatic communications role. The white building was very conspicuous on a clear headland and seemed inconsistent with its strategic importance as an essential radio communications role, but its prominence may have been designed to register this closer relationship.

An emergency radio station was built in a concrete bunker to the immediate south as a back-up in the event of enemy damage to the main station. It would provide protection for radio equipment that could still be utilised to keep in contact with shipping, aircraft and other links overseas.

The headland was considered a strategic location in the defence of Auckland, together with other forts and gun emplacements placed around the Hauraki Gulf. Submarine nets were erected between Browns Island and Musick Point; the concrete anchor stone remains on the foreshore.

After the bombing of Pearl Harbour the American Naval forces stationed in Auckland utilised the station for a time. They brought with them modern equipment such as teleprinters, radar and automatic Morse keys, as well as those well known personal items: Camel cigarettes, candy and ball point pens.

Another important link the station served was with the New Zealand Coastwatcher Unit. It comprised radio technicians, each accompanied by two army soldiers, and was located on remote Pacific islands to monitor the approach of enemy naval and military forces. They relayed information back to their Fiji headquarters, and thence on to New Zealand, via Musick Point. Several of these radio technicians came from the station. They suffered extreme hardship and some were captured. They were killed, or shipped off to Japan; or tortured and required to work.

The surviving Coastwatchers and other Europeans from the Gilbert and Ellice Islands (now Kiribati and Tuvalu) suffered the most. They were captured and later moved to Betio Islet, part of the Tarawa Atoll. Here their hands were tied and secured to coconut trees for up to four days before interrogation by the Japanese commandant. They were then confined to an enclosure used to house local people who were mentally ill, and required to work on the construction of a wharf at Betio. On the afternoon of 15 October 1942, the island was bombed by American warships and aircraft. One prisoner apparently escaped and waved to them. A native eyewitness reported that in their anger the Japanese rounded up the entire group of 22 and brutally murdered them, decapitating many.

A Court of Enquiry in Japan at the end of the war was not able to identify those guilty of committing atrocities outside of the recognised conventions of war. The evidence disclosed that the brutal murders were not carried out by Japanese soldiers but by conscripted coolie labourers. These conscripted people were attached to Japanese forces for menial work and often placed in charge of prisoners of war.

After the Second World War, both maritime and aviation radio communication were operated from Musick Point Memorial Radio Station. Increased air traffic resulted in Civil Aviation taking

Roll of Honour for those army and radio personnel who were murdered on Tarawa Island.

www.nzart.org.nz/assets/branches/sarc/roll_of_honour

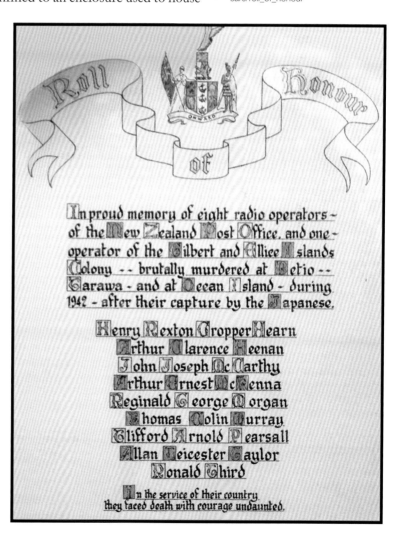

In proud memory of eight radio operators – of the New Zealand Post Office, and one operator of the Gilbert and Ellice Islands Colony -- brutally murdered at Betio -- Tarawa - and at Ocean Island - during 1942 - after their capture by the Japanese.

Henry Rexton Cropper Hearn
Arthur Clarence Heenan
John Joseph McCarthy
Arthur Ernest McKenna
Reginald George Morgan
Thomas Colin Murray
Clifford Arnold Pearsall
Allan Leicester Taylor
Ronald Third

In the service of their country they faced death with courage undaunted.

over the upper floor while the Post Office operated shipping communication from the ground floor.

In 1957 long range high frequency radio communication with overseas aircraft was transferred to the airport at Mangere. The Mechanics Bay airport site was incorporated with port development and the buildings demolished, so the Musick Point radio station is the sole surviving building associated with New Zealand's first international air services. Civil Aviation moved out to the airport in 1965–66 as interference was less than that caused by the developing area at Bucklands Beach.

Telecom New Zealand operated Auckland Radio ZLD from Musick Point until September 1993. It was still providing a Morse code service for commercial shipping and maritime services as this was favoured by foreign fishing boats that had to relay their daily positions. The closure of the station made many operators redundant.

In 1992 five land claims were lodged with the Waitangi Tribunal, the main claimants being Ngai Tai, Ngati Paoa and Ngati Whatua. These claims have not yet been resolved.

With the change from state ownership to a private company, Telecom decided to sell the property, but local opposition finally resulted in the residential zoning application being declined. A deal was negotiated with Telecom in 1990, a nominal sum being paid in compensation. It took until mid-1993 for Musick Point to become Crown-owned land again.

Telecom still holds a lease over the property and has kept communication with some Gulf Islands. They sublease the building to the Auckland Suburban Amateur Radio Club.

In 2002 the Musick Point Preservation Society was formed with the objective of saving and restoring the building and ensuring continued public access to the area. The society incorporated representatives from local groups, amongst which was the Auckland Chapter of the National Committee for Engineering Heritage. The Musick Point Preservation Society is now known as the Musick Point Trust.

On 12 January 2003 a large crowd of local dignitaries, post office operators who had served at the station, radio clubs, aeronautical clubs and enthusiasts, local people and their friends attended the re-dedication of the building by the United States Ambassador who unveiled another commemorative plaque. It was 65 years since the loss of Captain Musick and his crew.

Before arrangements could be made by IPENZ National Committee for Engineering Heritage to award a plaque to the site, approval was necessary from the owners (Land Information New Zealand), the occupiers (Auckland Suburban Radio Club), and, as a courtesy, The Musick Point Trust.

IPENZ was given the opportunity at the ceremony to present and affix their plaque which sums up and commemorates the history of the Musick Point Radio Station. It reads as follows:

MUSICK POINT RADIO STATION

IPENZ RECOGNISES THAT THIS SITE HAS AN IMPORTANT

PLACE IN NEW ZEALAND'S ENGINEERING HERITAGE.

IT SPANS MORE THAN 50 YEARS OF NEW ZEALAND'S EARLY RADIO

COMMUNICATIONS HISTORY FROM 1941, AND WAS ASSOCIATED

WITH THE AVIATION PIONEER EDWIN C MUSICK AND THE

OPENING UP OF PACIFIC AIR ROUTES.

IT HAD SPECIAL IMPORTANCE DURING WORLD WAR II FOR

ALLIED FORCES IN THE PACIFIC CAMPAIGN, AND PROVIDED RADIO

COMMUNICATION WITH THE COASTWATCHERS UNIT.

FOR 40 YEARS MOST OF AUCKLAND'S AVIATION AND MARITIME

RADIO COMMUNICATIONS WERE ROUTED THROUGH THIS SITE.

IPENZ

THE INSTITUTION OF PROFESSIONAL ENGINEERS NEW ZEALAND

References and further reading

Matthews, Jane, 'Musick Point Memorial Radio Station', in *Long Live the Modern: New Zealand's New Architecture 1904–1984*, edited by Julia Gatley, Auckland University Press, Auckland, 2008.

Mathews & Mathews Architects Ltd, in association with Bruce Hayward, John P. Adam and Lynn Williams, *Te Waiarohia o Ngai Tai Paa, Te Naupata Musick Point, Conservation Plan,* Auckland, 2008.

Morris, Doug, *Auckland Radio Alpha and Omega,* Auckland.

NZ Association of Radio Transmitters *Captain Musick* http://www.nzart.org.nz/assets/branches/sarc/capt-musick.htm

NZ Historic Places Trust, *Te Naupata/Musick Point,* Registration No. 9335.

Warkworth Satellite Earth Station

by
Neil Mander

Background

With the completion of the COMPAC submarine telephone cable system in 1963 and the extension via the SEACOM system to south-east Asia in 1967 the demand for high-quality voice and telegraph circuits continued to grow.

In October 1965 New Zealand used a geostationary satellite INTEL-SAT-1 to obtain additional telephone circuits across the Atlantic Ocean to the United Kingdom. Initially these were time-switched each day to fit in with traffic peak flows across the Atlantic. Early concerns that the extra signal transit time via the satellite hop might cause difficulties in holding satisfactory conversations were quickly dispelled.

But there was an ever-increasing need for telephone, data, telex, telegraph and television circuits, especially as colour television broadcasts were about to start in New Zealand. A communications satellite system was seen as the best answer.

Satellite System

Because the technology was still developing, a major uncertainty was which system we would get access to. One possibility was a low-orbit, multi-satellite system, which would require very directional, steerable antennas to track satellites as they moved across the sky in low Earth orbit. The other was a geostationary satellite system, which would require a somewhat larger antenna to point at a relatively fixed position in the sky.

If a low-orbit system were implemented, at least two antennas would be needed so that while one was tracking a satellite across the sky, the second would be aimed ready to pick up the signal from the next one as it came into view.

Geostationary satellites at a height of 35,786 kilometres above sea level at the equator have a single hop (that is, sender-satellite-receiver) signal propagation time of about one quarter of a second. Because of the much longer signal path and hence signal strength loss, a larger antenna would be required with a higher power transmitter, and a more sensitive receiver.

This latter arrangement was the one chosen, and remains today, not only for international communications (telephone, facsimile, data and studio-to-studio television links) but also now for television broadcasting. People are familiar now with the small dish antennas used to receive Sky and satellite Freeview broadcasts. A few larger two-metre antennas are also used for television reception from other geostationary satellites with poorer signal strength because New Zealand is off the centre of their transmitted beam and they are close to our horizon and therefore have a greater path loss.

Site Selection

Once the decision had been made to build a satellite earth station the next task was to find a suitable site. There were many criteria to be met in selection of the site to be used for the antenna and associated station equipment, and some of them conflicted.

Early planning for future expansion of services required a site suitable for up to four antennas, with adequate space between them. There had to be a five-degree elevation horizon in the event of low orbit satellites being used, but a valley with hills around was desirable to provide some shelter from the prevailing winds, and give good screening from radio noise. This noise results from electric and electronic equipment and radio transmitters and can interfere with the weak signals in the 4 GHz earth station receive band. It can come especially from maritime or land-based radar as well as VHF and UHF radio equipment. Power lines could introduce electrical noise from leakage from their insulators and from connected electrical machinery. The earth station transmit band, at 6 GHz, had the potential to interfere with terrestrial microwave links and this also had to be investigated.

Satellite earth station antennas are typically designed for a maximum wind speed of 70 miles per hour (112 kilometres per hour) while remaining in the normal operating position. At greater wind speeds the antennas are automatically moved to the stow position, pointing straight upwards.

A site north of Auckland was desired so that air traffic into and out of Auckland airports did not cross the signal path between antenna and satellites. This was not so much to protect people but to minimise interruptions to the signal itself. At the same time there had to be reliable mains power to the site, and also a good broadband path back to the International Gateway Exchange in Auckland.

To minimise possible earthquake damage, a site away from the main earthquake zones was required. Northland met this criterion. Foundation conditions had to be good, with a solid rock base at a reasonable depth on which to build the nearly 2,000 tonne concrete and steel foundation, and to

Warkworth Earth Satellite station from the air during construction.

Courtesy McConnell Dowell Constructors Ltd

Foundations for the
Satellite dish.

Courtesy McConnell Dowell
Constructors Ltd

support the antenna weight of 377 tonnes. For instance, clay above mudstone had to be avoided. (This particular formation is known as the Onerahi Chaos, a frequent condition in Northland.) Areas of suitable Waitemata series sandstone are ideal and were present at the Warkworth site.

Good liaison with local people, especially the farmers and land owners, was called for as the purchase of property easement for access was involved. One farmer expressed concern on what effect the radio transmissions might have on his cattle and milk production. Reliable access was needed for the construction machinery, especially that needed for the heavy lifting associated with the erection of the antenna, and to enable the delivery of heavy equipment.

A reliable and clean supply of fresh water was needed for firefighting as well as ordinary use. This was obtained by a combination of rainwater and bore water. A reliable mains power supply was vital.

Accommodation and facilities had to be provided for the construction and maintenance staffs. The previous practice for remote sites had been the establishment of a dedicated settlement. In this case, because the site finally selected was reasonably close to Warkworth, houses were built in the township itself. As a result, staff and their families quickly became an established part of the community.

Four potential sites were identified and then singled down to the final choice, five kilometres south of Warkworth. To enhance public relations the main building was designed with visitor facilities including a space-themed ceramic mural in the foyer and a distinctive microwave tower, with a hyperbolic profile to complement the main antenna.

Antenna System

In technical terms, satellite system parameters of the time required a 30 metres diameter dish antenna and the standard design was a steerable cassegrain with an elevation-azimuth mount and auto-tracking. The transmit path employed 3kW klystron transmitters (normally run at around 100 watts). The receive path used duplicated gaseous helium-cooled low-noise parametric amplifiers running at 17 deg Kelvin (i.e., 17 degrees above absolute zero which is 273 degrees below 0 degrees C). Later, after 'room-temperature' low noise receivers (LNR) were developed, they were purchased and installed to provide great reliability with substantially reduced maintenance.

Intelsat (International Telecommunications Satellite organisation) owned and operated the satellites and set the performance requirements for earth stations. The earth station performance 'figure of merit' had to be a minimum G/T of 40.7 dB (decibels) to meet requirements. G is the receive gain of the antenna at five degrees elevation in dB, and is typically 60 dB for a 30 metres diameter antenna. T is the system noise (antenna noise pickup plus LNR noise) expressed as dB from noise temperature. This was typically 18 dB – hence 60-18 = 42dB for G/T.

In developing the contract two problems arose. The first involved lifting the main hub into place. Even using the two largest cranes in the Auckland area the lift would have been very risky as the cranes would have been at their limits. The only crane capable of carrying out the operation on its own was a very large walking crane at the New Plymouth Power Station, which was nearing completion. The tender was therefore based on this crane being dismantled, taken by ship to the Whangarei wharf, transported to site and reassembled. This was going to be a costly exercise and as NEC wanted to reduce the tender price they asked for this item to be removed from their bid and they would be responsible for the cost of lifting the hub into place.

Lifting the hub into place.

Courtesy McConnell Dowell Constructors Ltd

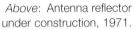

Above: Antenna reflector under construction, 1971.

Courtesy McConnell Dowell Constructors Ltd

Above right: Warkworth Earth Satellite Station in 1971. A view of the station, showing the main terminal building, the tower for the antenna for the microwave link back to Auckland, and the large antenna pointing to the satellite.

Courtesy J. R. Diamond collection, photographer unknown

As it turned out by the time the structure was ready for the big lift much larger cranes were available in the Auckland district and a dual lift was carried out.

The dish consists of a large number of separate panels, each of which had to be perfectly positioned by using precise surveying means. Without previous experience the cost of this work would have been impossible to estimate. However, the government had previously asked the Department of Scientific and Industrial Research (DSIR) to set up a section that could carry out precise survey work to aid in the creation of industries such as paper mills. Consequently, the DSIR agreed to carry out the survey and adjustment of all the plates at no cost.

Multiplex Equipment

Standard multiplex carrier telephony equipment was used, whereby single-sideband modulation technology is used to combine 12 voice-grade circuits into a Group. Five Groups were combined into a Supergroup. Combinations of these formed the standard 24-, 60- and 132-channel basebands used on the satellites. These were then frequency-modulated onto the microwave carrier for transmission to the satellite.

A standard 16 Supergroup baseband was available on the microwave system connecting back to the international telephone exchange in the Airedale Street building in Auckland.

Television Broadcasts

Colour television broadcasts were beginning in New Zealand at the time, and it was seen that there would be a requirement by the broadcaster for high-quality video links to and from other countries for news reports and coverage of important events.

One major problem was that New Zealand had adopted the 625-line PAL standard while a few other countries, notably the USA and Canada, were continuing with the older 525-line NTSC standard. These standards were incompatible, so it was necessary to convert from one standard to the other, using a newly developed Field Store Standards Converter which occupied an entire row of equipment. In fact, the design was so new, with much novel use of technology, that some appreciable local input and innovation was required to achieve and maintain satisfactory operation.

Power Supply

The mains power supply to the site was at 11kV with a local step-down transformer to provide a three-phase 400/230 volt feed at 50 Hz.

The incoming mains supply was rectified and fed to a 300 volt DC lead-acid battery which in turn fed a static inverter to supply the essential load bus-bar providing power to the transmit klystrons, Low Noise Receivers (LNRs) and other vital equipment. This was a new development in place of previously-used rotary machines.

Continuity of service in the event of mains failure was provided by two 300 kVA auto-start engine-alternator (EA) sets. While the EA sets came up to speed, no-break AC power was fed to the essential load bus bar by the 300 volt battery and static inverter.

Air Conditioning

To ensure reliable and consistent equipment performance a working environment with steady temperature and low humidity was required. To provide this, an extensive air conditioning system was designed and installed.

Contractors

The prime contractor for the antenna and electronics was NEC of Japan and their local agents Wm Scollay and Co. Ltd, along with other suppliers: Fujitsu for transmission equipment and Rank-Cintel of UK for the TV Standards Converter.

Design and supervision of the earthworks, roading, site development, main building and microwave tower were carried out by the Ministry of Works with Wiles and Jones as main building contractors. McConnell Dowell was the main contractor for the antenna structure.

Completion

The station, owned and operated by the then New Zealand Post Office, was completed and opened for service on 17 July 1971, working for a few months to INTELSAT III before changing onto the INTELSAT IV satellite, which had the capacity for 4,000 telephone circuits and two television circuits.

The initial total of 29 circuits to Australia, USA and Hong Kong had expanded to 164 circuits and eight destinations by 1976.

The station was available in good time to provide additional temporary telephone traffic capacity and for television to be transmitted live to millions of overseas television viewers during the Commonwealth Games in Christchurch in January 1974.

Later Developments

The original 30 metre antenna was taken out of service on 18 June 2008 and demolished shortly afterwards.

The second antenna and station building were opened on 24 July 1984. At a special function in December 1983 Dr Kobayashi of NEC planted a tree to mark the occasion. This antenna was removed from service in November 2010 and is now used by the Auckland University of Technology for radio astronomy work.

Other antennas have been installed on and near the site. These include an Auckland University of Technology radio-telescope, and antennas receiving television broadcasts, data from weather satellites and the like.

Acknowledgements

Thanks are due to John Diamond, NZPO Engineer, for his willing provision of much background information and photographs of the project.

Glossary of terms

One gigahertz (GHz) represents a frequency of one billion Hertz (cycles per second).

Cassegrain refers to a telescope, optical or radio, which has a large primary concave mirror which reflects the signal up to a secondary smaller convex mirror which re-reflects the signal down to the feed horn or observing eye-piece, etc.

Elevation-azimuth refers to a telescope or antenna mounting system which has its horizontal axis (elevation) supported on a vertical axis (azimuth).

References and further reading

Burdett, P. A., 'New Zealand Satellite Earth Station', *New Zealand Engineering*, Vol. 26, No. 5, p.122–127, 15 May 1971.
Geostationary Orbit http://en.wikipedia.org/wiki/Geostationary_orbit
Wilson, A. C., *Wire & Wireless: A History of Telecommunications in New Zealand 1890–1987*, Dunmore Press Ltd, Palmerston North, 1994.

8.4

COMPAC Submarine Telephone Cable System

by
Neil Mander

Background

The first telegraph line in New Zealand, an overhead wire mounted on poles, was installed between Christchurch and Lyttelton in 1862. By 1866 telegraph lines had extended through the South Island and a submarine cable was laid across Cook Strait. In 1876 the first cable link with Australia was laid, only 10 years after the first successful cable across the Atlantic Ocean. Other submarine cable links followed, to Australia, to Fiji and on to Canada via Fanning Island in 1902.

These were supplemented from 1912 with high-frequency radio links providing telegraph and then telephone circuits from 1930. The performance of these radio circuits was subject to the vagaries of the ionosphere, which varied with the time of day and the state of the sunspot cycle. They suffered from interference from other radio signals.

Traffic capacity was very limited, with the submarine cables handling only telegraph signals, which initially were a modified form of Morse code using direct current pulses.

In 1956 advancing technology enabled the first Trans-Atlantic Telephone Cable (TAT-1) to be brought into service to provide 36 voice-grade circuits between the United Kingdom and the United States. This circuit capacity was soon increased to 48 circuits.

By 1958 planning was underway for a Canada-United Kingdom cable, CANTAT, which was opened in December 1961. Planning started for a round-the-world Commonwealth system to follow on from that. The COMPAC (Commonwealth, Pacific Telephone Cable**)** system was the section crossing the Pacific Ocean from Vancouver to Honolulu, Suva, Auckland and Sydney.

The Auckland-Sydney system was completed in early 1962, with the

Laying the shore end at Lyall Bay, Wellington, of a new Cook Straight telephone and telegraph cable in 1936.

Sir George Grey Special Collections, Auckland Libraries
AWNS193060610-44-9

Auckland-Suva section following in July 1962, and the long haul across the Pacific Ocean to Hawaii and on to Vancouver in October 1963. Cable laying was carried out by the cable ships *Retriever* and *Mercury*. The system provided up to 80 telephone-grade circuits for toll calls and for voice-frequency telegraph systems each providing 24 50-baud telegraph circuits for public telegraph, leased telegraph and telex use. At Vancouver circuits were linked by microwave link across Canada and then into the CANTAT trans-Atlantic cable. The new high-quality circuits were welcomed by all users.

A later extension of the Commonwealth submarine cable system westwards took the international link from Cairns in Australia, to Madang in Papua New Guinea, then on to Guam, Hong Kong, Jesselton and to Singapore with a microwave link to Kuala Lumpur, under the title of SEACOM. This system was completed on 30 March 1967.

The cable ship *Mercury*, which laid the major portion of the COMPAC cable in 1962 and 1963. The huge bow sheaves are used for laying the shore end of the cable and for cable recovery and repair work. For deep-water laying the cable and repeaters are paid out a chute at the stern of the ship.

Cable & Wireless Plc 2009, courtesy Porthcurno Telegraph Museum, United Kingdom

The Technology

The first trans-Atlantic telephone cable took advantage of advancing technology, principally low-loss coaxial cable with high-density polythene as an insulator instead of the traditional gutta-percha, and highly reliable valve-operated amplifiers or repeaters. Two cables were laid, one for each direction of transmission, with repeaters at 37 nautical mile (69 kilometres) spacing.

The CANTAT and COMPAC systems, as well as later systems, used a single, light-weight, non-armoured coaxial cable to carry both directions of transmission. The strength member of the cable was a torsionally balanced, steel wire core with a copper foil layer around it to make up the centre conductor of the coaxial cable. High-density polythene provided the insulator between the core and the outer conductor of copper tapes spiral-wound around the cable. An outer layer of polythene covered the cable. Steel wire armouring was used on cable laid in shallow water where there was a risk of damage from trawling or boat anchors, or where the cable was buried in open country sections.

Each submerged repeater was housed in a rigid, high-strength steel cylinder nine feet in length (nearly three metres), ten and a half inches in diameter (25 centimetres), and designed to resist the water pressure at depths of down to 4,000 fathoms (7300 metres). Bandpass filters in each of the valve-operated repeaters at 26.3 nautical miles (43 kilometres) spacing, enabled each repeater to cope with both directions of transmission. Traffic capacity was 80 voice-grade circuits.

The amplifiers in the repeaters used vacuum tubes (valves) of an established, well-tested and very reliable type. Double-end power feeding was used on each cable section with half the

Lightweight coaxial cable used for COMPAC and SEACOM submarine cables.

SEACOM publicity leaflet, 1967

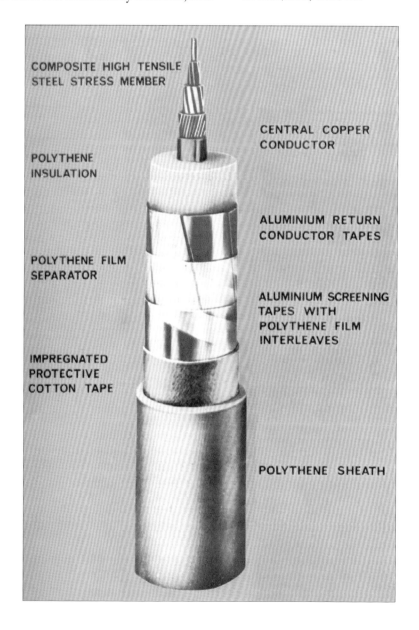

COMPOSITE HIGH TENSILE STEEL STRESS MEMBER

POLYTHENE INSULATION

POLYTHENE FILM SEPARATOR

IMPREGNATED PROTECTIVE COTTON TAPE

CENTRAL COPPER CONDUCTOR

ALUMINIUM RETURN CONDUCTOR TAPES

ALUMINIUM SCREENING TAPES WITH POLYTHENE FILM INTERLEAVES

POLYTHENE SHEATH

full voltage being supplied from each end. In emergency the total power-feed voltage could be applied from either end of the cable. The power-feed current of 430 milliamps (mA) was reduced to 415 mA after several years in order to ensure reliable performance for at least the expected life span of 20 years with no degradation in performance. Transistors were coming into use in many areas of consumer and commercial electronics but the performance in terms of noise, stability and reliability did not yet meet the required tight specifications.

Equalisers were installed in each repeater to match and cancel out the variation in loss of the cable across the frequency spectrum. Additional adjustable equalisers were installed (four in each of the Auckland-Sydney and Auckland-Suva cable systems) during the cable laying process to deal with minor variations in loss as the cable was laid. The end-to-end performance was monitored closely during the laying process, and these equalisers were adjusted and sealed into submersible housings spliced into the cable.

At the terminal stations single-sideband modulation was used to assemble 16 voice-grade circuits into a basic Group occupying a bandwidth of 60 to 108 kilohertz (kHz), and then five Groups were single-sideband modulated to the transmit path bandwidth of 60 to 300 kHz. In the receive direction five Groups in the high-band 360 kHz to 608 kHz were demodulated down to basic Groups, which were either through-connected to the next system in the chain, or demodulated down to audio for local use.

Toll operators used the derived circuits to enable telephone subscribers to make international toll calls.

Cable terminal stations were designated either as an 'A' station or a 'B' station, alternating along the system. 'A' stations such as Auckland transmitted the low band and received the high band. 'B' stations such as Sydney and Suva transmitted the high band and received the low band.

A comprehensive set of pilot tones was injected at various stages of the modulation equipment, and then continuously monitored to ensure stability of the overall system.

For a period, time-assignment speech interpolation (TASI) equipment was used on circuits across the Atlantic Ocean, to shoe-horn additional derived circuits into the existing limited number of 'real' circuits, by making use of the silent periods between speech bursts.

The New Zealand Section

Site Selection

Facilities were required in New Zealand to provide communications towards Australia and to Fiji and beyond. Also, a proportion of the circuits had to be through-connected, thus bypassing Auckland.

Depending on the location, one or two beach landings would be needed, together with communications links back to the international telephone exchange at Auckland. Sites were examined on both the west and east coasts between Auckland and Cape Reinga. Points considered included the changes in length and number of repeaters needed for each landing, beach conditions, the cost and technical difficulty in linking from the landings back to the international telephone exchange, and staff accommodation and facilities needed. The final selection made was for the Sydney cable to land at Muriwai Beach, and for the Suva cable to land on Takapuna Beach, relatively close to the landings of the then existing telegraph cables. Power feed and transmission equipment would be accommodated in a new terminal building adjacent to the then North Shore Line Depot in Northcote Road, Takapuna. Audio circuits would be connected over pairs in ordinary duct multi-pair cable back to the telephone exchange in Wellesley Street, Auckland. The main route for this was over the harbour bridge with a back-up available via Devonport.

The cable route from Muriwai followed the route of the existing telegraph cable via Kumeu and Hobsonville, with an upper harbour crossing to Island Bay near Birkdale, and then via the normal duct system to the terminal building in Northcote Road. Where the cable route traversed private property a 20 foot (6.1 metre) easement was arranged with the owners.

Because of the distance, it was necessary for one land-based repeater to be installed on the Sydney cable, at 1.9 miles (3.06 kilometres) from the Muriwai Beach. A concrete pit was installed and a local creek diverted through this to provide cooling water and hence a constant operating temperature.

Because the cable system was powered by direct current over the centre conductor, an earth connection was required at the cable terminal. This was in three main sections linked together: a sea earth electrode, the station buried earth mat and the combined cable sheaths of all the lead-sheathed cables entering the station.

Cable Laying and Jointing

In urban areas the cable was pulled into underground ducts in similar fashion to that used for ordinary telephone cables. In rural areas the cable was laid into trenches dug by jeep-mounted trenching machines. Once laid, jointing of the cables was carried out by specially trained teams of jointers. The steel wire core was brazed, copper tape wrapped around the steel wire core and brazed to provide a low-resistance centre conductor, then high-density polythene was injection-moulded around that. The outer conductor copper tapes were then formed around the outside and brazed together. The finished joint was X-rayed to ensure a high-quality joint.

Precautions taken to ensure the safety and security of the system included the extension of existing prohibited anchorages to prevent damage to the cables near the beaches, clear signposting of the existence of the cable, and a daily patrol of the overland section of the cable to prevent damage arising from roadworks and other, unauthorised earthworks.

Terminal Building

The main requirements were for accommodation for the cable termination equipment, including the power feeding equipment, the transmission equipment, power supply equipment including mains rectifiers, batteries, stand-by diesel generators, air-conditioning equipment, workshop and staff amenities.

Extensive air conditioning was required in order to maintain an environment which had a constant temperature and humidity, and which remained dust-free. A completely closed space was required, with no opening windows. The air in the building was recirculated through the air conditioning plant, with only a small proportion of fresh air being admitted in order to maintain an acceptable environment for staff.

A building was designed and planned in very quick time, on a site adjacent to the Takapuna Line Depot on Northcote Rd, Takapuna. This work was carried out by the Ministry of Works and the building was completed by the target date of 1 June 1961.

Power Feed Equipment

The 50 repeaters in each of the two cables (to Sydney and to Suva) had to be supplied with continuous power, originally at 430 milliamps (mA) but later reduced to 415 mA, at a voltage of some 2.7 kilovolts (kV) with double-end feeding, or up to 5.4 kV in the event of single-end feeding being required. The current had to be controlled within tight limits, with care given to avoidance of over- or under-voltage, or of over- or under-current conditions. At any given moment, two out of three power-feeding cubicles were online, sharing the load in about a one to nine ratio. Failure of either cubicle would result in the other immediately taking up the full load. The third cubicle could be switched in without any interruption to service. Magnetic amplifiers controlled the power feed current, protecting the system from variations in earth potentials arising from magnetic storms caused by solar activity. Chart recorders continuously recorded the power-feeding current and voltage.

Because of the high voltages used, a comprehensive system of inter-connected switches and locks was provided to ensure complete protection for staff as well as for the cable and repeaters.

Transmission Equipment

Echo-suppressors were installed on all toll circuits to avoid any objectionable echo. The one-way propagation time for a signal between Sydney and Auckland was 15 milliseconds, and was greater on longer circuits.

The derived circuits were connected on copper pair cables through to the Auckland International Telephone Exchange, initially at Civic House in Queen Street, Auckland, and then later at Airedale Street. Toll operator staff set up international toll calls on request from telephone subscribers, ticketing the start and finish times for each call for later billing.

Voice-frequency-telegraph (VFT) equipment provided 24 50-baud telegraph channels over a standard voice-grade circuit, using frequency-shift modulation. Public telegraph (for telegrams), leased telegraph and telex trunk circuits were provided.

Power Supplies

It was important to maintain continuity of power supply to the cable power-feeding equipment, bearing in mind the need to ensure continuous service and also to avoid the risk of degradation to the submerged repeaters in the event of power feed disruption. Extensive and duplicated mains rectifiers, batteries and motor-generators were used to ensure continuous supply to the power feeding cubicles and also to the transmission equipment. Auto-start diesel engine-powered generators provided back-up for the mains.

Much of this control equipment was designed and built in New Zealand, although the motors and generators were all purchased from overseas suppliers.

Later Developments

Disused telegraph cables were used for earth-current recording as part of an ongoing research project of one of the English universities. The variation of induced voltage in step with tides was measured.

Conclusion

The new toll circuits were welcomed as being much superior to the previous radio circuits, which were often subject to fading and interference. The comment was often made that talking to someone in the UK was now clearer than talking to someone here in the same city in New Zealand.

The Auckland-Sydney section of the system ceased working on 5 October 1983 because of a cable fault a few miles off the Sydney beach.

The Auckland-Suva section was eventually taken out of service in 7 December 1984, as by that time newer cable and satellite systems with much larger traffic capacity were in place.

The Satellite Earth Station just south of Warkworth opened on 17 July 1971, providing 29 circuits to Australia, USA and Hong Kong.

The new 480-circuit TASMAN cable system linking Auckland and Sydney opened in February 1976, and the ANZCAN cable system via Norfolk Island opened at the end of 1984 with 1380 circuits.

Glossary of Terms

A baud is a digital signalling element per second. A speed of 50 baud was about 80 words per minute for the teleprinter code in use at that time.

References and further reading

Commonwealth Pacific Cable Symposium, New Zealand Institution of Engineers, Vol. 17, No. 7, p. 233–267, 12 July 1962.
Fanning Island http://www.janeresture.com/kiribati_line/fanning.htm
History of the Atlantic Cable and Undersea Communications
    http://atlantic-cable.com/Cableships/Mercury/index.htm
Trans Atlantic Telephone cables http://en.wikipedia.org/wiki/TAT-1
Wilson, A. C., *Wire & Wireless: A History of Telecommunications in New Zealand 1890–1987,* Dunmore Press, Palmerston North, 1994.

CHAPTER NINE

Aviation

For centuries, man has dreamt about soaring in the air like a bird and since the age of enlightenment has attempted to put the dream into practice.

The French brothers Joseph-Michel and Jacques-Étienne Montgolfier demonstrated their hot air balloon in 1783. The first flight by a heavier-than-air machine was made by Wilbur and Orville Wright on 17 December 1903, although arguably they were preceded by Richard Pearse in South Canterbury in March of that year.

Remarkably, the first successful aeroplane flight in New Zealand occurred a scant eight years later when 23-year-old Vivian Walsh flew an imported Howard Wright bi-plane named *Manurewa* (Soaring Bird) from Glenora Park in Papakura, Auckland. It had been imported by a syndicate called the Aero Club of New Zealand, who expected to receive a kit of parts, ready to assemble, but instead got a collection of materials from which to make the parts, with the exception of the engine and the propeller.

Vivian made repeated flights and he and his brother used the

9.1

Walsh Brothers Flying School

by Colin Zeff

The Walsh brothers aircraft, the Howard Wright biplane Manurewa, at Glenora Park, Papakura, February 1911.

Sir George Grey Special Collections, Auckland Libraries 2-V11

Curtis flying boat flown by
Vivian Walsh at Mission Bay
in 1916.

Sir George Grey Special Collections,
Auckland Libraries 7-A3419

Walsh flying school at
Mission Bay.

Sir George Grey Special Collections,
Auckland Libraries 7-A260

experience gained to improve the design of *Manurewa*, based on their growing knowledge of flying and the mishaps that occurred, but in 1913 the syndicate was dissolved and the Walsh brothers lost control of the plane.

Undeterred, and with new financial backing from car importer Reuben Dexter, they commenced the construction of a seaplane. The brothers were sons of Yorkshire immigrants and although afforded a good education had no formal training in engineering, aviation (such as it was), or any trade. That they set out to design and construct an aeroplane that could take off and land on water was an amazing undertaking in itself. This machine finally and successfully took to the air on New Year's day 1915 and by March 14 of that year had carried its first passenger.

From then on there was a strong demand for flights from intrepid passengers and a thriving business developed. By that time the First World War was in progress and the value of aeroplanes as reconnaissance tools was starting to be recognised, although the New Zealand Government had yet to be convinced.

The Royal Flying Corps in Britain fielded an ever increasing fleet of aircraft and pilots were being recruited from all the Dominions except New Zealand. By mid 1915 the Walsh brothers were sufficiently confident in their abilities to be able to offer to train pilots for military service in Europe. The New Zealand Government was not interested, but the demand from individuals who wanted to learn to fly for the purpose of offering their skills to the Royal Flying Corps was sufficient for the New Zealand Flying School to be formed.

The school consisted of one flying boat and one self-taught instructor set up in a shed on the foreshore at Orakei. Flying training commenced with three pupils on 2 October 1915. Powered by a 10-cylinder Anzani engine, the flying boat had scarcely enough power to lift the student pilot and the instructor into the air, but it proved sufficient for learning the basic skills of aviation.

By 28 November the school had moved to Mission Bay, where two of the students went for their first solo flights. Notably, this was the first occasion on which Vivian Walsh had witnessed a plane in flight, having previously been the only pilot.

Shortly after this, the school bought another aircraft; a Caudron bi-plane that had originally been brought to New Zealand by the pioneer aviator J. W. H. Scotland in Christchurch. It was sold to the Walsh brothers in damaged condition and they set about rebuilding the plane and converting it to a flying boat for use by the school.

Preparing for a seaplane flight at Mission Bay.

Sir George Grey Special Collections, Auckland Libraries 7 A6265

In 1916 the flying school moved to Kohimarama, leasing land adjacent to the beach owned by the Melanesian Mission.

The first regular intake of 12 prospective pilots occurred in early 1916, with students coming from all over New Zealand. The pupils had to be between 18 and 30 years of age, in good physical shape, and front up with a fee of £100 (well over $12,000 in today's money).

Successful students who passed the qualifying tests could go on to get a commission in the Royal Flying Corps after a further course at a military flying school in Britain. The Imperial Government then refunded £75 to the commissioned pilot.

In addition to flying training, pupils at the school received instruction in flight theory, aircraft mechanics and other technical instruction. Pupils had to provide their own tent for accommodation and pay for board.

In May 1916 the school imported a Curtiss flying boat with a 90 horse-power engine, which proved superior to the two aircraft already in use. Financing the growing business proved to be difficult and eventually the then mayor of Auckland, James Gunson, appealed for public support on patriotic grounds.

In early 1917 the Walsh brothers constructed another flying boat with an 80 horsepower Curtiss engine, bringing the effective training fleet to three aircraft, operated by three instructors, George Bolt, Bob Going and Marmaduc Matthews.

The average time to complete the course was three months. In 1916 15 pupils graduated from the school, rising to 25 in 1917 and 44 in 1918. In total, over a thousand pilots were trained up until the school finally closed in

September 1924. Still in financial difficulty, it was bought by the government and the operations were transferred to Hobsonville.

In 2008 a tribute to the Walsh brothers, celebrating their achievements, was placed in the Selwyn Reserve, Mission Bay. The bird sculpture by artist Fred Graham has a six-metre wingspan made of titanium rods and hangs suspended above the ground as if in flight.

References and further reading:

Hopkins, Jim, *Words on Wings: An Anthology of New Zealanders in Flight*, Harper Collins, Auckland, 2004.

Mounce, John and Williams, Richard, *100 years of Flight in New Zealand*, MOTAT and Penguin Viking, Auckland, 2010.

Mulligan, David, *The Kiwi's First Wings: The Story of the Walsh Brothers and the New Zealand Flying School 1910–1924*, Wingfield Press, Wellington, 1960.

Royal Aeronautical Society New Zealand Division Vivian & Leo Walsh, 2010 www.raes.org.nz/nzat/vivian_and_leo_walsh

Wright, Matthew, *Wings Over New Zealand: A Social History of New Zealand Aviation*, Whitcoulls, Auckland, 2000.

Auckland International Airport

by
Mike Lancaster

A very comprehensive and well illustrated book titled *Where New Zealand Touches the World*, by Martyn Thompson and Alice Clements, was produced in 2003 for the Auckland International Airport Limited. This book covers the political history and construction extremely well, but for the engineering heritage purposes a shorter story is required.

History

Since the first pioneering flights at Papakura in 1911, described in the preceding section on the Walsh Flying School, Auckland has had several airports for a variety of uses: recreational, military and commercial. The Auckland Aero Club, founded on 24 April 1928, leased farmland from a Mr Peacock in Mangere. This first airport was established on what is basically the site of the present one. In the same year the famous flyer Charles Kingsford Smith made the initial crossing of the Tasman Sea in the *Southern Cross*. Landing at Wigram near Christchurch, he later flew on a tour of New Zealand to arrive at Mangere Aerodrome, as it was then known, on 18 September 1928. The next important arrival was Jean Batten, a member of the Auckland Aero Club, who came in 1936. When she landed at Mangere Aerodrome at the end of her first solo flight from England to New Zealand, she was welcomed by a crowd of 6,000 people. The following year in 1937 Union Airways, New Zealand's first major airline, adopted Mangere Aerodrome as its first official airport.

The government took over all of the aircraft facilities at Mangere just before the outbreak of the Second World War in 1939. All territorial pilots and instructors were called up for the Royal New Zealand Air Force (RNZAF).

Construction had begun in 1937 of an air force base at Whenuapai, designed to take a squadron of Wellington bombers ordered under the expansion programme of 1937 to 1939. With the outbreak of war, the Wellington bombers stayed in England and Whenuapai was used as a wartime training base. Post-war it became the centre for RNZAF transport and maritime operations.

Above: Sir Charles Kingsford Smith arriving at Mangere in 1928.

South Auckland Research Centre/ Papatoetoe Historical Society, Footprints 02149_pr.jpg

Left: Jean Batten arriving at Mangere, Auckland in 1934 after her record-breaking flight from England to Australia.

Sir George Grey Special Collections, Auckland Libraries 7-A3705

Left: Auckland Aero Club's airfield at Mangere, May 1947.

South Auckland Research Centre MGE III, 1, No 45 Footprints -01193_pr.jpg

Aerial View of Whenuapai
Airport, 1959.

Alexander Turnbull Library WA-51494-G
Whites Aviation photo

NAC aircraft at Whenuapai
in November 1965.

Alexander Turnbull Library, WA-03728,
Whites Aviation photo

From 1948 until 1965 Whenuapai also became Auckland's civilian airport as commercial flights moved there. Only the aero club, which had been in abeyance during the war, remained at Mangere, to focus on recreational flying and instruction. Why was Whenuapai chosen as the centre for municipal operations, when a preliminary general survey by the Public Works Department had indicated that the Mangere area was the most favoured site for a municipal airport? It was the one capable of further development to the ultimate requirements of larger international services. The choice was dictated by cost. The temporary arrangement on offer at Whenuapai proved too attractive to the Auckland City Council and had been accepted in 1946 because it involved no cost to the city.

Accordingly Whenuapai became Auckland's Municipal Airport, where civilian aviation competed with the needs of the RNZAF. An additional pressure was put on the airbase as larger, faster commercial aircraft were beginning to emerge from the drawing boards of international designers. Whenuapai was simply not designed to handle this new breed of aircraft. Its runways were too short and not constructed to take the heavier weight of the new generation of commercial passenger aircraft. The hills surrounding Whenuapai posed yet another problem. Bigger aircraft needed more, clearer airspace. At this stage all international flights came via Australia and the main trans-Tasman flyer, Tasman Empire Airlines (TEAL), upgraded its fleet in 1946 using flying boats for international services, but land based aircraft gradually replaced them, needing airports and runways. TEAL introduced its first DC6 flights to Australia in 1954. Flying boats continued flying to the Pacific until 1960.

With an eye to the future, the New Zealand Government asked a United

Kingdom civil aviation team, headed by Sir Frederick Tymms, to report on aviation in New Zealand. Their final report presented in September 1948 featured issues such as crash and fire services, landing fees and airport ownership, as well as suggesting that the flying boats were no longer the best solution. The report concluded that there was need for an international airport. The question of location was still unanswered but the continued use of Whenuapai was soundly rejected. The report recommended that sites at Mangere and Pakuranga be investigated urgently and that funds be provided for the necessary meteorological and engineering studies.

In 1958 the government commissioned Leigh Fisher Associates, an internationally respected aviation consulting firm from San Francisco, to survey and report on the design and construction of Auckland International Airport. They recommended an airport runway of initial length of 2,590 metres but capable of extension to 3,300 metres.

After years of investigations and talks about the future of an international airport in New Zealand, the director of Civil Aviation, Mr A. Neville, spelt out in his 1960 annual report to Parliament that Auckland was the logical site for a jet-age airport because of its geographic location, importance as a commercial centre, and large population base. His report stated that Mangere should be planned as a fully international airport as there appeared to be no economic justification for more than one truly international airport in this country. Following this report, meetings were held between the Minister of Works Hugh Watt and the Auckland City Council about the construction of an international airport. After much debate finally agreements for cost sharing were signed on 10 October 1960 by the government and Auckland City, allowing the work to go ahead.

The Auckland Aero Club, which had continued to thrive at Mangere, moved to the Ardmore field in February 1961 to make way for construction of the new Auckland International Airport.

Construction

With 170 large earthmoving machines available from South Island hydro dam construction, it was agreed between Auckland City representative Reg Savory, the Minister of Works Hugh Watt, and the Commissioner of Works Fred Hanson that the earthworks, moving nearly eight million cubic metres of soil, could be done by the Ministry of Works. This saved about a year of construction time and under project engineer Ted Flynn work proceeded in 1960. There were difficulties with pockets of peat and soft clay requiring removal and replacement with suitable filling material, but the basic earthworks were completed in May 1962. The Ministry of Works also constructed a massive stormwater system and

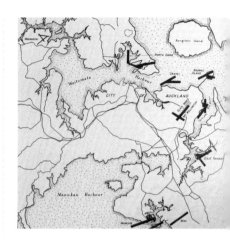

Possible sites for Auckland International Airport.

NZ Engineering, July 1955, paper by J. Wright: 'Some problems associated with siting of an airport for Auckland'

Top: Auckland Airport
international terminal,
c. 1980.

Sir George Grey Special Collections,
Auckland Libraries 1021-40

Above: Aerial view of Auckland
International Airport, 2010.

Courtesy Auckland International
Airport Ltd

some 40 kilometres of subsoil drains. The scoria base and concrete pavements for the runway and taxi strips were constructed by contract by British firm Taylor Woodrow in a consortium with the New Zealand firm of Wilkins and Davies. These were completed by 1964.

For the initial airport only the basic control buildings and a cargo shed, used as an interim terminal, were built. Later on, after the formation of the Auckland Regional Authority (ARA), the main international terminal was built. The ARA became the manager of the airport. The rapid increase in air traffic and size of aircraft expansion has never ceased since the official opening on Saturday 29 January 1966. The main runway was extended to 3,300 metres in 1973 and plans for an additional runway north of the present one are being pursued.

Conclusion

With the possibility that the RNZAF might vacate its base at Whenuapai, there has been much discussion about either reverting to a dual civil-RNZAF operation or using Whenuapai as an additional civil airfield. The latter would be in competition with Auckland International Airport, and is a controversial topic amongst local authorities.

The airport at Mangere is of heritage importance as the first official airfield to have a powered flight in New Zealand, and as the country's first fully international airport.

References and further reading

Auckland Regional Authority, *Auckland International Airport, Its history and Development*, a booklet printed and published by Auckland Regional Authority to commemorate the opening of the Airport on 29 January 1966, December, 1965.

Thompson, M. and Clements, A., *Where New Zealand Touches the World: From Farm Paddock to South Pacific Hub – A History of Auckland International Airport*, Pearson Education, Auckland, 2003.

Wright, J., 'Some Problems Associated with the Siting of an Airport for Auckland', *NZ Engineering*, Vol. 10, July 1955.

CHAPTER TEN

Military Protection

Albert Barracks Wall

Albert Park and the nearby Auckland University campus form a peaceful island within the busy city centre, where visitors and lunchtime workers stroll among gardens bright with flowers. As university students walk through one of the older parts of their campus, they are likely to pass a length of sturdily constructed stone wall behind the Old Arts Building (now the Clock Tower). Probably very few give any thought to why this remnant of wall is there, or what its significance in the early days of Auckland may have been. The scene is in stark contrast to the stone buildings comprising a barracks magazine, prison, store and other military establishments of almost 150 years ago.

Its historical significance was first officially recognised by the Auckland Civic League in 1915 with a plaque to record the part played by friendly Maori in its construction. At that time Maori soldiers were fighting alongside New Zealand and British forces in the First World War. Although it may have been appropriate at that time, the wording was seen as unfortunate some 50 years later, when the plaque was severely damaged. It was removed in 1984 when the wall was being restored on the university campus.

An Historic Places Trust plaque on the south side of the wall near the General Library entrance reads 'This is

10.1

Albert Barracks

by
Rhys Thomas

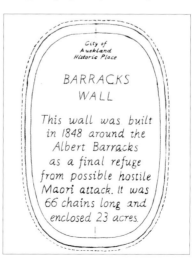

City of
Auckland
Historic Place

BARRACKS
WALL

This wall was built in 1848 around the Albert Barracks as a final refuge from possible hostile Maori attack. It was 66 chains long and enclosed 23 acres.

Copy of Albert Barracks wall original plaque.

Auckland Council Archives based on ACC015 Record no 12035/6

North side view of Albert Barracks Wall at Auckland University.

J. La Roche

South side view of Albert Barracks wall showing Historic Places plaque and University Clock Tower.

Rhys Thomas photo, enhanced by S. La Roche

a remnant of the Albert Barracks Wall which was started in 1846 and by 1852 enclosed some 23 acres of land.'

Servicemen were first established in Auckland in 1840 when some 50 men of the 80th Regiment were sent from the Bay of Islands, becoming the first official British settlers. When Auckland was selected as the capital by Governor Hobson, who later moved to the new seat of government, servicemen became an important part of the settlement for 30 years. Since the capital feared a possible Maori attack, both from Ngapuhi warriors in the north and from southern iwi, an increased number of soldiers were sent to Auckland. They constructed everything they required: their own quarters, stores, military hospital and magazine, using local volcanic rock, brick and timber to create the most substantial public buildings in the new town. A fortress was built for protection of the settlement on the promontory, to be known as Fort Britomart in 1842.

To further safeguard the town Sir George Grey, the new Governor, ordered the construction in 1846 of a stone wall three to four metres high and 1,300 metres long, and encircling some nine hectares which contained the Albert Barracks. Fort Britomart and Albert Barracks were designed to hold up to 1000 troops but only about 400 at any one time were ever quartered there. Besides being a fortification for the Barracks and town, the Governor said it should also be a place for recreation and interest for the townspeople.

The Albert Barracks wall was constructed by 'friendly' Maori trained in dressing stone under the supervision of the Royal Engineers, assisted by 25 sappers and miners from England. This resulted in a well constructed wall consisting of large basalt rock bonded with lime mortar, built as a typical mid-19th century fortification with bastions protecting the gates and a firing step along its length for troops to fire through the loopholes. It would have been an impregnable fort against any army lacking artillery.

A close inspection shows the skill that the Maori workmen acquired in a relatively short period to build this impressive wall. While historians quote the height of the wall as 15 to 20 feet (five to six metres), today's remnant of 85 metres length measures only approximately four and a half metres in height. Possibly a good proportion of the rest of the wall was higher than the section still in place.

After the departure of the military, the impressive barracks wall no longer had a practical purpose. Slowly it was dismantled; some of the stone was used in the construction of railway culverts in Mechanics Bay and the Kitchener Street retaining wall. Within the university grounds today, less than seven per cent of the original wall stands, the sole remnant of a sad loss to Auckland's engineering heritage.

Group of soldiers inside the Albert Barracks beside the military store, 1860s.

Sir George Grey Special Collections, Auckland Libraries 4-423

The Military contribution to Auckland

No actual hostilities occurred in Auckland but, while they continued in the Waikato and Bay of Plenty, military and naval forces were concentrated in Auckland's barracks and its outer areas until it acquired the appearance of a large armed camp. Fencible settlements were established at Howick, Otahuhu, Penrose and Onehunga as bastions protecting the southern approaches to Auckland. The population of the settlement of Auckland was 9,000 in 1849 and was growing rapidly, mainly because of the increasing presence of soldiers and sailors. By 1851 serving soldiers, the Fencibles and their families made up about 30 per cent of Auckland's population.

The military had a huge effect on early Auckland and its subsequent progress. It became the largest centre of population in the colony and this created resentment further south. The New Zealand Company had established

Drawing by P. J. Hogan of Albert Barracks in 1852, looking from the vicinity of Hobson Street.

Sir George Grey Special Collections, Auckland Libraries 4-1288

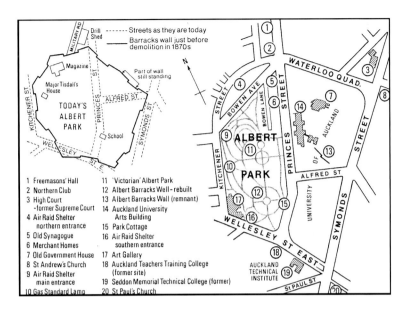

Plan of the Albert Barracks in relation to Albert Park and Auckland University, prepared by H. J. Brown and W. Colgan.

Published in 'The Past Today, Historic Places of New Zealand', courtesy H. J. Brown & W. Colgan

Above: Fencible House at Panmure.

Sir George Grey Special Collections, Auckland Libraries 4-2575

Right: Soldiers, probably at Albert Barracks in the 1860s.

Sir George Grey Special Collections, Auckland Libraries 4-453

colonies in the lower North Island and upper South Island and Auckland was publicly criticised as owing its position to the will of a Governor and its reliance on British money for enormous military expenditure. It was inferred that if government money ceased, Auckland's growth would 'melt' away. This fuelled antagonism between the two regions for many years.

Until the departure of the military, the servicemen were an integral part of the social life of the young town. Fort Britomart personnel contributed to the social life of Auckland, with balls being held and plays performed, and large crowds attending ceremonial functions such as the trooping of the colours and the pageantry on public holidays, particularly on the Queen's Birthday. Performances by the regimental band playing on the well-kept lawn of Government House (now the university staff common room) presented not only popular music and marches, but included dances with waltzes, polkas, schottisches and classical overtures from popular operas. Officers, most of whom had purchased their commissions and were well off, were well connected socially, and together with the governor's officials were the capital's social elite. The garrison had its own cricket and football clubs and mixed and played with the local population.

The Barracks Square in particular was a popular place to walk through, watch the parade, and chat to friends. It was here the soldiers used to drill every morning before breakfast, wearing their light blue tunics with velvet cuffs and collar, and dark trousers with a red stripe, no doubt an attraction for the youth.

There were a number of regulations promulgated governing admissions of the public to the barracks, such as:

> Sober well conducted persons may pass from gate to gate when opened.
>
> When passing through you are to abstain from smoking tobacco, especially near the powder magazine, do not loiter.
>
> Do not ride or drive through unless to transact business.
>
> Do not carry any bulky materials merchandise or other burdens.

While Auckland never came under armed attack, the military proved their worth in other ways. More than once when the town was threatened with annihilation by fire it owed its salvation to a swarm of soldiers who rushed out from the barracks to help. They also assisted with civil work, helping to form Khyber Pass with pickaxe and spade.

The part the military played in the early days of Auckland was significant and no doubt helped the fledgling town. Its influence did not end there. In 1858 servicemen ending their service period were to be returned home, but a large number elected to stay – of the 350 rank and file serving in the 58th Regiment, only 120 left. This was not exceptional, as imperial colonisation encouraged experienced soldiers to settle in the colonies after the departure of their corps. Over time a substantial number of the 1,400 from the regiment stayed as settlers. Not all were rank and file. Some medical officers resigned from the army to practise in Auckland. Several others with professional and artistic qualifications remained, including a noted musician who founded the Auckland Choral Society.

After the end of the Waikato campaign and the transfer of military operations to other parts of the country, a reduction in the troop numbers in Auckland was inevitable. But of greater significance was the decision of the home government to progressively withdraw regular troops from the colony. Once it acquired self government it was considered that New Zealand should be able to handle its own problems and become self reliant. In 1865 the first of the withdrawals started and was completed by February 1870.

After the final departure of the soldiers in 1870 both sets of barracks were closed and Fort Britomart land was handed over to the Harbour Board. It was decreed that the Albert Barracks be retained as a public endowment, with some six hectares being allocated for public recreation, the name of Albert was to be retained for the park.

For three decades the military had made an impressive impact on the early life of Auckland. The transfer of the capital to Wellington in 1865 and the withdrawal of the imperial troops were relatively dramatic but did not leave Auckland destitute. The town was strategically located between two harbours with increasing trade, absorbing the skills obtained from the military and the arrival of businessmen with money, education and ability, Auckland continued to advance.

Acknowledgement

Permission to use the writing of Wynne Colgan and Russell Stone from the publications listed below is gratefully acknowledged.

References and further reading

Colgan, Wynne, *'This Really Nobel Thoroughfare' Princes Street and Albert Park*, p.140–147, The Past Today: Historic Places in New Zealand, New Zealand Historic Places Trust, Pacific Publishers, Auckland, 1987.
Historic Places Trust, Albert *Barracks Wall (University of Auckland)*, Registration No. 12.
Stone, Russell, *Logan Campbell's Auckland: Tales from the Early Years*, Auckland University Press, 2007.

10.2

Albert Park Air Raid Shelters

*by
Rhys Thomas,
Bryan Bartley
and
Elizabeth
Aitken Rose*

Albert Park, the central city park, was once Albert Barracks, a colonial defence post built in 1845 to withstand a Maori attack. Although never under siege, it was a military base until finally disbanded in 1870. When Auckland City Council was formed in 1871 there were no public parks handed to the Council. According to G. W. Bush's book *Decently and in Order*, the Albert Barracks area at that time was 'accessible to the general public who were desirous of escaping for the nonce the odours and eyesores of the town'. The Council officially took over the Albert barracks in 1879 and architect James Slater won a competition to design the layout of the park. Once the military buildings were cleared away in the 1880s it was developed as a six hectare park with gardens in formal Victorian style.

During the Second World War, when a Japanese bomb attack was feared, the city engineer James Tyler designed an extensive air-raid shelter network under the park with a capacity of 20,400 people. Some mechanical equipment was used at the entrances, but the main excavation was carried out by hand by up to 300 council staff. It cost £120,000, three quarters of which was paid by the government. The construction involved some 1200 cubic metres of volcanic and sandstone rock; 140,000 square metres of timber lined its tunnels and galleries, which were arranged in a grid under Albert Park and Bowen Reserve.

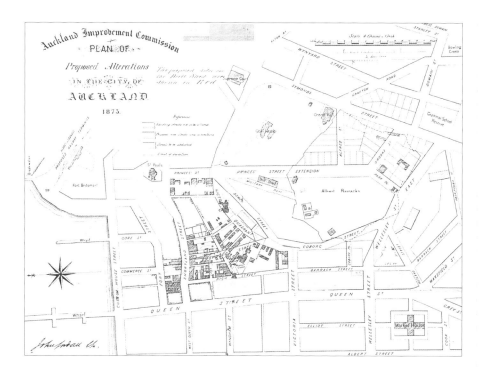

Auckland City plan for Albert Park, 1873.

Auckland Council Archives AIC 003/1

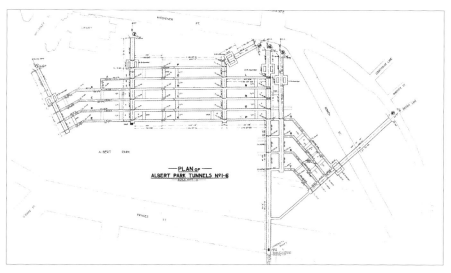

Plan of tunnel complex under Albert Park.

Auckland Council Archives ACC 015 Record No 8439/7

The main tunnels, 3.7 kilometres in length and stretching from the eastern end of Victoria Street to the foot of Constitution Hill in Parnell, were just 2.7 metres high by 4.6 metres wide, with a semicircular roof and timber lining. Off these main tunnels was a grid of accommodation galleries 2.1 metres high by 2.1 metres wide, with wooden seating. The total length of these accommodation galleries was 1,800 meters. The main tunnels were fitted with baffles near the tunnel entrances constructed from timber, lead and stone designed to absorb the shock of a bomb blast. Smaller tunnels from the side of the main tunnels

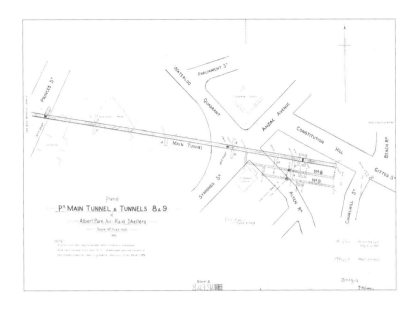

Plan of air raid shelter tunnels
under Old Government House
through to Constitution Hill.

Auckland Council Archives
ACC015 8439/2

provided access around the baffles and there were air conditioning fans and emergency electric lighting provided by a diesel engine from an old meat works. To assist forced air ventilation there were no dead ends in the tunnels.

First aid posts were installed as well as a loudspeaker system. Of the original nine tunnel entries, three are behind the decorative oval wall at the top of Victoria Street East, and two others are the steel door opposite Bacons Lane in Kitchener Street and the stone facing at the bottom of Constitution Hill.

A contributor to this text, Bryan Bartley, was a student at Seddon Memorial Technical College in Wellesley Street when these tunnels were excavated. When they were ready for testing in 1945, the whole college population filed, in good order, across the road into one of the Wellesley Street portals and stopped for a short period, before returning through another portal. Memories remain of nervous excitement; warm, humid, earthy, fresh air; dim light which one got used to and rough-sawn boards. The roof, which seemed high, was supported with timber frames. Anxiety about claustrophobia

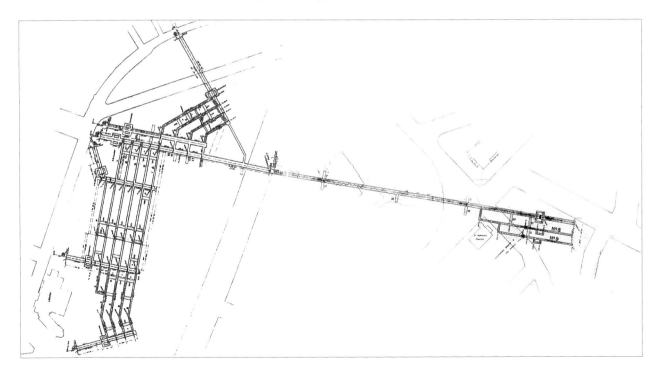

soon went and it became an interesting, if challenging, experience and adventure in confidence building.

The war with Japan ended soon after. Fortunately, the tunnels were never needed to be used as air raid shelters, the purpose for which they were designed. Soon the timber supports were deteriorating and when the war concluded in 1945 the tunnels were filled with unfired clay bricks. There have been many

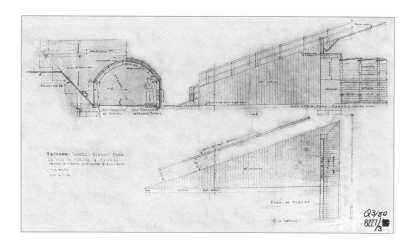

Above: Tunnel entrance to air raid shelters.

Auckland Council Archives
ACC 015 8227/3

Left: Closed-off entrances now behind the decorative wall at the top of Victoria Street East.

Sir George Grey Special Collections, Auckland Libraries 7-A-13963

proposals over recent years to re-use the tunnels for various purposes, including a traffic by-pass, car parking and a tourist attraction, but so far none have come to fruition. In 2005 one of the old ventilation shafts collapsed, causing a subsidence in Albert Park, and generated renewed interest.

References and further reading

Albert Park Tunnels http://en.wikipedia.org/wiki/Albert_Park_Tunnels
Auckland City Council Management Plan www.aucklandcity.govt.nz/council/ documents/managementplans/albertpark
Taylor, Nancy M., *The Official History of New Zealand in the Second World War 1939–1945 Volume 1*, Historical Publications Branch, Wellington, 1986.

Opposite page: Overall plan of air raid shelter tunnels from Victoria Street through to Constitution Hill.

Compound picture from Auckland Council Archives ACC 015 Record No. 8439/7 and ACC 015 Record No. 8439/2, compiled by S. La Roche

10.3

North Head: Engineering Auckland's Victorian Defences

*by
David Veart*

By the 1870s the internal conflict of the land wars was mostly over and the colonists turned their attention to possible threats from outside the country. New Zealand at this time was very much part of the British world and from the 1850s onward the main threat to the British imperial power came from the rapidly expanding Russian empire. It was feared that Russian forces would move down through Afghanistan to attack British India. New Zealanders were also very aware of the Russian naval presence at their Pacific base at Vladivostok.

With no defences at New Zealand's ports, the government came under increasing pressure to provide some. The boldest of these initiatives was a hoax article in the Auckland newspaper the *Daily Southern Cross* of 18 February 1873 describing an attack on the city by the Russian cruiser *Kaskowiski*. This modern weapon of war with its 'submarine pinnace' and 'mephitic water gas' had seized the government steamer and was holding the city to ransom. Not realising it was a hoax, people panicked but the point had been made; the city had no way of defending itself.

Numerous official reports on the state of the defences were prepared and in 1882 British defence expert Sir William Drummond Jervois was appointed New Zealand's governor. Jervois had been involved in planning defences both in Britain and in other parts of the Empire, including Australia. Among his recommendations was that New Zealand appoint a professional military engineer.

In December 1883 a Royal Engineer officer, Major Henry Cautley, was appointed as Jervois' assistant and in 1884 Jervois delivered a public address summarising their thoughts on the

Firing the eight-inch Armstrong disappearing gun on North Head, 19 September 2010.

Sandra Jack, Department of Conservation

subject. He recommended that forts be constructed at the four main ports and that these be armed with the Rifled Muzzle Loader (RML) guns that the government had already ordered, together with the most up to date weapons available, the extraordinary 'disappearing guns'. These pieces of artillery were designed to use the force generated by the recoil to drive the gun back into its underground pit between shots. The use of a hydro-pneumatic system, pressurised by the recoil, meant that these guns could be returned to the surface after being reloaded and aimed out of sight, under the ground. Major Cautley designed a series of very elegant, albeit expensive, forts to emplace this artillery, including batteries at North Head at the entrance to Auckland's harbour.

At this point the government had the large rifled muzzle loader guns in storage. The plans for Cautley's series of beautifully designed forts unfortunately were deemed too expensive to build. Just to add to the mix, in March 1885 another Russian war scare occurred. Russian forces moved into northern Afghanistan and war between Britain and Russia seemed imminent. Orders for the new disappearing guns were placed and the Armed Constabulary, as well as 300 unemployed men, were rushed to North Head to start building defences against the expected Russian attack. The war with Russia came to nothing and the New Zealand government now found itself with the new artillery emplaced in temporary holes in the ground. Another solution was needed.

The answer to the government's dilemma came in the form of a Royal Artillery officer, Captain Edmund Tudor Boddam, who was busy building forts in Tasmania. Boddam had developed a system of construction which was very much cheaper than Cautley's more traditional methods. As Boddam described it in his official report of 1886:

> We have done away with the heavy brick arches usually heretofore adopted, and substituted old rails and concrete, at a reduction of about one-half in cost; and in many other instances made considerable reductions in the costs of materials and labour, without impairing in any way the efficiency of the work.

Concrete was cheaper to use because it required no skilled bricklayers or expensive bricks. It could be mixed and poured by unskilled labour. In most cases during this period prisoners did the work on the forts and a barracks at North Head was converted into a prison to house up to 40 inmates. The only skilled workmen required were the carpenters used to build the timber formwork into which the concrete was poured (in a timber rich country carpenters were more common than bricklayers), and a blacksmith to make the metal fittings. At North Head even the blacksmith was a prisoner for most of the 19th-century period.

As well as the use of 'old rails and concrete' Boddam used innovative solutions to other problems. Much of his design work entailed the use of separate

Seven-inch rifled muzzle loader crew on North Head, 1885.

Courtesy Department of Conservation, photo C25201006231120 from the collection of Mr C. J. Watt, whose grandfather Gunner Alford is at the left rear.

Six-inch Mark 7 gun on North Battery, North Head.

Courtesy Department of Conservation

modules. The gun pits, magazine blocks and personnel tunnels were separate designs and could be fitted together to form a fort suitable to each site with the many minor details contained in a 'General Specification'. He also used pre-cast concrete details for things such as corbels, loop-hole apertures and window and lamp recess architraves. Modern contractors have observed that the good design of Boddam's forts has helped them to survive despite the shortcomings of some of the materials used.

While he was in New Zealand Boddam was promoted to Lieutenant Colonel and his efforts were praised by his superior officers. Sir G. S. Whitmore wrote in 1886,

> …in Major Boddam the colony possesses an officer of singular energy, ability, and versatility of talent. Works on so large a scale were probably never attempted in so many different places by any government with so small amount of supervision, and the incessant labour devolving on Major Boddam, and got through by him is almost incredible.

The structures he designed at North Head, however, are his greatest memorial. They stand now in a Historic Reserve managed by the Department of Conservation. Despite long periods of neglect, Major Boddam's legacy still forms the major part of the North Head landscape today.

References and further reading

Coastal fortifications of New Zealand
    www.aucklandcity.govt.nz/council/documents/managementplans/albertpark
Cooke, Peter, *Defending New Zealand: Ramparts on the Sea, 1840–1950s*, Defence of New Zealand Study Group, 2000.
Mitchell, John, *The Disappearing Guns of Auckland*, thesis (PhD, anthropology), University of Auckland, 1995.
North Head Defences, History of the reserve, Life at the fort, DoC website www.doc.govt.nz/conservation/historic/by-region/auckland/Auckland-area-north
North Head Historic Reserve, *Hauraki Marine Park Self Guided Walk*, DoC brochure, 2007.

By the 1920s Auckland's coast defences were obsolete. Many of the forts dated from the 19th century and the most modern installation was a 6-inch battery at North Head built in 1905. The main concern for military planners was that these older defences were too close to the ports they were meant to defend, and modern warships could have shelled the city with little fear of counter-attack. Auckland's defences needed to be upgraded and plans were prepared for a new chain of forts to protect the harbour. The most impressive of these planned fortifications were to be 9.2-inch batteries. These guns were the largest commonly used for coast defence but they were very expensive. For this reason the batteries were not built immediately and Auckland's main defence throughout the Second World War came from a modern 6-inch battery built on Motutapu Island in the late 1930s.

The situation completely changed in December 1941 with the Japanese attack on Pearl Harbour and the subsequent entry of the United States into the war.

The government was prepared. Three months before Pearl Harbour a report had been written for the government by General Sir Guy Williams giving a higher priority to coastal defence, mostly as a precaution against raiders. An important part of this report was the recommendation to start construction of the larger 9.2-inch batteries shelved earlier because of cost.

There was, however, a new problem in carrying out these recommendations; it was not the expense this time, rather there was no guarantee from the over-stretched British manufacturers that a firm delivery date could be set. In a significant development for New Zealand's future international relations this problem was effectively resolved by the United States Navy. As part of the planned counter-offensive in the Pacific the Hauraki Gulf was to be used as a secure fleet anchorage and extended coastal defences were needed as part of this plan. As a result of the new American requirements the priorities of the British manufacturer were altered, delivery dates set and work on the 9.2-inch batteries started.

The design work was placed in the hands of the Public Works Department. It had been usual up until this date for New Zealand's coastal defences to be built using designs sent from Britain. The battery on Motutapu for example had

10.4

Stony Batter: Auckland's Last Fortress

by
David Veart

Stony Batter gun sites.

Courtesy Department of Conservation

been built using a standard British plan. However, the situation in New Zealand at this time required another, more localised engineering solution. British batteries at this date used a system of layers of concrete and steel burster slabs (used on the surface of a fortification to detonate projectiles before they could penetrate deeply enough to cause great damage) to protect the underground magazines and services. Steel of the type required was virtually unobtainable in New Zealand at this time so the three batteries were redesigned locally as tunnelled rather than built structures, with the depth of the excavations rather than concrete and steel providing overhead protection.

Construction work at Stony Batter.

Courtesy Department of Conservation

Construction work for 9.2-inch gun installation.

Courtesy Department of Conservation

To standardise the batteries and to speed up work, existing designs were chosen and modified. All the larger underground chambers were based on the double-track Tawa Flat railway tunnel, while the smaller access tunnels used the standard railways personnel tunnel. At Stony Batter the local volcanic boulders, from which the site gets its name, were crushed and concrete mixed and transferred to the mobile steel and timber formwork that lined the tunnel sections.

Each of the batteries was originally designed to emplace three 9.2-inch guns with deep underground magazines to store ammunition. Associated with these were pumps to provide the hydraulic power to move the guns and to work the automatic ammunition rammers that fed the heavy shells to the guns. To supply electricity for the fort, engine rooms were built deep underground, each with two large and one smaller Ruston Hornsby diesel engine. These were linked to generator sets and oil storage and exhaust systems were built nearby. All this was linked by hundreds of metres of personnel tunnels, with long flights of stairs and access from both the gun pits and at ground level.

Three of these 9.2-inch batteries were built in New Zealand, two in Auckland and one in Wellington. The Auckland batteries were located at Whangaparaoa and at Stony Batter on Waiheke Island. The battery at Stony Batter was in an inaccessible island location and it was impossible to get a private contractor who was willing to manage the difficulties of the site. For this reason Stony Batter was built by the Public Works Department, an arm of the New Zealand government.

By October 1943 work had started. The initial intention that the construction would be completed within 12 months proved to be hopelessly optimistic and the requirements for materials and for skilled labour were never met. These problems were compounded by design changes and other difficulties brought about by wet weather. One particularly vexing problem was that the access tunnels had been made with corners too acute to get the generator base plates into the engine rooms and parts of the tunnel network had to be rebuilt to get around this dilemma.

Another problem that developed as the work progressed was a lack of proper financial control. This inevitably led to large cost overruns and it is difficult from the surviving records to calculate the true cost of this enormous complex. Years later Ministry of Works' staff estimated the cost of the battery in 1982 dollars as being $13,600,000 (well over $43,000,000 in today's money).

Progress on the construction reflected events overseas. At the time work began the Japanese Empire posed a real threat and the batteries were given the highest priority. As the threat diminished the job was scaled down. The first sign of this was in 1943, when the reduction of the battery's armament was suggested. This came about in 1944 when the number of guns for each fort was reduced from three to two. By 1945 the government had new priorities and large numbers of workers were transferred to other work building the hydroelectric power stations on the Waikato River.

Construction continued slowly after the war. In 1947 it was recommended that only the most essential work be completed, that is that the pump chambers be fitted out so that the guns could be operated, the main engine room be completed and a general tidy-up be done prior to the battery being placed on a 'care and maintenance basis'. The guns were not officially proof fired until 1951,

9.2-inch gun at Stony Batter.

Courtesy Department of Conservation

although there is evidence that an 'unofficial' test firing was carried out in 1946. In 1955 all material that would be liable to deteriorate was removed, an event which signalled the end of the battery. By this date, the middle of the cold war, an era of nuclear threat, long-range aircraft and intercontinental ballistic missiles, the old form of coastal defence seemed very outmoded. Taking the lead from Britain, New Zealand wound down its coastal defences and the coastal defence regiments were disbanded. By 1962–3 this process was almost complete. Stony Batter was stripped of its remaining equipment and was abandoned, the only one of the three 9.2-inch battery installations to suffer such a fate. It is now a Historic Reserve, looked after by an enthusiastic restoration society.

References and further reading

Corbett, Peter, *A First Class Defended Port*, Department of Conservation, 2003
Historic Places Trust, *Waiheke Battery*, Register No. 7472.
Historic Stony Batter Waiheke Island, DoC website http://www.doc.govt.
    nz/conservation/historic/by-region/auckland/hauraki-gulf-islands/
    stony-batter-historic-reserve-waiheke-island/

10.5

Mt Eden Shot Tower

*by
Bryan Bartley*

The Mt Eden Shot Tower marks the site of the former Colonial Ammunition Company (CAC) and has a Category 1 rating by the NZ Historic Places Trust.

CAC was formed in 1885, by Major John Whitney and W. H. Hazard. This was at the time of the 'Russian Scare' when Tsar Alexander III brought some of his naval fleet into the North Pacific to Vladivostok and it was feared that he was about to expand his empire. Fortifications were built with all haste and the need for ammunition independent of the supplies from Britain became urgent. CAC was the first munitions factory in Australasia and later established a factory in Melbourne.

CAC prospered and apart from the needs of the military, the company provided bullets for hunters and shotgun cartridges for duck shooters.

The shot tower was built in 1914 to produce the small spherical lead pellets for shotgun enthusiasts. The pellets fired from the gun formed a pattern when aimed at a bird. They were earlier produced in Nelson, by a Mr Lylie, using a casting process that was laborious and slow in production.

The first operator of the new Auckland shot tower was the same Mr Lylie, assisted by his two daughters. Lead blocks were raised to the top of the tower

Mt Eden Shot Tower, 2009.

B. Bartley photo

by a lift, melted in a furnace and poured into a pan with many small holes in the bottom so that small drops fell down the 30-metre height of the tower as perfect spheres which solidified in the air and splashed into soapy water at the base. They were polished and sized, with rejects being returned to the molten metal. Production up to 1000 tons per year was possible.

Colonial Ammunition Company premises, Normanby Road, Mt Eden, 1902.

Sir George Grey Special Collections, Auckland Libraries 1-W1057

Our shot tower is somewhat unique in being a light steel structure and built by an Auckland blacksmith, W. Wilson & Co. Other shot towers, all built in the 19th century, are two in the UK, four in the USA, three in Australia – all are in the form of brick chimneys.

CAC was an essential industry through both the world wars and each time expanded its manufacturing significantly. At the end of World War II it was producing up to 25-pound shells.

Imperial Chemical Industries (ICI) of the UK had been major manufacturers of explosives with the NOBEL trademark and following Nobel's patents for gelignite, supplied explosives to the New Zealand mining, quarrying and tunnelling activities and bought control of CAC in about 1960. The General Manager of ICI explosives in New Zealand was Dick Hazard, no doubt related to the CAC founder W. H. Hazard.

A little-known unique activity of CAC was the commercial harvesting and canning of toheroa, the large shellfish found on the west coast beaches north of Auckland. This was carried on for many years, until about 1975 when the fishery was closed.

References and further reading

Historic Places Trust, *Colonial Ammunition Company Shot Tower*, Register No. 87.

Energy Supplies

On 5 April 1864 it was reported in the local newspapers that most of the population of Auckland had turned out to see the city's new street lighting turned on. This technological advance was the result of the formation of New Zealand's first joint stock company, the Auckland Gas Company. The company and its associated works, gas storage tanks and infrastructure were to be part of Auckland's cityscape for over 100 years.

The company started production in a gasworks located at the corner of Wyndham and Nelson Streets in the city, the gas generated from coal brought initially as ballast by ships from England. Later this was replaced by coal from Newcastle in Australia with some from Greymouth in the South Island. Despite a few early problems gas consumption grew, and in 1877 more gas storage capacity was needed. In response the company built a much larger gas holder on a new site at the foot of College Hill. These gas holders with

11.1

The Auckland Gas Company

by
David Veart

Auckland's first gasworks, at the foot of Nelson Street in the 1860s.

Sir George Grey Special Collections, Auckland Libraries 7-A11393

their distinctive gas flare finials were to be a city landmark for over a century. A supermarket now occupies this site.

Expansion continued and by the end of the 19th century the old city gas-works site was no longer large enough to allow further expansion. The company then moved to Beaumont Street in Freemans Bay, where a new works with attached offices and service buildings was constructed. The Italianate admin-istration building is all that now remains of what once was a 5.2-hectare site.

From the start there was a significant engineering component to the construction and management of a gasworks. As my father, a second genera-tion 'gasman' and the distribution engineer at the Auckland Gas Company for many years, commented in a paper delivered to the Institute of Gas Engineers in 1999, 'Simple logic dictated that if you want street gas lighting you need a gas-making plant, gas pipes and a gas engineer to plan, install and operate the enterprise'.

The first engineer-manager was Mr J. N. Wark, whose job it was to accom-pany the essential equipment from England, assemble it and start producing gas as soon as possible. This, however, was impossible as he arrived at a time when war with Maori in the Waikato meant that skilled tradesmen were impossible to engage. Other gas engineers followed him; Henry Atkinson in 1877, and then Harry Levick, brought out in 1905 to help construct the new Beaumont works. These men were from Britain, but New Zealanders, trained here, followed them. My father remembered them as hard taskmasters who helped trainees to remember their lessons by time spent 'cutting the tops off thousands of rivets on a holder crown under repair … or digging out the bottom layer of spent oxide in a purifier'. He did, however, comment that while these tasks were treated as punishments by the cadets, they were also someone else's everyday job.

Gasworks were dirty, dangerous places to work. While my father's descrip-tion below is from an earlier period it also fits my childhood memories of time spent in the Auckland retort house, the place where the gas is made and the heart of a gasworks.

> The production of coal gas would commence within the Dante's Inferno of the horizontal retort house floor. Flames licked around the edges of any badly fitted retort doors, a greeny yellow raw gas from the ascension pipes oozed upwards, the dull roar of the exhausters coming from the brickwork and the gangs of indistinguishable workers with coke sacks protecting their shoulders, felt hats and bushranger face masks to protect against hot gases, dust and smoke. (Albert Veart Notes, collection of D. Veart.)

Auckland Gasworks, 1928.

Auckland War memorial Museum,
C24692

The first years of the 20th century were a time of prosperity for the Auckland Gas Company. By 1907 the new works at Beaumont Street was supplying 977 gas lamps and 10,818 customers. After that time competition from electricity grew, with the new council-owned generating station at Kings Wharf opening in 1908. Other problems affected production as well. Coal shortages during the First World War led to price increases and strikes during the 1920s meant that at one stage gas production ceased altogether.

Higher prices, dissatisfied customers and the new, cheaper, state-owned hydro electricity from Arapuni led to a fall in gas consumption. The government control of electricity supplies meant that other impediments were placed on gas sales. For example gas appliances were forbidden in state houses and electric supply authorities insisted that new electric hot water heating could only be installed in homes with electric stoves. Out went the old gas appliances and gas sales fell.

The Second World War saw the Auckland Gas Company in dire straits. Australia banned export of Newcastle coal, the best gas production coal in the world which made up half of Auckland's gas production. The loss of this coal reduced output by 20 per cent. As well, the plant was old and worn out and in winter gas often had run out by six o'clock in the evening. Something had to be done.

A new general manager was appointed – ex-Hamilton borough engineer Rupert Worley, who had revived the ailing Hamilton gasworks. His assessment was that almost all the gas-making equipment at Beaumont Street was obsolete. A gas engineer, C. F. Broadhead, was appointed to prepare a formal report. He agreed with Worley: the place was severely run down. As a result of this study a new retort house was ordered from Britain, a continuous vertical plant known as a Glover-West, and it was in operation by 1948. This new, highly efficient plant had one unexpected side effect: coke production trebled. Coke is what is left after the gas has been generated and the huge mountains of coke filling

Auckland Gasworks, October 1964. Note gasholder tanks at rear.

Sir George Grey Special Collections, Auckland Libraries 7-A1307

every vacant part of the gasworks site was a feature of the Beaumont Street landscape for years.

The post-war period with the new plant and increased prosperity meant the Gas Company did well, with occasional problems such as the 1951 waterfront strike, which limited coal supplies and meant gas was rationed for three months. Further savings were made possible by the opening of the Auckland Harbour Bridge. In 1959 the company built a high-pressure pipeline under the bridge to the North Shore, allowing the closure of the uneconomic Devonport gasworks.

Another event in 1959 was to have far-reaching effects on the company – the discovery of natural gas at Kapuni in Taranaki. Initially the government wanted to use this gas solely for the generation of electricity. The gas industry argued that this was a very wasteful way to use the resource and an enquiry was called. The Washington firm of Zinders was engaged to advise and reported that the electricity proposal was flawed and that burning the fuel directly was a more efficient use.

As a result of this report a pipeline was built from the Taranaki gas fields and Auckland first received natural gas in 1970. Prior to this much of the old distribution network, suitable for the old product but not for natural gas, was

Auckland Gasworks coal delivery, 1931.

Sir George Grey Special Collections, Auckland Libraries 4 -4655 rebuilt to limit gas loss and thousands of conversions of older gas equipment were carried out.

With the arrival of natural gas the Auckland Gas Company went from being a gas producer to being more of a transmission, distribution and marketing organisation. Most of the old plant relating to coal gas production became obsolete. The retort house, the distillation towers, the laboratories and, finally, even the huge gas holders were all removed. The gas engineer, the backbone of an industry for over 100 years, was also approaching obsolescence, in the original sense of the word at least. But, as my father wrote in 1999, 'No doubt there will be a gas engineer, if not in command, at least in the background keeping the integrity of "gas" in good hands'.

Devonport Gasworks, 1884.

Takapuna Library D GBB 0003

References and further reading

Pritchard, Assoc. Prof. M. P. L., and Tabb, B. J., *One Hundred Years of the Auckland Gas Company,* Auckland Gas Company, 1967.

Veart, A., *New Zealand Institute of Gas Engineers 75 Years On.* Unpublished paper, 1 October 1999.

Veart, A., *Lamp Light to Natural Gas: A History of the New Zealand Institution of Gas Engineers,* New Zealand Institute of Gas Engineers, 2000.

Worley, R., 'Auckland Gas Company Limited', in *Auckland-Waikato Historical Journal,* Vol. 37, September 1980, pp 36–40.

Worley, R., 'Auckland Gas Company Limited', in *Auckland-Waikato Historical Journal,* Vol. 38, April 1981, pp 37–40.

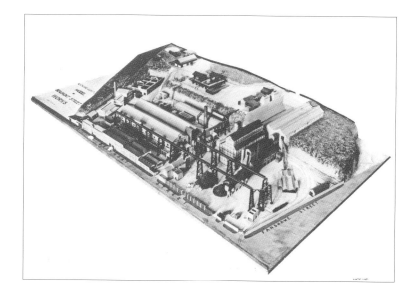

Model of Auckland Gasworks.

Auckland War Memorial Museum C24724

Auckland City Destructor

*by
Bryan Bartley
and
Elizabeth
Aitken Rose*

The site of today's Victoria Park Market was once the central refuse collection area for Auckland City. Disposal of refuse was a pungent city issue throughout the latter part of the 19th century. In the 1870s collection was contracted out and dumping occurred out of sight and smell of citizens. In the 1880s, however, citizens were required to dispose of their own rubbish and vacant allotments became convenient informal tips. Rats were a serious problem. Fear of the bubonic plague in 1900, after some cases were reported in Sydney, caused the council to consider a municipal refuse destruction plant.

In 1904 a tender of £16,840 (worth more than $2.6 million today) was accepted from J. Barre Johnston Ltd of Sydney for the construction of a Meldrum destructor to incinerate the collected refuse. This was completed in 1905.

The complex of polychromatic brick construction included the council's works depot, blacksmith's and carpenter's shops, stables and a 38-metre-high chimney. Alfred Wrigg (city engineer from 1899 to 1906) supervised construction. He was also responsible for supervising the Auckland electric trams and for paving Queen Street with asphalt.

As Auckland grew, so did the requirement for electricity. The council was vested with the public supply of electricity by the Auckland City Electric Lighting Act 1900, and Australian engineer W. T. G. Goodman was employed

The brick building that once housed the Destructor, now Victoria Park Markets.

B. Bartley

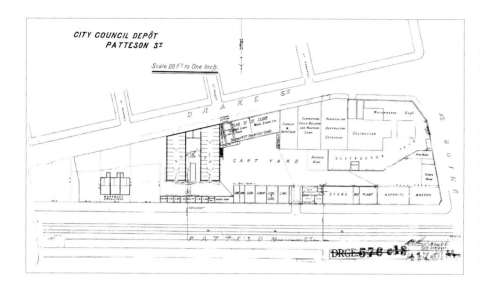

Plan of Auckland City Works depot, 1915.

Auckland Council Archives ACC 015 Record No 4174/3

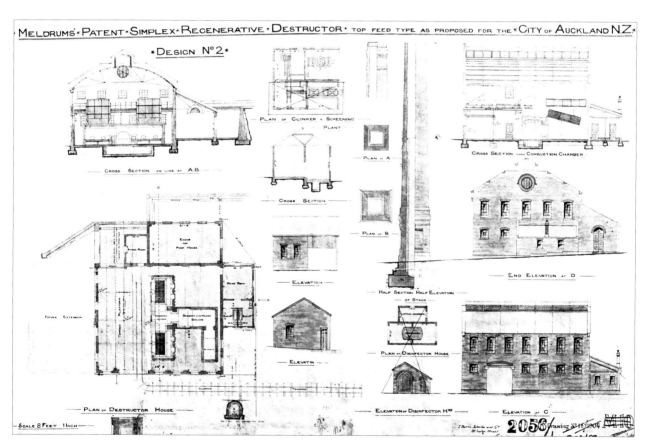

to report on the feasibility of using the destructor to generate electricity in 1906. His proposals were accepted, although he criticised the council for failing to incorporate a generating plant in the original design, despite a series of earlier reports endorsing the potential of electricity.

Meldrum Destructor.

Auckland Council Archives ACC 015 Record No 2056/1

First public electricity generator in Auckland, 1908.

Sir George Grey Special Collections, Auckland Libraries 7-A4319

Turnbull and Jones won the electrical contract for £11,808 (about $1.75 million). The cost subsequently escalated, with revisions in potential demand and the provision of additional boilers and new feeders. In 1908, the electricity was provided to the first 12 customers. Within four months demand exceeded supply and coal was used to supplement the burning of rubbish. The generation plant was replaced in 1913 by the Kings Wharf coal-fired station, again built by the council.

The capacity of the destructor was increased during the 1920s and 1930s, but by 1960, as controlled landfill grew in popularity, it was disposing of a mere 10 per cent of the city's rubbish. The plant was closed in 1972, although the complex continued to act as a rubbish collection depot until 1981, and it was subsequently converted into the Victoria Park Market.

References and further reading

Bush, G. W. A., *Decently and In Order: The Centennial History of Auckland City Council*, Collins, Auckland, 1971.
Historic Places Trust, *Auckland Municipal Destructor and Depot (Former)*, Register No. 7664.

11.3

A Brief History of Electricity in Auckland

by
Bryan Leyland

The earliest public supply of electricity in New Zealand was from a hydro-power plant at Reefton in 1886. This was said to be the first public supply of electricity in the Southern Hemisphere. The generating plant was installed to provide power to a goldmine. In 1886 an ordinary working man would typically earn one shilling per hour and electricity was sold for six pence per kilowatt hour (kWh). In today's terms this is roughly equivalent to $10 per kWh – 50 times the current price!

The earliest recorded use of electricity in Auckland was in 1882 in the private home in Princes Street of Moss Davis and his family. Among the family was the 10-year-old future brewery baron, mayor and Auckland benefactor Ernest Davis.

In 1887 a generator installed at the Northern Roller Milling Company provided electricity for street lighting in Queen Street over the Christmas period. As the Auckland City Council could not afford to install permanent electric lighting, Queen Street was lit by gas lighting until 1903. At this time the council purchased electricity from the Auckland Tramways Company to power some lights in Queen Street.

Although Wellington had a supply from a private company in 1893, Auckland lagged behind because, all through the 1890s, the council strongly resisted all attempts by private companies to build a power station. In 1900 the council persuaded the government to pass the Auckland Electric Lighting Act, which gave the council exclusive authority to run an electrical generating plant.

In 1902, the first electric trams ran in Auckland. In 1905 a dentist in Endean's Building was the first private consumer connected to a mains supply.

In 1908 a very limited public supply of electricity was made available from a powerhouse sited next to the Auckland City Destructor, the rubbish-burning facility in Freemans Bay. The destructor burned coal and some rubbish. The station was opened on 10 February 1908. Because of the very high demand, a new generating plant was ordered shortly afterwards. The station finished up with three 225 kilowatt (kW) generators driven by reciprocating steam engines. This power station drew its cooling water from the sea. The original building still exists and is now the site of the Victoria Park Market.

In technical terms, the electricity supply was three-wire direct current (DC) with 460 volts (V) between the two main conductors (effectively 230 + 230 V). Supply for lighting and other uses was taken at 230 V DC, while larger motors operated at 460 V.

There was also a power station for the trams and this must have been in service from about 1900. It also drew its cooling water from the sea and the returning warm water passed through the Tepid Baths in Customs Street

Steam engines and generators
at King's Wharf Power Station.

King's Wharf Power Station
switchboard.

West. This provided warm water for swimmers all year round. When the station shut down, a coal-fired boiler was installed to keep the pool warm.

In 1908 it was also realised that the site in Freeman's Bay was too small to accommodate the increasing demand so a 4-acre (1.6-hectare) site at Kings Wharf was purchased in 1909. This had direct access for colliers and to waterfront rail sidings for coal from Huntly. Construction began in 1910 and the new station was commissioned in February 1913. It had two 750 horsepower (hp) and two 1500 hp (1100 kW) triple-expansion steam engines driving direct current generators. There were two small steam turbines driven by the exhaust steam from the 1500 hp reciprocating engines and, later on, a 7500 hp (5600 kW) steam turbine generator. It had six coal-fired Babcock and Wilcox boilers operating at 165 pounds per square inch (lb/in^2) or approximately 11 bar (modern power stations operate at pressures in excess of 200 bar).

In 1914 orders were placed for new generators that added 2200 kW of direct current generation and 1500 kW of alternating current generation.

These were commissioned in 1920. In 1920, 13,000 kW of steam turbine-driven alternating current generation was ordered. The Kings Wharf station operated in parallel with a power station in Hobson Street that was built to supply power to the tramways. When spare capacity was available, it took over some of the domestic power load.

Not long after it was commissioned, the Kings Wharf power station provided all the power to the tramways and the power station at Hobson Street was shut down.

A number of rotary converters were installed at Kings Wharf. The rotary converters normally operated to convert alternating current to direct current to take advantage of the better efficiency of the newer steam turbine-driven alternating current generators. When the system load was high, the old direct current generators, driven by triple-expansion steam engines, were brought back into service. If there was surplus direct current power available the rotary converters operated 'inverted' to supplement the alternating current supply.

If the power station suffered a total blackout (because of overloading or because of blockage of the cooling water intake screens), the operators had to first start the reciprocating engines, generate direct current to drive the rotary converters, and then use the alternating current to start the feed pumps and cooling water pumps for the steam turbines. According to one of the operators, by the end of the process, they were totally exhausted!

In 1921, the Auckland Electric Power Board (later Mercury Energy and now Vector) was formed by a special act of Parliament to supply power to Auckland. It took over the Kings Wharf power station and the power supply to the tramways. When it was formed, the Auckland Electric Power Board had 8,533 customers. In 1972, it had 171,500.

While the Auckland Electric Power Board was steadily expanding the Kings Wharf power station, the government was investigating hydropower on the Waikato River, and undertook to provide Auckland with a supply from the new Arapuni station in 1928. Although its maximum demand was only 4975 kW, the board agreed to take a minimum of 15 megawatts (MW) when Arapuni was commissioned. To ensure this demand, the new board embarked on a vigorous programme of line-building and acquiring new consumers.

King's Wharf Power Station automatic stokers.

Sir George Grey Special Collections, Auckland Libraries Municipal & Official Handbook City of Auckland 1922

In the meantime, power demand was often greater than the capacity of the Kings Wharf power station and shortages were not uncommon. At one stage the use of electrical heating in city offices was banned. Other problems included a large number of electrical fires along the footpaths because, instead of cables, electricity was supplied by copper bars buried in troughs filled with pitch. If the pitch cracked, and water got into the cables, the resultant explosions and fire were often spectacular and, at times, quite dangerous. The standard method of detecting hotspots was for the engineer concerned to walk along the footpath in his stockinged feet, a scene that often generated some ribaldry. But the method did not guarantee success: once, when a hotspot was found, they dug up the hot-water pipe feeding the Tepid Baths!

In 1924, the power station at Hobson Street was shut down and the entire tramway load was supplied by the Kings Wharf power station. One unfortunate result was that the Tepid Baths no longer had a supply of hot water, but this was soon rectified.

In the winter of 1925 the first hydropower was supplied from the old station at Hora Hora. This was originally built to supply electricity to the Waihi mine and the gold crushing battery at Waikino in the Karanghake Gorge. Supply was only 2,000 kW and it soon became necessary to increase the generating capacity at Kings Wharf to 4,000 kW.

New Zealand was one of the first countries in the world to introduce what is now called 'demand-side management'. In those days, it was simply called 'peak load control'. It was pioneered by Lloyd Mandeno, who, while he was the engineer with Tauranga Borough Council in the 1920s, built a new power station at McLaren Falls. At that time there was commonly a high peak demand in the evening from cooking and lighting, not much load during the day and a very low load in the early hours of the morning. Lloyd designed and built storage electric water heaters that were insulated with pumice. He ensured that they could not be switched on during times of peak demand simply by having a two-way switch above the stove labelled 'stove' or 'hot water'. The householders could have one or the other, but not both.

In 1928, the average weekly electricity bill was about six shillings. In modern-day terms, this would be in the region of $60. In the late 1920s, the State Hydro-Electric Department instituted a bulk tariff that charged £5 for each kW of peak demand and nothing for units consumed. As a result, most of the power boards in New Zealand introduced some form of peak load control. In the end, what is now known as 'ripple control' became the dominant technology and was extremely effective in limiting electricity demand during peak demand periods. Sadly, since the advent of the electricity market, it is used less and less.

When the Power Board instituted a new domestic rate that included a special water heating rate, using time switches to minimise peak demand, Lloyd Mandeno's storage water heaters soon spread to Auckland. Within 12 months, 2,000 storage water heaters had been sold.

In the mid 1920s the first 22 kilovolt (kV) cables were laid between the new substation at Penrose and Kings Wharf. By the standards of the day, these cables were close to the limits of technology. They had three copper conductors surrounded by many layers of oiled paper tape and each core in turn was surrounded by a lead sheath. A lead over-sheath was then extruded over the three lead-sheathed conductors. Jointing the cables was a time-consuming operation; layers and layers of paper tape were carefully wrapped around each soldered joint. Each joint was several days' work for a jointer and his mate. These cables were still in service more than half a century later.

Alternating current (AC) power was transmitted around the city at 6.6 kV and, as the system developed, more and more 'zone substations' were added. Each was fed by a pair of 22 kV cables from Penrose substation. Early substations were at Epsom, Kingsland, Newmarket and Point Chevalier. Newmarket and Point Chevalier also provided direct current for the trams and trolleybuses. The equipment at Point Chevalier – and maybe at other substations – was fully automatic and operated under remote control. Inner-city trams and trolley buses were supplied from the old Hobson Street substation. The two rotary converters in the Greenlane Road Tram Barn in Epsom and others in Newmarket were replaced by mercury arc rectifiers in the 1950s. One of the rectifiers is now in the Museum of Transport and Technology (MOTAT) at Western Springs.

Power from the new huge hydropower station at Arapuni (huge by the standards of the day) was first available on 2 June 1929. Unfortunately, two years later it had major problems with leaks in the headrace canal that caused ground movement that threatened to tip, literally, the whole power station into the river. The station was shut down for about 18 months while repairs were carried out. During this time, the Kings Wharf station was brought back into service and, because of rapid load growth, carried on operating until the 1960s.

The period from the 1930s through to the mid-1960s was one of frequent power shortages, especially if there was a dry year. Every winter, rolling blackouts in the evening were a routine occurrence and were advertised in advance. They were needed because the rate of construction of new hydropower stations could not keep up with demand, which was growing at about 7 per cent per year. People became accustomed to periods without hot water, and being without power for an hour or two during winter evenings. In those days, every house had candles and an open fire, so there was always some light and, if necessary, cooking could be done over the open fire.

Shortages became much less frequent once the 600 MW direct current link carrying hydropower from the South Island was commissioned in the mid-1970s. The table below, illustrating the growth in the available capacity supplying the Auckland central business district, indicates how fast the load grew.

Year	Equipment	Installed Capacity		Firm Capacity
1955–1959	Kings Wharf Power Station		20 MVA	40 MVA
	Penrose-Quay 4 x 22 kV circuits		40 MVA (4x10 MVA)	
		Total:	60 MVA	
1959–1968	Kings Wharf Power Station		20 MVA	100 MVA
	Penrose-Quay 4 x 22 kV circuits		30 MVA (4x10 MVA*)	
	Penrose-Quay 2 x 110 kV circuits		100 MVA (2x50 MVA)	
		Total:	150 MVA	
1968–1973	Penrose-Quay 4 x 22 kV circuits		30 MVA (4x10 MVA*)	80 MVA
	Penrose-Quay 2 x 110 kV circuits		100 MVA (2x50 MVA)	
		Total:	130 MVA	
1973–1977	Penrose-Quay 2 x 110 kV circuits		100 MVA (2x50 MVA)	90 MVA
	Kingsland-Liverpool Inter-tie		40 MVA	
		Total:	140 MVA	
1977–1997	Penrose-Quay 2 x 110 kV circuits		100 MVA (2x50 MVA)	200 MVA
	Kingsland-Liverpool Inter-tie		40 MVA	
	Roskill-Liverpool 110 kV		120 MVA (2x60 MVA)	
		Total:	260 MVA	

Source: Mercury Energy Ltd, 1998.
Note: 1. Firm Capacity is defined as worst case, single contingency event.
    2. * Limited to 30 MVA by available capacity from Penrose 22 kV bus.

(MVA = mega-volt-amperes. It is equal to or greater than the MW.)

In 1998, the Auckland central business district suffered a major power failure which lasted for five weeks. As with most disasters, it did not have a single cause. The scene was set with the failure of one of the old 110 kV gas-filled cables between Penrose and Quay Street during the summer. Due to problems in obtaining jointing materials, there were delays in repairing this cable.

A month or so later, the other cable failed (possibly as a result of a temporary overload not long before the failure) and this immediately put a heavy load on the two oil-filled cables feeding the Liverpool Street substation just off Queen Street. Not long after that, and while the cable was still working within its assigned rating, one of these cables also failed. As a result, power was switched off to parts of the central business district in order to avoid overloading the remaining cable. A day or so later, this remaining cable failed even though it, too, was operating within its assigned rating.

It was eventually established that the cause of the failure was defective design of the cable joints themselves. The cable joints were designed to cope with the amount of thermal expansion that occurred in cables with copper conductors when the cable was close to its maximum operating temperature. Unfortunately, these cables were among the first on which aluminium conductors were used. These expanded by a much greater amount. If, at that same time, the joints had been redesigned, the failure would not have occurred.

For several weeks, most of the offices in the central business district were forced to close down and remove their operations to somewhere else (if they could). Some were able to hire diesel generators and Mercury Energy staff and contractors also mobilised a large number of diesel generators to boost the supply. A small fleet of generators installed on a vacant plot of land in Grafton gully contributed about 10 MW to the city. Vector even hired a gas turbine-driven ship, tied it up alongside one of the wharves, and connected it to the 6.6 kV system. This added about 10 MW to the supply.

Full supply was restored to the central business district by building a new 110 kV overhead line all the way from Penrose to the Liverpool Street substation. By good luck, Transpower had recently ordered poles, insulators and conductors for a 110 kV line in Taranaki. These were diverted to Auckland and with a lot of ingenuity and by working around the clock, power was restored.

The shortage really brought home to everyone how important it is to have a reliable supply of power, and the need to have emergency generators that are reliable and able to run for long periods if necessary.

A few years later, Vector completed the excavation of a tunnel from Penrose to Liverpool Street and on to Hobson Street. It carries two 110 kV cables and two 33 kV cables to Newmarket. It will soon carry 220 kV cables fed from the Otahuhu substation. These cables will cross the harbour bridge and thus provide a 220 kV supply to Albany substation. At the moment (early 2011), everything north of the Waitemata Harbour is totally dependent on the single 220 kV double circuit overhead line. If that fails, everything north of Auckland Harbour loses power.

One of the many advantages that electricity supply has brought to Auckland is reduction in air pollution. People who believe that the air pollution in Auckland is bad would have been horrified at the pall of smoke over the city on a calm day caused by the Kings Wharf power station, steam-powered ferries, steam trains, thousands of chimney pots, industrial steam engines and the gasworks in earlier days. Electricity has greatly reduced air pollution and improved the quality of life for our citizens. Along with natural gas and fuel oil, electricity now provides most of the heat energy and power required for households and industry. The air we breathe is far less polluted now that open fires have been replaced by heat pumps, and coal-fired boilers and steam engines have been replaced by hydro, geothermal and gas-fired power stations.

References and further reading

Leyland, Bryan, 'Auckland central business district power failure', *IEE Power Engineering Journal*, June 1998.

Leyland, Bryan, 'Auckland central business district power failure', the Ministerial enquiry, *IEE Power Engineering Journal*, December, 1998.

Rennie, Neil, *Power to the People: 100 years of Public Electricity Supply in New Zealand*, Electricity Supply Association of New Zealand, Wellington, 1989.

CHAPTER TWELVE

Industrial Development

Introduction

The story of New Zealand Steel Limited is one of developing an internationally competitive process for utilising the country's previously useless but vast ironsand deposits and indigenous low ranking coal. It is the story of establishing a highly successful domestic and export steel industry based on unique raw materials and a unique process developed by New Zealand engineers and technologists. The Glenbrook process and project received an IPENZ plaque in 1990 for engineering excellence.

12.1

Steel from Ironsand

by
Sir John Ingram

Aerial view of New Zealand Steel Plant, 2009.

NZ Steel CIMG0080c

245

Early History

Some two and a half million years ago Mt Taranaki and its old volcanic relations disgorged vast quantities of titanomagnetite material which was ground by the action of the sea and wind and deposited in sand dunes behind headlands up and down the North Island's west coast.

These black magnetic sands attracted interest from the time of the first European explorers. Captain Cook had noted the deposits on his first visit in 1769, and later the material's accessibility, its density, magnetic properties, colour and metallic appearance excited the interest of the Pakeha settlers.

The early attempts to smelt the material marked the beginning of a series of unsuccessful trials, tribulations and bankruptcies that unfolded over the next 120 years. From 1840 to the end of the 19th century there were literally scores of attempts to smelt ironsand, some by small companies, others by provincial or national governments and some by public companies.

In 1857 the Taranaki Provincial Government offered a reward of £1000 to the first person who could produce 100 tons of merchantable iron from ironsand. The prize was not claimed!

The Waihi Gold Mining Company built a blast furnace in New Plymouth in 1914. Under the direction of Mr J. A. Heskett, using briquettes of ironsand and finely pulverised coal, five tons per day of iron were initially produced but the furnace kept clogging and the process stopped.

It was about this time that the cause of the problem was identified. The reduction of the titanium dioxide in the ore at high temperature resulted in the formation of carbides and nitrides, a viscous slag which blocked the draught of the furnace and stopped the process. It was later recognised that to avoid this problem the reduction (conversion of oxide to metal) had to take place at a lower temperature without melting the material.

During this time three patents were granted on the processing of ironsand but none had an impact on the challenge. Their significance lay in the growing interest in direct reduction and the growing influence of science and engineering in resolving problems, instead of trial and error. Two of the patents were in the name of university graduates, Galbraith and Cull.

Cull, after graduating in engineering from Canterbury University College in 1906, undertook some ironsand research there, and his patent was granted in 1908. It comprised a preheater and reduction chamber directly discharging partly reduced ironsand concentrate into an electric arc furnace. His trials were unsuccessful.

Cull left the Engineering School and had a distinguished engineering career in Auckland before returning to Christchurch as professor of civil engineering.

Direct Reduction Development

The development of direct reduction processes in the 1950s caused the government to sponsor an investigation into the resources and processes available, forming the New Zealand Steel Investigating Company under the chairmanship of Mr Woolf Fisher (later Sir Woolf Fisher). With the help of Department of Scientific and Industrial Research scientists and the Battelle Memorial Institute in Ohio, New Zealand ironsand and coal were shipped to the northern hemisphere over the next five years and trialled in various pilot plants.

Finally the investigating company considered that the resources, a process and a market existed for the establishment of an economic domestic steel industry. The press announcement in 1962 caused considerable excitement, particularly in the industrial/manufacturing sector. At last New Zealand was to get its own integrated flat products steel works, after more than 120 years of failure in the attempt.

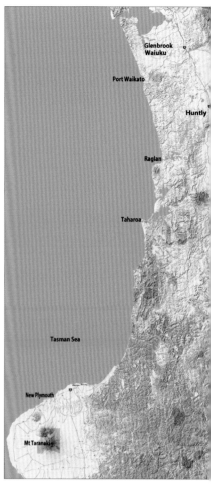

Above: Map showing Glenbrook, Port Waikato, Huntly, Taharoa and Mt Taranaki.

S. La Roche composition

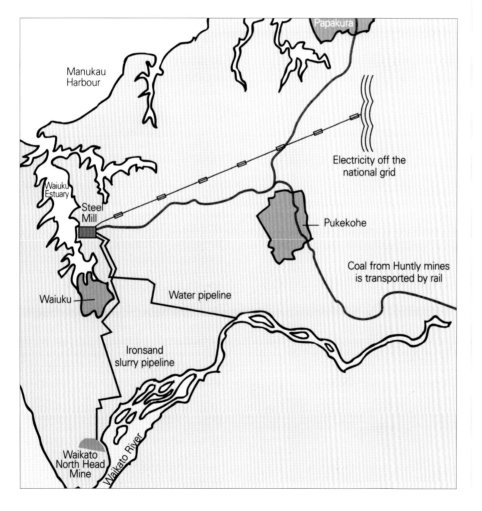

Left: Map showing the Glenbrook Steel Mill, the ironsand mine, slurry and water supply pipeline to the steel mill.

NZ Steel leaflet, Natural Resources and Energy

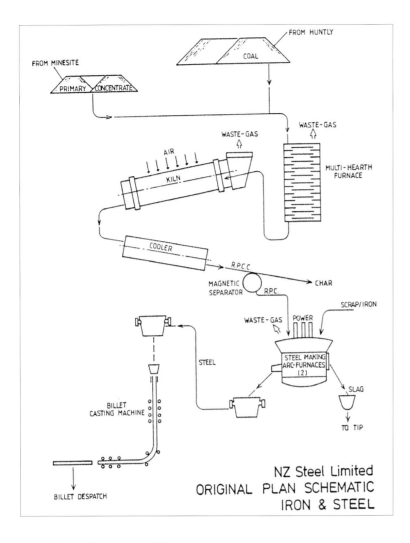

NZ Steel Limited
ORIGINAL PLAN SCHEMATIC
IRON & STEEL

NZ Steel Ltd Original Plan
Schematic Iron & Steel.

J. H. Ingram paper, Fig. 1

Investigations into the extent of ironsand available at Waikato North Head revealed a reserve of about 150 million tonnes of primary concentrate (57 per cent iron) which at current usage, 1.2 million tonnes per year, is enough to last over 100 years. It was decided to build the plant at Glenbrook, close to the ironsand mine, Huntly coal, and available land with good foundations. It was also in close proximity to the bulk of the domestic market in Auckland and to export shipping.

The plan was to build a prototype iron and steel plant of 150,000 tonnes per year capacity of continuously cast billets, together progressively with finishing plants (galvanising plant, paint line, pipe plant and hot rolled coil finishing equipment), all operating initially on imported semi-finished steel. Later, when the iron and steel process was optimised, additional capacity would be installed, together with rolling mills to substitute the imported semi-finished steel with local product.

The government underwrote the floating of a new public limited liability company and New Zealand Steel Ltd was born. At this point the government owned about half of the company and was in effect a joint venture partner, but later sold all of its shares to the public at a substantial premium.

The Prototype Plant

The process selected for the iron and steel plant utilised the SLRN (Stelco-Lurgi-Republic Steel-National Lead) direct reduction kiln, 75 metres long and 4 metres in diameter, which was fed with ironsand pellets. The coal, providing the carbon as a reductant and the energy for the process, was blown into the kiln at the discharge end and the pellets reduced to sponge iron during their passage down the kiln. After cooling to ambient temperature to avoid reoxidation and allow magnetic separation from the surplus carbon and ash, the sponge iron pellets were stored before being refined into steel in the steel plant.

All very well in theory and in the pilot plant trials, but in practice an absolute disaster. The process as bought and designed did not work!

Prototype Problems

First the pellets broke down in the kiln, reverting to the black talcum powder-sized grains from which they were made. They were picked up by the waste gas and distributed far and wide over the countryside or accreted as massive iron lumps on the walls of the kiln.

Secondly, there were nine process steps between the receipt of the ground ironsand concentrate from the mine and the reduced sponge iron pellet storage, each with a discrete item of plant and with no intermediate storage. The not infrequent breakdown of any item would interrupt the process, causing instability, which made consistent operation impossible.

Operating campaigns were a few days or weeks instead of the planned 10 months, each followed by the heart-

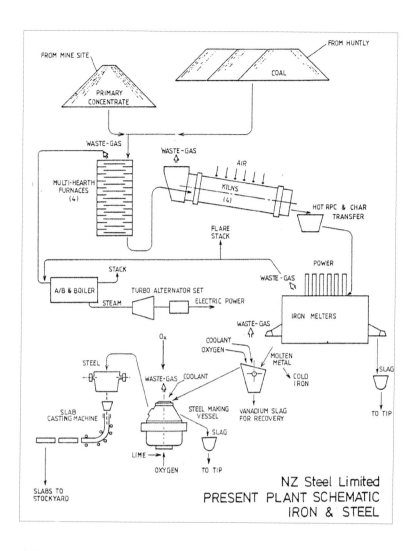

NZ Steel Ltd Present Plant Schematic Iron and Steel.

J. H. Ingram paper, Fig. 2

breaking job of breaking and removing stubborn accretions, including, on one occasion, repairing a split in the kiln shell caused by the excessive use of explosives during accretion removal.

The process designers, plant manufacturers and engineering consultants provided experts aplenty who tendered advice and apportioned blame, pointing to each in turn. There was an enormous conflict between the demands of the arc furnaces for sponge iron, the market for steel billets and the bank for cash on the one hand, and the need to slow down, think, experiment and learn on the other.

During this period and up to 1973 the company made big losses, cushioned by the profitability of the galvanising plant and profits from the export of ironsand concentrate from Taharoa. Sir Woolf Fisher, the then chairman, remained confident throughout and was wonderfully supportive of the company management. The government provided five million dollars of new capital as preference shares. This was subsequently repaid.

Dr Nigel Evans.

Courtesy Bryce Williamson and
NZ Institute of Chemistry

Peter Bates.

Courtesy Bryce Williamson and
NZ Institute of Chemistry

Dr Richard Cooper.

Courtesy Bryce Williamson and
NZ Institute of Chemistry

Prototype Innovations

At the time of its founding the company recruited several postgraduate engineers and technologists who were sent overseas for steel industry experience. On their return they, particularly Dr Nigel Evans, Dr Richard Cooper and Peter Bates, became the core of the company's technical services department. It was their analytical ability, innovation and determination that played a major role in the ultimate development of the extremely efficient iron and steel making process.

In spite of strong protests from the overseas experts, on the recommendation of its technical services department the company decided to trial-feed the kiln with unground primary concentrate. It had been observed in the laboratory that these grains, unlike the fine grains of secondary concentrate, did not grow biddybid-like whiskers, obviously a major cause of accretion growth, during the reduction process.

The tests were successful, plant availability greatly improved and accretion growth was much reduced. Other changes were necessary to cope with feeding concentrate instead of pellets. The evolution of carbon monoxide fluidised the bed so it acted like thick slurry and the resulting surges caused problems, including variations in the degree of metallisation. Brick dams were built in the kiln to reduce, in effect, the kiln slope. After trials, surplus dams were removed on the run with the army sharpshooters shooting out the relevant key bricks.

For the first time the plant operated smoothly, but design output was not achieved. One third of the kiln length was used for drying and heating the burden and devolatilising the coal so it was decided to install a multiple hearth preheating furnace ahead of the kiln. The evolving gases were burnt to provide the works' steam requirements and the output was increased to 150,000 tonnes per year.

At last an efficient process was developed for converting New Zealand ironsand to iron as reduced primary concentrate (RPC), but the cost of converting this to steel was not viable. First, the discharge from the kiln had to be cooled before exposure to air to avoid re-oxidation and to allow magnetic separation of the iron grains and surplus carbon. Thus the heat of about 200 kilowatt hours per tonne was lost. Secondly, the relatively high slag volumes meant long arc furnace tap to tap (cycle) times with high energy costs. Thirdly, the alternative acid and basic slags during the melting and then refining cycle shortened refractory life, incurring high costs in both refractories and furnace downtime.

Process Optimisation

Because of the high cost of steel production, the cost of the end product – steel billets – was not internationally competitive. Without cross-subsidy and domestic protection the iron and steel plants would have to be closed with big redundancies and the end of using indigenous materials.

It was decided therefore to research an optimum process and then test if it was feasible to fulfil the original proposal of expanding the plant into an integrated flat products works, replacing the imported steel for the paint line, the galvanising line, the pipe mill and ultimately the hot and cold rolled sheet and plate for the domestic market.

It was recognised that producing pig iron as an intermediate product between the kiln and steel making would result in three major benefits. First, the hot kiln product (RPC and un-used carbon) could be fed directly to a melting furnace and the wasted heat saved. Secondly, a modern, highly productive oxygen steel-making process could be utilised using carbon and oxygen as the energy source in lieu of electricity as in the arc furnaces. This greatly reduced electricity demand and refractory costs. Thirdly, the vanadium present in the ore and reduced in the kiln to vanadium metal would be soluble in the pig iron. Its subsequent recovery as vanadium-rich slag and sale would subsidise the steel making costs by an average of $30 per tonne.

Although plants existed in South Africa and Scandinavia using submerged arc melters for making pig iron from ore or partly metallised ore, it had not previously been achieved using sponge iron (RPC), the product of the Glenbrook kilns. The problem was to make a pig iron of high enough carbon content, more than three per cent, to enable the extraction of the vanadium-rich slag and to provide the energy to operate the basic oxygen steel furnace.

A pilot plant comprising a batch pilot kiln and small 500 kilovolt ampere furnace was built at Glenbrook. After lengthy trials it was established that a suitable quality pig iron could be obtained if certain operating parameters were adopted.

The Expansion Project, 1981

Having established that the new process would work, a feasibility study was undertaken which indicated that an integrated works could be built and provide a good rate of return to both the shareholders and the nation.

It was, however, recognised at the time that to ensure an economic capital cost per tonne of production, the rolling mill complex would have to include a number of state of the art innovations such as a coil box. A description of these is outside the scope of this writing but may be seen in the paper 'Pioneering

IHI Hot Strip Mill with management watching.

Courtesy NZ Steel, Scan0030

a Process' described under 'References and further reading' at the end of this section.

The project, comprising an increase in steel production of five times to 700,000 tonnes per year, and the installation of hot and cold rolling mills, was far too big for the company to undertake alone. The government would be invited to participate in a form of joint venture, just as it did when the company started.

The choice for the company was simple. It had to either persuade the government to agree to and participate in the expansion, or in a few years face the closure of the existing iron plant, steel plant and mine site with massive redundancies and become merely an importer and processor of imported steel. There was a firm determination to avoid the latter.

The government agreed to consider an involvement and negotiations began with representatives of Treasury, Trade and Industry and supplier departments. At first the officials were sceptical that the company's forecasts could be achieved but with an intensive interchange of financial and technical information and visits, their doubts were mollified. Through this extensive period ministers and cabinet committees were kept informed of progress.

A major concern for the company was to ensure that profits and dividends could be maintained throughout the construction period. This could be achieved only if the project was undertaken off the company's balance sheet. Therefore a new company would be established to undertake the project, New Zealand Steel Development Ltd (NZSD), 60 per cent owned by the government and 40 per cent by New Zealand Steel. The capital of the company would be nominal but the government would guarantee the loan finance if necessary. New Zealand Steel Ltd would progressively take over NZSD once production had reached certain levels.

Hot Coil Box in rolling mill.

NZ Steel, Hot Coil

A heads of agreement document was drawn up to include these points, and others concerning limited market protection for a period following the completion of the project, an obligation by the company to maximise local content of plant and machinery and the availability of coal and electricity. The New Zealand Steel board considered that this agreement, although not enforceable on successive governments, provided sufficient protection for the shareholders. It agreed that the project should proceed, following final government approval.

Prior to the 1981 election two other substantial capital intensive projects were proposed as a part of the government's 'Think Big' policy: the aluminium smelter at Aramoana and a synthetic gasoline plant at Motunui. There was no official comment but it was suggested these projects would take precedence over the expansion of New Zealand Steel (which, originally proposed by the New Zealand Steel Investigating Company in 1962, was never a part of 'Think Big') either because they had a better net national benefit or because they required no government input or risk. However, neither project materialised at that time and New Zealand Steel got the go-ahead in November 1981.

The company was ready to go and earth moving contracts were let by NZSD almost immediately, the prime minister turning the 'first sod' a few weeks later.

The project was run by NZSD, at arm's length from New Zealand Steel Ltd. However, because of the physical linking of the project and the existing works and the ultimate responsibility belonging to New Zealand Steel, a number of the directors and executives, including the managing director, had dual responsibilities. Sir Alan Hellaby chaired both boards, being joined by three New Zealand Steel directors and four government appointees, including resident director Mr A. G. Stirrat, previously chief design engineer of the Ministry of Works. He made a major contribution to the project.

As construction work reached a peak, demarcation problems between various unions reached massive proportions. Inter-union disputes, sometimes violent, broke out pitting welders and engineers against boilermakers; riggers and labourers against engineers; roofing plumbers against carpenters against boilermakers, and so on. The inter-union nature of the disputes left contractor management helpless and many work hours were lost. Similar problems at the Marsden Point Refinery were solved by special government legislation but similar measures were declined for the NZSD project.

Significant additional costs were incurred by the company in meeting the very high local content target, much of the work being on the limit of the local works capacity. Requests to the government for some relief in this area were declined.

Double digit inflation added to cost overruns but project reviews confirmed the project was viable.

In 1984 Labour won the snap election and Mr Roger Douglas (later Sir Roger Douglas) was made Minister of Finance. He did not accept the heads of agreement signed by the previous government and indicated he would not continue to guarantee the NZSD loans. Prolonged negotiations ensued during which overseas consultants examined the company's feasibility study and process. The government finally proposed that it would absorb the NZSD loans

'Big John' addressing NZ Steel staff.

NZ Steel, Scan 0116

and that New Zealand Steel should take over the government's 60 per cent share of NZSD by issuing New Zealand Steel shares to the government. This would cause considerable loss of value to the shareholders. The board considered this proposal against the possibility of withdrawing from the project and continuing to operate the company's other assets. Considering the interlinking of the project with common services and operating with an antagonistic government, this was not a practical proposition.

With the transaction complete, the government became the 90 per cent majority owner of New Zealand Steel Ltd. Newspaper headlines claimed the move as a 'bail-out'. New Zealand Steel, however, considered that the absorption of the NZSD loans by the government was an appropriate compensation for the new government's abrogation of the heads of agreement and acquisition of the company.

The expanded iron and steel plants began operating in 1986 and the rolling mills complex and associated plant in 1987.

In October 1987 the government, unlike its predecessors, was so desperate to divest itself of the company that it sold New Zealand Steel to Equiticorp Ltd, a merchant bank-type company remote from the steel industry. Further, because the plant was still commissioning, the sale price was far from optimum.

In early 1989, Equiticorp was placed under statutory management. Negotiations between the statutory manager and China Minmetals Corporation to buy New Zealand Steel were disrupted by the Tiananmen Square massacre in June and not resumed.

The company was later sold to a consortium led by BHP, which later became 100 per cent BHP owned. The company is now owned by BHP Steel's

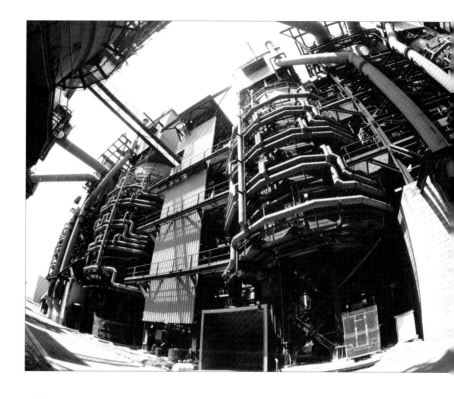

Exterior view of multi-hearth furnaces.

NZ Steel, Scan 0126

KOBM vessel for converting iron to steel.

NZ Steel, Davy

Above: Molten Iron being charged into the steelmaking vessel.

NZ Steel, Charging

Above: Steel Slab emerging from the casting machine.

NZ Steel, High Res Slab

successor, Bluescope Steel Ltd, but the name has reverted to New Zealand Steel Ltd.

It is perhaps ironic that the Equiticorp statutory manager subsequently took action against the government in connection with Equiticorp's payment package. Substantial damages in favour of the statutory manager resulted.

Progress Under New Owners

The control of the company changed to the new owners in late 1989. Significant capital expenditure was undertaken, and the design level of productivity achieved. In 2009 the company operated for a full year without one lost time accident, an exceptional achievement. Glenbrook is one of the cleanest integrated flat products steelworks in the world. The company's largest capital investment in environmental control is in gas cleaning equipment to ensure that the quality of gases leaving their stacks betters the levels agreed in the Air Permit issued under the Resource Management Act.

Manufacturing Success

The domestic availability of high quality competitive flat steel products, with shorter lead times, an increased range of specifications and small order item sizes,

'The New Zealand Steel Production Process'.

NZ Steel Brochure BH821124
W3885 P6

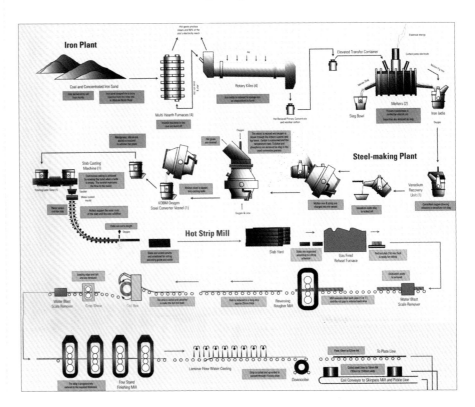

together with skilled technical advice, has greatly benefited the very diverse local manufacturing industry. A 'boutique steel company' is an apt description.

Economic Success

In year 2000 figures, if New Zealand Steel had not existed the current account deficit would have risen by about 600 million dollars per year, or about 0.6 per cent of gross domestic product.

Environmental Care

Although the company's record of contribution to the environment started with a stutter, mostly in self defence, with the early formation of an environmental committee chaired by the managing director to keep local people and their representatives informed of progress (or lack of it), it has grown into one that is nationally acclaimed as excellent.

Since the change in ownership of the company in 1989, BHP directed all their businesses to establish an environmental system based on international standard ISO 140001. The company therefore uses this formal system to monitor and improve its environmental performance.

In 1994 the company received a Green Ribbon Award from the Ministry

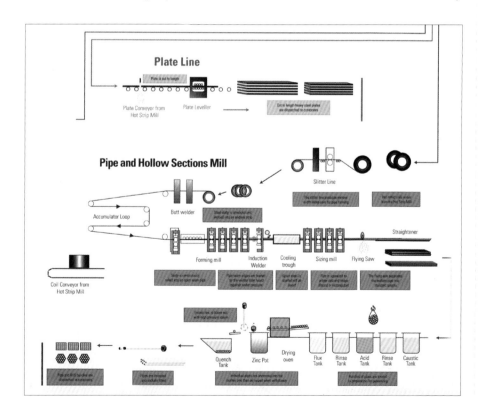

'Skin Pass Mill, Plate Line and Pipe and Hollow Sections Mill'.

NZ Steel Brochure BH821124
W3885 P6

of the Environment for a major environmental and economic achievement: that some 550,000 tonnes of slag per year, previously discarded to land fill, are now recycled, reused or sold profitably – the latter replacing materials previously quarried.

Further, the hot gas from the iron plant multi-hearth furnaces, kilns and melters is burnt in a cogeneration plant to produce about 60 per cent of the 1,000 gigawatt hours of electricity consumed annually on the Glenbrook site. This has led to a decrease in carbon dioxide emissions at thermal stations by some 300,000 tonnes per year. The company was recognised for this outstanding contribution to the environment by being awarded the Energy-Wise Companies Campaign Award in November 1998.

Contribution to Society

The arrival and expansion of New Zealand Steel has changed Waiuku and to a lesser extent Pukekohe into thriving local towns, no longer solely dependent on dairying and horticulture. Furthermore the company policy to subcontract many of the services at the mill has led to a strong growth in the range of small local engineering businesses. The variety and strength of sports, service, cultural and leisure clubs has increased significantly and it is interesting to note the high percentage that now have New Zealand Steel employees as office bearers.

Relationships have greatly improved with the Tainui hapu Ngaati Te Ata, the guardians for Waiuku, the mine site and Glenbrook. The company can point to many areas of agreement where it has been able to contribute to the welfare of the hapu following agreement on certain problems at the mine site.

The changes at Taharoa for the Maori community, Ngati Mahuta, also a hapu of Tainui, have been far more dramatic: the arrival of New Zealand Steel literally thrust a small community with no electricity and access except by horseback into the 20th century. Taharoa C, the Maori shareholders with whom the mining lease had been negotiated, have invested their royalties wisely in successful commercial enterprises such as farms. But importantly in providing scholarships, both secondary and tertiary, for the education of their young people.

The words of Prime Minister Norman Kirk at the opening ceremony in November 1972 have been truly vindicated: 'The development of these ironsands will transform the lives of the owners, their children and their grandchildren for generations ahead. It has provided a future.'

Recognition by the Engineering Profession

The achievements of BHP New Zealand Steel Ltd were recognised in 2000 by IPENZ in presenting one of its Millennium Awards to the company for its contribution to manufacturing, to the economy, to the environment and to society.

In responding to the award Dr Norm Clark, finishing plants manager of BHP NZ Steel as it was then known, and a work colleague of the three engineers mentioned below, said,

Many people over many years have contributed to this achievement. However, at a time when the country is celebrating the success of Team New Zealand, I would especially like to acknowledge a small group of Team NZ Steel, who took overseas technology, which quite frankly did not work, and transformed it into the elegant iron-making process which is still the heart of the company thirty years on.

There was a knight at the top, Sir Woolf Fisher, an entrepreneur who strongly supported his young engineers against the conventional wisdom of many overseas experts and who held together the financial backers through desperate months.

There was John Ingram, later Sir John, an engineer and past president of this institution, who made pivotal recommendations based on a sound technical understanding of the problems and the proposed solutions. Then there was a team of three young NZ engineers: Dr Nigel Evans, Peter Bates and the late Dr Richard Cooper. Their great achievement was to put in place a technology for making steel from ironsand and Waikato coal which was simple in concept, and which has proved capable of delivering continual financial and environmental improvements at BHP NZ Steel.

The process was not entirely novel. In fact it can now be seen as the logical end-point of a series of experiments on ironsand which started as soon as the first European settlers arrived. And of course many engineers have worked improvements since the time of Evans, Bates and Cooper. So in accepting this award we look across nearly 150 years of engineering endeavour and commensurate financial courage. It makes one feel very humble.

Conclusion

There is at Glenbrook a highly efficient, and low cost, flat products integrated steel plant which uses ironsand ore and low-ranking Waikato coal. Although a very small integrated works by world standards, it is the largest industrial site in New Zealand by far and contributes greatly to the national economy. Around half of the company's production is exported and the balance sold on the domestic market. The company is very profitable and competes against imported steel with no tariff protection. It is probably one of the very few steel works which continued to operate at full capacity throughout the recession that began in 2009.

The success of the company vindicates the board's confidence in the young engineers and technologists who developed the new process, in the management who recommended the development should proceed and in the brave pioneering decision of the board, particularly Chairman Sir Alan Hellaby, to enter the commitment.

Appendix

Expansion Project Main Contractors and Plant Suppliers

Stage I. Iron and Steel Plants

Project Principal – NZS Development Ltd
Managers and Engineers – Davy McKee (Stockton) Ltd
Multi Hearth Furnace & Rotary Kilns – Lurgi Gmbh
MHF Waste Gas Scrubber – Flakt Australia Ltd
Co-generation plant – NEI Pacific Ltd
Iron Melter – Elkem a/s Engineering
KOBM – Davy McKee (Stockton) Ltd
Slab Caster – Sack Stranggiesstechnic
Billet Caster – Concast Standard AG
Air Separation Plant – Cryoplants Ltd and NZ Industrial Gases Ltd

Stage II

Project Manager – NZ Steel Development Ltd
    Project Engineers – Nippon Kokan KK
Main Contractors – Ishikawajima-Harima Heavy Industries Ltd (IHI)

Sub Contractors

Preheat furnace – IHI
Hot strip mill – IHI
Pickle line – Sumitomo Heavy Industries
Reversing cold mill – Hitachi
Combination mill – IHI
Uniflow Annealing Plant – Chugai-Ro
Water treatment – Ebara Infilco

Mine site

Concentration plant Managers and Engineers – Beca Carter Hollings and Ferner
Bucket Wheel Excavators – Orenstein & Koppel
Slurry Pipeline – McConnell Dowell Construction Ltd

References and further reading

Bold, D. A., 'A vision unfulfilled: the iron and steel industry in New Zealand 1842 to 1975', PhD thesis submitted to University of Auckland, 2001.

Evans, N. T., 'Development of the SL/RN process at New Zealand Steel Ltd', 37th Ironmaking Conference, American Institution of Mechanical Engineers, 1978.

Evans, N. T., IPENZ Millennium Award Submission for BHP New Zealand Steel Ltd, 1999.

Ingram, J. H., 'Pioneering a Process', Keynote Address, Mechanical 88 Congress, part of the College of Mechanical Engineers, The Institution of Engineers Australia celebration of the Australian bicentenary, Brisbane, May 1988.

12.2

Slurry Transportation Ironsand Concentrate – Mine Site to Glenbrook

by Sir John Ingram

Slurry transportation from the mine site to Glenbrook began in 1986. This was the world's first polyurethane-lined high pressure underground pipe line with welded flanges transporting dense abrasive coarse material by positive displacement pumps. The project extended the known bounds of slurry pumping technology and was awarded an IPENZ plaque for engineering excellence.

The increase in usage of primary concentrate due to the iron and steel plant expansion (from about 250,000 tonnes per year to over 1.2 million tonnes) meant continuing use of road transport for the 18-kilometre journey was neither economic nor practical. Other options had to be considered. These were: slurry transportation, aerial ropeway, conveyors, pneumatic capsules and railway.

Slurry transportation was initially ruled out, as no slurry systems longer than a few kilometres existed for such abrasive material with its combination of grain size and density. There was reluctance to risk extending the bounds of technology to such an extent for such a vital service.

Diagrammatic illustration of slurry transport system.

NZ Steel leaflet 'Water and Essential Resource', Fig 1

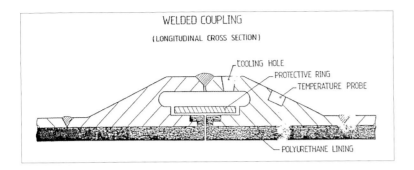

Diagram of welded coupling
on the slurry pipeline.

J. H. Ingram paper, Fig. 3

Of the remainder, railway appeared the most practicable and lowest-cost option, particularly as the link would be constructed with New Zealand Rail's capital. Unfortunately the local farmers along the proposed route who did not like the idea of a railway going through their property objected strongly, establishing the Concerned Landowners Association to fight the intention. Negotiations with the association began, and the route was modified as far as possible to avoid particularly sensitive areas such as the artificial lake (known locally as Lake Lollipop) belonging to Mr Heard, the association's president. It soon became clear, however, that an alternative method of transportation had to be found if construction delays were to be avoided.

Following discussions with a favoured contractor it was decided that the slurry alternative, much preferred from an environmental point of view, should be reviewed in the light of significant advances recently made in pumping and pipeline technology. Finally it was agreed that the company would write a specification which met its requirements as regards life, safety, reliability and costs, and that a committee comprising contractor and company engineers would be established to ensure the optimum result.

In due course a contract was let for the design and construction of the slurry system. It involved two Geho positive displacement flexible diaphragm pumps (the diaphragm separating the slurry from the piston and other moving parts), one at the mine site terminal and one about half way to Glenbrook. The requirement of a 25-year life, safe and leak free, demanded a polyurethane lined

Above: Pipeline coupling being prepared by McConnell Dowell.

Courtesy McConnell Dowell Constructors Ltd

Right: Flange joint being welded by McConnell Dowell.

Courtesy McConnell Dowell Constructors Ltd

steel pipe with a welded radiographed pipe joint to provide complete confidence in the integrity of the weld prior to backfill. This joint was a patented world first. To prevent damage to the pipe lining during welding a thermal barrier was built into the forged flange, forming an annulus through which air and water mist were passed to dissipate heat during welding.

The slurry transportation is very successful, an example of amazing ingenuity applied to a complex problem. It is cost effective and low maintenance, with energy consumption of only about eight kilowatt hours per tonne. There is no adverse effect on the environment. After well over 20 years of service, an inspection of the pipe showed no evidence of deterioration of either the lining or the pipe. The pipeline is expected both to meet pressure tests to comply with recertification requirements and to remain in service for many more years.

The Concerned Landowners Association did the company a good turn.

Geho high pressure slurry pumps.

Courtesy NZ Steel Ltd

Ironsand Properties, Primary Concentrate
Bulk Density: 2090 kg/m3
Size range: 45–212 micron

Contractors for Slurry Pipeline
Design, quality assurance, inspection and commissioning: Slurry Systems Pty Ltd
Construction and project management: Mc Connell Dowell Construction Ltd

References and further reading

Ingram, J. H., 'Pioneering a Process', Keynote Address, Mechanical 88 Congress, part of the College of Mechanical Engineers, The Institution of Engineers Australia celebration of the Australian bicentenary, Brisbane, May 1988.

Lush, S. M., and Pope, P. B., *The NZ Steel Development Ironsand Slurry Pipeline*, 12th International Conference on Slurry Technology, 1987.

Lye, M., *Ironsand Slurry Pipe Line: Selection and Design Considerations*, IPENZ Auckland Branch (unpublished), 1984.

12.3

Chelsea Sugar Works

by
Alec Aitken
and
John La Roche

The Chelsea Sugar Works is notable because it is still operating as New Zealand's only sugar works after commencing operation in 1884. It has a Historic Places Trust Category 1 rating, Register Number 7792. It is one of the longest-functioning industries in New Zealand and holds great importance as a landmark industrial building in Auckland's history.

History

Edward Knox, Chairman of Colonial Sugar Refining Company (CSR) of Australia visited Auckland in 1881 and purchased 76 hectares of land on which to build a sugar refinery to provide refined sugar for the New Zealand market. The New Zealand Government had offered a bounty to the first company to establish a sugar refinery in New Zealand and the closeness to sugar cane sources in Fiji made the site at Birkenhead attractive. The New Zealand Sugar Company was formed in 1883 with CSR and the Victorian Sugar Company of Australia. Two thirds of the shares were held by the Australian companies and the remainder by New Zealand shareholders, including prominent Auckland businessmen Sir Frederick Whitaker, Alan Kerr Taylor, L. D. Nathan and J. L. Wilson.

The refinery site at Chelsea on the north side of the Waitemata Harbour was ideal with deep water close to the shore. There was ample fresh water, an essential requirement for a refinery, available from the Duck Creek water catchment area within the purchased land. The name Chelsea originated from the first refinery customs officer, Mr Judd, whose home was in Chelsea in London, England.

Initial construction works were designed by Auckland consulting engineers Boylan and Lundon. The process design for the works, with a capacity of 10,000 tonnes per year, was provided by James Muir, CSR's engineer. Muir had built sugar refineries in Scotland and England before joining the company in Australia to design refineries at Pyrmont and Broadwater Mill. The Chelsea site required the removal of a headland and excavation by pick and shovel of 130,000 cubic metres of clay. A level site of two hectares was needed for buildings, tramways and workshops. One and a half million bricks were produced from the excavated clay and fired with a kiln built on the site. The bricks were used to construct two dams and the buildings which are still in use. Timber

Construction of Chelsea Sugar Refinery in 1883 with rows of bricks stacked to dry before firing.

North Shore Libraries B0091

for buildings was cut from native trees on the site. Two major wharves were constructed, one to load and unload the processed and raw sugar, most of which was to come from Fiji, and the other was for unloading coal. Holes for the wharf piles had to be blasted into the solid rock of the harbour bed. The coal wharf has since been dismantled when coal firing was replaced with natural gas.

At 37 metres high, the tallest building is the Char House, where the raw sugar is purified. Four hundred tonnes of machinery and equipment was built in Greenock, Scotland and shipped to Chelsea. The water supply was assured by constructing two dams across Duck Creek. Two additional dams were added later.

The process involves receiving bulk shipments of raw sugar from sugar mills that process the sugar cane, mainly in Australia and Fiji. After being unloaded from the ship, raw sugar is stored awaiting purification. The refining process starts with raw sugar being mixed with concentrated sugar syrup to soften the impurities on the surface of the crystals before washing with water and centrifuging to remove the washing water. The washed crystals are then dissolved with hot water before lime and carbon dioxide are added to help remove impurities. The solution is then filtered through very fine filter cloths. Char is a charcoal formed from burning animal bones and is used to remove any remaining impurities and colour. The clear liquor is then boiled in a vacuum to form crystals of pure sugar that are then dried-sterilised with ultraviolet light, prior to grading and packing. Residual syrup can be made into brown sugar, golden syrup or treacle.

Chelsea Sugar Refinery, 1885. The excavation done with picks, shovels, horses and scoops to remove the headland can be seen on the right. The dam across Duck Creek was yet to be formed.

North Shore Libraries B0061

Chelsea Sugar Refinery
showing workers
homes, 1888.

Sir George Grey Special Collections,
Auckland Libraries 4-1011

Until 1961, 90 per cent of the sugar production at Chelsea was shipped across the harbour to the Auckland wharves in a fleet of seven flat-bottomed lighters. These lighters were fitted with steam winches and derricks to hoist sugar bags into and out of the hold. The building of the Auckland Harbour Bridge changed all that when road transport direct from the refinery could be used. Once city water supply became available in 1960, dependence on the Duck Creek supply diminished and natural gas replaced coal as an energy source.

However, the company has a strong environmental and conservation policy. In 2009 it was decided to draw and treat water from Duck Creek, reducing the company's dependence on city water. Maintaining a high quality water supply for the refining process using activated carbon filtration and ultra-violet light is needed. The company is very conscious of the need to minimise energy use and monitor operations to minimise waste and prevent pollution.

Beautification of the site has long been practised. In 1900 the company undertook a revegetation programme using both native and exotic species. In 1975 the company won the Waitemata Garden prize for the best factory environment on the North Shore. In 2008, 37 hectares of land, including the lakes, regenerating forest and open spaces were sold to the Heritage Park Trust to ensure the area is retained as a park for future generations. The park adjoins Kauri Point Centennial Park, making it the largest bush reserve in close proximity to Auckland.

Refinery capacity has been extended many times and over 200,000 tonnes per year is now processed, with about 20 per cent being exported, mainly to Australia.

Community

Smokey Chelsea Sugar works, 1925.

Sir George Grey Special Collections, Auckland Libraries 1-W708

To build the works in 1882, 150 men were employed, most living in tents. These men were the first to be offered jobs when the refinery started and 100 took up the offer. The company built 35 houses for staff and also provided a school and reading room and privately-owned shop. Access was also provided for 150 workers living in Birkenhead and elsewhere. Provision was made for ferrying staff, materials and equipment across the harbour prior to the Harbour Bridge being built.

In what is believed to be one of the first staff welfare schemes in New Zealand the company organised a benefit fund in 1890 that subsidised the deduction of 3 pence per week from wages to cover sickness, accident and death. At that time the company had a policy to take on and train boys, particularly the sons of men employed at the works.

Kauri gum digging was allowed in the 1910s and 1920s, when local residents could supplement their income by collecting and selling the gum to a dealer in Fort Street for about $3 a sugar sack. There were labour disputes in the 1920s and on-going complaints about the soot from the refinery chimneys blackening Birkenhead washing. The depression in the 1930s was a difficult time, when the company had a tradition of providing low interest mortgage loans for workers, and of not laying off workers who held company mortgages. Some single men and newly married couples had to go on week-on and week-off existence but at least they held on to their jobs.

The suburb of Birkenhead has been closely linked with the Chelsea Sugar

Chelsea Sugar works in 2011, viewed from Birkenhead.

S. La Roche

works ever since it was established in 1883. The Borough had a population of 334 in 1886, including 189 who lived at the Chelsea village owned by the company. By 1900, when the population of Birkenhead Borough was 1,000, one third of the men of the borough were sugar workers. The park surroundings are used by dog walkers, joggers and duck-feeding families. Throughout the years the company has been generous in allowing public access to its land. In 1960 the Sugar company went on town water supply and decided to subdivide part of the Duck Creek catchment 106 hectares to form the Chatswood Subdivision with 1,000 sections.

References and further reading

Chelsea Sugar Works http://en.wikipedia.org/wiki/Chelsea_Sugar_Refinery

Historic Places Trust, *Chelsea Refinery and Estate*, Register Number 7792, June 2009.

History of Chelsea Sugar Works, http://chelsea.co.nz/net/sugar-history/default.apsx The History of New Zealand Sugar – Chelsea Sugar

Lowndes, A. G., (ed.), *South Pacific Enterprise: The Colonial Sugar Refining Company Limited*, Angus and Robertson, Sydney, 1956.

McClure, Margaret, *The Story of Birkenhead*, Birkenhead City Council, 1987.

Introduction

Why choose a rock quarry as an item of engineering heritage?

Hard rock quarries have produced the most fundamental civil engineering material, for the construction of roads, since the dawn of civilisation and aggregate for concrete, since Roman times. Rock for the pyramids was quarried and the quarries are now of historic significance. Similarly our cities were built from quarried material so we should celebrate the technology and achievement of those who made it possible. Their contribution to our standard of living is as great as any sector of society and still continues. Try to imagine a city and all the services that make it up, but without concrete or road metal.

Winstone's Lunn Avenue Quarry was opened in 1936 to utilise a basalt lava field adjacent to Mt Wellington, about eight kilometres from the centre of Auckland City. Since that time it has been the main source of aggregate for the city and an important factor in the building of modern Auckland. Now is an appropriate time to record a brief history of this early activity, while first-hand information is still available, as the quarry stopped producing in 2005.

New Zealanders once used on average six tonnes per person of quarry material each year, but this has now increased to more than eight tonnes per person. Three quarters is for roading and one quarter for concrete. You and your near family may account for 35 tonnes every year. Where does yours come from?

If you ask your friends that question, you will find that few know, or have ever thought of the matter. So the conclusion must be that the environmental impact of a modern quarry is negligible. If not, everyone would know where they are and what nuisances they cause. Quarries continue to operate year in and year out, largely unheard and unseen, serving their community.

The environmental impact of the distribution of the stone products, by heavy road transport, is, however, significant, particularly from noise and fumes. Fortunate is the city with a good quarry close at hand, to minimise transport, both in cost and nuisance value. Auckland was such a city, and the quarry which played an important part in its construction is the subject of this chapter. While we record some of the history of Lunn Avenue Quarry and its engineering heritage, there are many points of engineering interest in the way the quarry operated.

Early History

Winstone Limited developed from two brothers who started in 1859 with horses and carts to sell coal and firewood. The company developed with the early colony, manufacturing, trading and distributing permanent building materials, except timber. One hundred years later, with the third generation of

12.4

Winstone's Lunn Avenue Quarry, Mt Wellington, Auckland

by
Bryan Bartley

Basecourse Plant No2 Plant

No1 Plant   Clean Metal

Singapore Crusher

42" Primary Gyratory Crusher

The quarry plants and general view, c. 1960.

Courtesy Fletcher Challenge Archives
6251P-107

Mr Percy Winstone, c. 1945.

Courtesy Fletcher Challenge Archives
6251P -40

Winstones, it was one of the 10 largest companies in New Zealand. Company fortunes fluctuated and it is now part of the Fletcher group of companies, with the quarry activities called Winstone Aggregates Limited.

In the mid 1930s Mr Percy Winstone bought, through his cousin Frank, a land agent, 100 hectares of 'useless' rock land eight kilometres from Auckland City Centre, with the idea of using the stone. The site was a single basalt lava flow from the nearby scoria cone, Mt Wellington. Although the flow was a few thousand years old, it was without significant overlying soil or significant weathering. The lava flow was unique in having been ponded to about 37 metres thickness, whereas other similar lava flows are often only 10 metres in thickness because the molten basalt rock has flowed easily.

Quarrying had started in 1936 and by 1938 a Traylor primary crusher was installed. This was soon found to be too small, so with the urgency of the wartime economy, Mr Percy Winstone went to Singapore and, just before the Japanese invasion, brought back a 48-inch by 42-inch Traylor primary jaw crusher.

The story goes that Mr Percy, as he was always known, bought it out of his No. 2 account, without reference to his brothers or the board for approval. However, it was the biggest crusher in the country and proved to be a brilliant choice. In 1960 it was moved to another quarry and was still in operation until it was retired in the 90s after 57 years of steadily crushing hard rock.

It was always called the 'Singapore' crusher and was able to crush the big rock from the quarry face, although secondary blasting (popping) was still necessary for the very large rocks. If a very large stone did reach the crusher it would ride over the moving jaw and not be crushed. Various methods were used to overcome this problem, such as hooks, tongs or wire strops to turn the stone. Steel wedges on ropes were also used. If all failed the crusher would be stopped, a wire sling attached and the stone lifted out by a jib crane on a truck chassis fitted with a logging winch.

If the flat drive belt or the power supply failed when the crusher was full, it had to be emptied by hand and crane before it could be restarted. On one occasion the quarry manager, Mr Hunter, returned from a funeral in his best Sunday suit, to find the crusher being thus emptied. He jumped in with his men to help. That was his leadership style, and not unusual at that time.

Basecourse Plant (No. 2 Plant)

With the 'Singapore' crusher in place a second plant was built with a similar Traylor crusher. Two-stage crushing using a Jaques gyratory crusher from Melbourne was satisfactory for the upper face rock from the top of the flow, which was very vesicular (gas bubbles in the rock). This basecourse had the ability to crush under the wheels of a roller and lock into place in the road. Although it did not comply with later specifications, it was much sought after and the specifications would be ignored.

Clean Metal Plant (No. 1 Plant)

With the basecourse rock from the upper face removed, the main face below was of higher quality, denser rock and was used to produce the concrete, asphalt and road-sealing chip materials.

Mr Bruce Winstone.

Courtesy Fletcher Challenge Archives
Winstone Centennial publication 1961

Mr Bruce Winstone, a qualified civil engineer, returned from war service and took over the quarry from his uncle, Mr Percy.

In the late 1940s a large-scale re-building of the No. 1 plant was begun. This was the third upgrade in less than 10 years. Bruce Winstone determined that very adequate design standards would be used so that the growth of production could be accommodated. This proved to be very sound management and the plant performed well through the 1950s to 2005 when it closed. Bruce Winstone was ably assisted by the then Quarry Superintendent (Quarry General Manager) Leo Foster, who had considerable mechanical engineering and leadership ability. Bruce was also assisted by Larry Watts, who did the structural design, and was seconded for two years from the partnership of Gray and Watts, which became Gray Watts and Beca, now Beca Carter Hollings and Ferner Ltd and Beca International Consultants Ltd. Because Winstone Ltd was faced with a glut of clay roofing tiles from its factory, the tertiary crusher building had a roof of Marseilles tiles, making it probably the only crusher building outside Europe with a tiled roof.

A 100 RB electric shovel was purchased new from England about 1949.

100RB electric face shovel with 5 ton Bedford truck, 1952.

Courtesy Fletcher Challenge Archives 6251P-31

This had a five-tonne bucket and was powered by a 1,100 volt trailing cable from junction boxes set in the quarry floor. A rotary converter set, mounted on the counterweight, provided DC power for the various drive motors. The shovel had been built in England, tested and taken apart for shipping. When it arrived, the quarry staff had a serious problem erecting the machine, as there were no written instructions and all the small parts were boxed in any order, with the nuts and bolts, right down to gutter bolts, being mixed in sacks. Once erected the machine had a long life and outlived a number of diesel face shovels.

In principle, any stone that could pass through the bucket could enter the Singapore crusher, but there were exceptions. One problem was that if a 100 RB (Ruston Bucyrus) shovel tooth broke loose and was delivered to the crusher, it could, in one orientation, destroy the punch-plate safety device and wreck the crusher.

New Primary Gyratory Crusher

Primary gyratory crusher with Autocar truck, c. 1964.

Courtesy Fletcher Challenge Archives 6251P-48

With the increasing growth of Auckland after the war, Mr Bruce Winstone decided that the capacity of the quarry should be increased, by adding a 42" Nordberg gyratory crusher with a radial top feed opening of 42 inches (1.1 metres) to replace the 'Singapore' crusher. This, the largest rock-crushing machine in the country, provided extra production, allowed larger dump trucks to be used and reduced greatly the secondary blasting, which was labour intensive and dangerous. The crusher was installed in the quarry floor close to the faces of that time. The long conveyor from the primary gyratory crusher to the plant reduced the haulage cost of primary crushed rock.

Crusher Problems

Imports into New Zealand were subject to 'Imperial Preference' at that time (1950s). In selling all our primary produce to Britain, we were obliged to buy British goods, so the General Motors trucks from the UK were Bedfords and the American Nordberg crusher was manufactured by Fraser Chalmers in England. Early in the commissioning, the Nordberg 42" crusher stalled with power overload on the 225 kilowatt motor and had to be cleared by hand. This would take at least half a day, possibly a whole day, and became very demoralising. The English office couldn't help; so many urgent communications with Milwaukee produced the response that the power supply was inadequate and needed to be increased to double the full-load torque. That still wasn't enough so the power supply was increased to three times full-load torque. There was some improvement, but the crusher still stalled. Nordberg admitted a fault in the design and supplied new parts. After two years of trial and considerable effort it started to perform satisfactorily.

For the superstitious: at the start-up ceremony, through a misunderstanding, the crusher was launched with a bottle of sparkling cider instead of the best champagne and the building was number 12a.

The 42-inch primary gyratory crusher compared with Winstone head office building, c. 1958.

Courtesy Fletcher Challenge Archives 6251P-69

Quarry Face Working

Wagon Drills

In the 1930s and 1940s drilling for blasting used wagon drills, which drilled near-horizontal toe holes. A wagon drill comprised a large pneumatic hammer mounted on two carriage wheels and used a set of drill rods of complimentary lengths. The ends were forged by the blacksmith in a well set up shop for forming the ends of the rods, and for sharpening and tempering them.

This method was the only way to blast the eight-metre-high upper face

Above: Wagon drill in operation, c.1965.

Courtesy Fletcher Challenge
Archives 6251P-102

Above right: Drilling big rocks for secondary blasting, c.1960.

Courtesy Fletcher Challenge
Archives 6251P-92

Minidril diamond drilling rigs, c.1954.

Courtesy Fletcher Challenge
Archives 6251P-99

where the top of the rock was too rough for machine access. For the main 15-metre-high face it was necessary to blast out the bottom with horizontal holes, but with some top holes, drilled vertically to blow out the middle and upper stone. A very rugged face resulted and had to be barred down with crowbars by men swinging over the face, on safety lines, to remove all loose rocks before the wagon drill could again start at the toe.

Diamond Drills

Drilling methods improved with introduction of Mindril E500 diamond drills. These were high speed rotating drills using 32 millimetres diameter hollow rods with pressure water flushing the diamond studded bits. The drillers became very skilled with these rigs, achieving faces that were straight and clean. It was not necessary to bar down the face, to the same extent, as drills were not working on the toe. Some drillers on the blasted pile drilled the big spawls for secondary blasting.

Twenty-eight-millimetre diameter gelignite was used to charge the main face holes. This was a big improvement on past practice, particularly with millisecond delays. The small-diameter holes were vulnerable to occasional misfires where several holes were left fully charged. This was a worry for the quarry manager as the detonators were at the bottom of the holes. They were usually fired with everybody well clear because of the risk of flying stone. It was also a worry for the shovel driver, who could sometimes see pink gelignite and knew there might be a detonator in front of the bucket. At such times one could smell gelignite in the crusher house and screening plant.

Halco Drills

The use of Halco Stenuik drills in the mid 1950s was a further improvement. A problem with the pneumatic hammer on long drill rods is that the energy is absorbed in the drill rod. The drill makes slower progress with depth and the rods have to be of heavy section to withstand the impact. To overcome this problem the Halco drill had the hammer at the bottom of the hole adjacent to the bit and light tubes could be used in place of drill rods. The bits were 100 millimetres in diameter, allowing fewer holes and bigger blasts. The bigger holes were less likely to cut-off from moving stones and charging was easier with larger explosive cartridges. The use of remarkably cheap agricultural ammonium nitrate / fuel oil slurries soon developed a safe and reliable blasting technique. Occasionally a Halco hammer would be jammed or lost down a hole but it could usually be recovered after the shot was fired and could be used again.

Halco drills with hammer at bottom of the drill rod, c.1964.

Courtesy Fletcher Challenge Archives 6251P-51

Blasting Vibration

In later years, as housing developed nearby the quarry, blasting vibration became a cause of complaint. The vibration was well below the level of physical damage, but that is difficult to explain to an irate property owner. In 1951 the company brought in several world authorities on blasting vibration from the United States. On their advice, and with the help of the Department of Scientific and Industrial Research, vibrographs that could 'stand up in court' were made. These produced a photographic trace from a pendulum with high magnification. For all significant blasts from that time, vibration recordings were taken and logged. If a complaint was received the second vibrograph was sent out and evaluated at the complaint site. Although there were many complaints over the years the company was not involved in any

A typical blast from Halco drilled holes, c.1964.

Courtesy Fletcher Challenge Archives 6251P-53

Above: Tipping Bedford truck
at the Singapore crusher.

Courtesy Fletcher Challenge
Archives 6251P-6

Above right: Autocar trucks
with 20-tonne side tipping
bodies, c.1964.

Courtesy Fletcher Challenge
Archives 626P-61

court action. This is undoubtedly due to this detailed monitoring and the use of millisecond delay blasting, to minimise vibration.

With changing regulations and standards, modern electronic equipment is now used, providing more detailed information and even closer control. Earthquake seismographs are not sensitive enough for this duty.

Quarry Face to Crusher Transport

Originally, trucks from the company's town fleet finished out their life in the quarry. While this may have been cheap in capital outlay, it wasn't cheap in terms of reliability, down time and lost production. Hydraulic hoists were not suited to this heavy duty, with so many tippings per day. Cam and roller tippers were then common. To improve this situation, new Bedford five-ton chassis were purchased, and fitted with 'rock bodies' made in the quarry. A rope hoist was established at the primary crusher and the tipping controlled by the crusher operator. This greatly improved the reliability and turnaround time. Occasionally the hook (see image at top) would not engage properly and the tray would lift, with the truck pin on the tip of the hook. When part way up it could slip and the full tray come crashing down. This would awaken the driver, give him a bad fright and was potentially dangerous. Every effort was made to correct this fault. The crusher operator was given a carefully placed mirror and often the driver would climb out of the cab so the incidence and hazard was greatly reduced, but not eliminated.

The five-ton Bedfords were not well matched to the 100 RB shovel as they could only take one bucketful (see image top of page 272).

The 42-inch gyratory crusher building had a drive-through passage on each side of the crusher where side dump trucks were again operated by a hook and winch system. The Bedfords were unsuitable for this work, so two ex-army Autocar chassis were rebuilt, and each fitted with a 20-ton side dump rock body as a semi trailer.

These gave very good service and were replaced by Foden dumpers with side dump bodies. Later, when larger rear tipping dumpers became available, the building was modified and the winch system abandoned in favor of the now reliable heavy-duty hydraulic tipping.

Production Statistics

By 1969 Lunn Ave Quarry reached a production total of 1 million tonnes per year. By 1975 a peak of 1.3 million tonnes had been achieved. Output ranged between 1 million and 600,000 tonnes per year. Before the quarry closed it reached an output of over 2 million tonnes, using a large portable crushing plant. When the quarry was worked out by the year 2000, in excess of 35 million tonnes had been produced and used to build modern Auckland.

Restoration

There was much debate about what to do with this valuable asset. A hole had been created covering 100 hectares, with an excavated volume of 23 million cubic metres. Rubbish disposal was considered. From the environmental point of view this would save the long-distance haulage of the city refuse, but the possible leaking of leachate into the ground water was a deciding issue, along with the strong lobby from the high-quality homes now overlooking the site. The quarry is being reworked as a housing area and some 3,000 dwellings are being built to form a new suburb, called Stonefields.

Some see quarries as an environmental disaster for all time. The residents

Stonefields development, April 2011.

B. Bartley

settling into Stonefields would have no reason to think so. Other examples of restored quarry sites are Eden Gardens, Mt Smart Stadium, the lower playing fields for Auckland Grammar School and industrial sites at Wiri.

Conclusion.

This paper is intended as a tribute to those who worked hard to overcome the engineering problems associated with producing a fundamental civil engineering material. They did not enjoy many of the advantages that we now take for granted, such as heavy duty, high lift, mobile cranes, huge trucks and loaders. Quarry face working is now faster, safer and more economic, and crushers are steadily improving in performance and reliability. To design and build a plant that crushed and screened hard, abrasive rock for 50 years, with only minor change, is a tribute to the late Bruce Winstone and the few he brought around him to achieve it.

References and further reading

Simpson, Frank A., *The First Century: A Centenary Review of Winstone Ltd*, Winstone Ltd, Auckland, 1965.

12.5

Kawau Mining

by
John Duder

Setting aside Maori adze manufacture and European sealing, whaling and timber milling, initially for Royal Navy spars, it was the mining of manganese and then, by chance discovery, copper under the south-west coast of Kawau Island that was one of the first essentially industrial activities in New Zealand. First indications of minerals of interest were telltale blue-green colourings on cliffs, still visible today along with some of the trial adits and the preserved shells of the pumping station and the smelting house.

Entrepreneurs from New South Wales arranged with local Maori chiefs to buy Kawau Island in 1840 for around £200. A crown grant was issued to James Forbes Beattie representing Henry Tayler of the North British Australian Loan and Investment Company. Beattie formed the Kawau Company with £50,000 capital and brought Cornish miners from Falmouth. After discovering that unsmelted ore became hot and a fire hazard aboard ship, Welsh smelters were brought out and after repeated delays the smelting house finally started operation in 1849 in Swansea Bay.

The copper lode extended below the sea bed, necessitating a permanent

steam-driven pumping station as the shaft deepened. The main structure of that pump house with its distinctive brick chimney has been partly restored and, with the shell of the boiler, forms an unofficial memorial to those original Cornish miners. Sir George Grey's Mansion House at the entrance to the harbour is a much visited icon from colonial times; it was originally the home of the mine manager.

Also preserved is the shell of the smelting house now next to the Royal New Zealand Yacht Squadron's base up Bon Accord Harbour. Still visible on the foreshore is the deposit of heavy slag, the waste product of the smelting process. The well-bushed valley and hills behind the smelter now show no trace of the complete denudation caused by the felling of timber to fuel the smelter or the toxic effects of the smelting process.

The mining enterprise started around 1840 and eventually exported 467 tons of copper in 1845, rising to 1202 tons the next year. However, a rival company set up by Frederick Whittaker, a lawyer, and Theophilus Heale obtained by 'devious means a grant of land below high water mark' immediately beyond the original company's workings. Evidently this gave them control of the Kawau Company's wharf and certain reclamations on which to stockpile ore and worse, it enabled them to drive their shaft inland and remove ore from under

1850s drawing by John Kinder showing the copper works at Kawau.

Sir George Grey Special Collections, Auckland Libraries 4-1198

Ruins of the old smelting house in Bon Accord Harbour, Kawau, 1926.

Sir George Grey Special Collections, Auckland Libraries 7-A4700

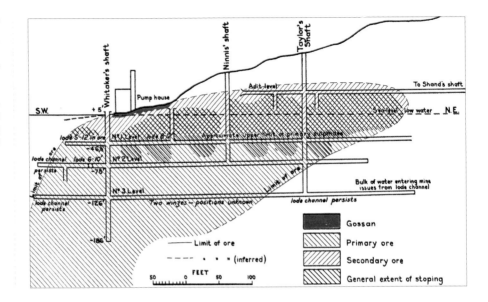

1898 attempt by Captain Holgate to reopen the Kawau Copper Mine.

the Kawau Company's land! That led to serious confrontation when the Kawau Company's miners broke through into the other's heading.

This was the beginning of the end; it was not until 1846, after Grey had become Governor, that the Supreme Court repealed the grant. Despite an injunction from the Colonial Secretary in favour of Whittaker and Heale, Grey made his own representations in London and the Kawau Company finally took sole possession in 1848 for £5000. But Whittiker and Heale's operations had allowed both mines to flood and by 1851 the miners had been discharged and the workings abandoned.

Some light on the human side of the venture was shed by the staff surgeon of HMS *Pandora*, visiting in the 1850s. Evidently there were some 300 Cornish miners and Welsh smelters and their families and 200 Maori on the island at the peak of activity.

Some activity on the adjacent island of Motuketekete failed in 1847 with flooded mines and the capsize of ore-laden lighters. That was the end of mining production on Kawau, although sporadic dreams of reactivation continued until as recently as 1970.

References and further reading

An Encyclopedia of New Zealand, 1966, Kawau Island http://www.teara.govt.nz/
en/1966/kawau-island/1

Clough, Rod, *The Historic Copper Industry on Kawau Island 1840–1855: Test
Excavations and Recommendations*, Science and Research Internal Report
No. 16 (unpublished), Regional Archaeological Unit Auckland, Department of
Conservation.

Salmond Reed Architects, *Coppermine Engine House and Wharf Site – Kawau Island*,
Conservation plan for Department of Conservation.

Williams, G. J., *Economic Geology of New Zealand*, Australasian Institute of Mining
and Metallurgy Victoria, Australia 1974.

12.6

The Cement Works of Northland

*by
Andrew Marriott
and
John La Roche*

Cement is the amazing engineering ingredient of concrete that can be formed into structures that are as hard as rock, very long lasting, and under most conditions requiring very little maintenance. Cement has been vital to New Zealand's development right from the earliest days of colonisation. Portland cement was patented in 1824 by Joseph Aspdin, a UK bricklayer from Leeds, who burned a controlled mixture of clay and limestone and ground it to form Portland cement. Its name, Portland, was used because the finished concrete imitated grey Portland stone quarried on the United Kingdom Isle of Portland in Dorset. This stone was used for buildings including St Paul's Cathedral and Buckingham Palace. Cement works were established in England from 1847 and cement was exported in barrels to New Zealand, Australia and many other countries. It was not until 1871 that cement was manufactured in USA.

Wilson's Cement Works, Warkworth

Nathaniel Wilson, the founder of New Zealand's cement industry, emigrated with his family in 1842 from Glasgow aged six years. Nathaniel initially trained as a shoemaker, but in 1864 he purchased a small holding of land adjacent to his parents' block south of Warkworth village, where his father William was a blacksmith. Close by, John Southgate had been making lime since 1851 by burning local limestone in a kiln. With limestone deposits on his land, Nathaniel built a lime kiln and in 1866 started to manufacture Roche lime (quick lime, calcium oxide, CaO). In 1878 he sent a ship-load of Roche lime to Auckland for the construction of the Parnell railway tunnel.

Warkworth cement
works, 1906.

Warkworth Museum No. 2586,
T. W. Collins photo donated by
B. Collins

Nathaniel became interested in Portland cement in 1883 after reading a book entitled *Science and Art of the Manufacture of Portland Cement* by Henry Reid CE. The book had been recommended to him by his friend, Mr J. A. Pond, the government analyst. After many experiments, by 1885 Nathaniel, with his brothers John and James Wilson, trading as J. Wilson and Company, became the first enterprise to commercially manufacture Portland cement in the Southern Hemisphere. However, there was a problem with the variability of the limestone which they finally overcame, with help from Mr J. A. Pond. They added pipi shells from the Mahurangi River and later from Clevedon to increase the lime content. There were also problems with the coke supplied by Auckland Gas Company, and for a short period Wilson's manufactured their own coke using Westport coal. During this period they had to overcome much prejudice and a preference by the authorities for imported cement. However, the large programme of public works at that time dramatically increased the demand for cement. By 1893 the company had to undertake major additions to their plant by installing additional grinding and boilers for steam to power the kilns.

Wilson's further expanded their works to increase production by utilising the latest in overseas technology, after Nathaniel had sent his engineer son William to the United States in 1898. As a result, rotary kilns and ball and tube grinding mills were installed. Annual production grew from 1,524 tonnes in 1897 to 7,620 tonnes in 1902 and, with a major expansion to the works in 1903, the annual production rose to 20,220 tonnes. At this time other companies established cement works at Limestone Island in Whangarei Harbour and at Milburn near Dunedin. By 1910 Wilson's works employed 180 people and was the major employer in Warkworth. The ready availability of Portland cement from the beginning of the century enabled rapid development of durable structures and port facilities, particularly in Auckland. Notable projects using Wilson's cement at the time included Rangitoto Beacon, Grafton Bridge, Queens Wharf, Rotorua Bath House and Napier Breakwater. Although Wilson's invested heavily in new machinery and processes, by 1918 the company was voluntarily wound up and amalgamated with the New Zealand Portland

Scow *Jane Gifford* at Mahurangi cement works, 1923.

Warkworth Museum No. 2293, T. W. Collins photo donated by B. Collins

Cement Company, whose works were on Limestone Island in Whangarei Harbour. It was here that most of the cement was being produced, while the Warkworth plant was producing mainly hydrated lime. Fires occurred at the Warkworth works in 1898 and again in 1922. By 1926 the closure of the works was imminent and machinery was being transferred to Portland at Whangarei before the Warkworth works were finally closed in 1929.

New Zealand Portland Cement Company Limestone Island, Whangarei Harbour

Ernest Schaw Rutherfurd produced the first batch of Portland cement; probably the first cement made in the Southern Hemisphere, in 1881 at Limestone Island. But it was not until 1895 that Rutherfurd and Company had erected a cement works and commenced cement manufacture on Limestone Island in Whangarei Harbour, not far from Portland. One year later Rutherfurd's business was taken over by Alan Hall under a new company called New Zealand Portland Cement Company. The plant was able to produce 46 tonnes of cement and 61 tonnes of hydraulic lime per week. A wharf at the island could take vessels of up to 3.3 metres draught bringing coal from nearby Kamo and Hikurangi and taking away the manufactured cement and lime. However, by 1918 when NZ Portland Cement Company bought out Dominion Portland Cement, most of the buildings and equipment were moved to nearby Portland works and the Limestone Island works closed. The island was then purchased by Northland Harbour Board. After many years of being grazed with livestock, it was gifted to the Whangarei district and it is now a planted and restored

Overlooking Limestone Island cement works.

Alexander Turnbull Library
1/2-001783-G

wildlife sanctuary with kiwis and other native birds and skinks. Golden Bay Cement has provided sponsorship for this project.

Wilson's (NZ) Portland Cement/Golden Bay Cement Company Portland, Whangarei

In 1912, William Wilson, who had retired from Wilson's Portland Cement Company two years earlier, noted a large hill of limestone near the Oakleigh River and decided it would be a good place for a cement works. It was close to where the new railway from Auckland was to run. William, with George Winstone, formed a company called Dominion Portland Cement Company. After visiting suppliers in USA, England and Europe, they imported the most up-to-date machinery and established a new plant at Portland not far from Limestone Island in Whangarei Harbour. The company secured the right to develop the Wairua Falls power station where they installed equipment to deliver up to 2,000 kilowatts to drive all the machinery at the works with a surplus to provide electricity to Whangarei and surrounding districts.

With the First World War still in progress conditions were difficult. Dominion Portland Cement Company, which was able to produce cement more efficiently than the NZ Portland Cement Company, often provided cement for them. It was finally decided in 1918 that Wilson's and the New Zealand Portland Cement Company would purchase the assets of the Dominion Portland Cement Company to become Wilson's (NZ) Portland Cement Ltd.

Fullers Engineering Co. of the United States was responsible for the design of the Portland works and also provided 11 grinding mills. The Wilkes Barre Company (also of United States) provided kilns, driers and coolers.

Extensive additions were made in 1953 to the plant to double its annual

Aerial view of Portland cement works.

Fletcher ACC 0367-10-2

capacity from 100,000 tonnes to 200,000 tonnes by building a new gantry building, crusher house, two cement silos and a slurry basin. By 1955, with a new kiln commissioned, the plant capacity was increased to 250,000 tonnes per annum, and by 1966, with six kilns operating, the capacity was 460,000 tonnes per annum using the 'wet process', where cement rock (an argillaceous marl) and limestone rock are ground to a fine powder in the form of a slurry. The energy required to dry the slurry prior to firing in the kilns made the wet process uneconomic and in 1983 the dry process was introduced to the No. 6 Kiln, with earlier kilns being scrapped or mothballed. With a plant capacity of 430,000 tonnes per annum the energy consumption was almost halved by moving to the dry process. New crushers and cement silos were built.

Reconstruction in 1980 was designed by Gatx-Fuller, the same company that did the original plant. Local contractors Whangarei Engineering Co. Ltd (WECO) and Wilkins and Davies were responsible for the construction work. With the latest improvements the Portland plant is a very sophisticated engineering project and its conversion to the dry process makes it, for its size, one of the most efficient plants in the world. In 1995 X-ray fluorescence laboratory quality control was installed and 'expert' high level process logic control

Conveyor from Limestone mine
to Portland cement works,
c.1985.

computer systems were introduced, increasing capacity to 600,000 tonnes per annum. In 2003 the direct coal-fired milling and firing system was changed to new duo-fuels burner systems using pulverised coal and alternative fuels such as pulverised wood waste or liquid fuels. These initiatives have improved efficiency and reduced the impact on the environment.

In 1970 Wilson's became part of Golden Bay cement owned by the Winstone Group of companies. The company was purchased in 1988 by Fletcher Building Ltd and its brand name became Golden Bay Cement. This company now supplies cement from the Portland plant throughout New Zealand by truck and ship. New Zealand cement production in 2009 was 1.43 million tonnes, with 930,000 tonnes coming from Golden Bay's plant in Whangarei and 500,000 tonnes from Holcim's Westport plant.

References and further reading

Clark, G. M., *More Than Just a Little Island: A History of Matakohe Limestone Island*, Published by Friends of Limestone Island, Whangarei, 2001.

Friends of Matakohe/Limestone Island www.limestoneisland.org.nz

Golden Bay Cement www.goldenbay.co.nz

Institution of Professional Engineers heritage www.ipenz.org.nz/heritage.

New Zealand Portland Cement Company (Cyclopaedia of NZ, Auckland Provincial District, Victoria University of Wellington) http://www.nzetc.org/tm/scholarly/tei-Cyc02Cycl-t1-body1-d2-d7-d37.html

Pearson, Dave, Architects Ltd, *Wilson's Cement Works, Warkworth, A Conservation Plan for Rodney District Council*, 2005.

Thornton, Geoffrey, *New Zealand's Industrial Heritage*, Reed Books, Auckland, 1982.

Thornton, Geoffrey, *Cast in Concrete: Concrete Construction in New Zealand 1850–1939*, Reed Books, Auckland, 1996.

Wilson, T. H., *History and Growth of Wilsons Portland Cement in New Zealand*, Calders Design and Print Company Ltd, Whangarei, 1956.

CHAPTER THIRTEEN

Buildings

Structural engineers play a very important part in the preservation of heritage buildings. From earliest times in New Zealand, buildings were strong and carried the vertical loads of weight, storage of goods and the activities of people. The horizontal forces of wind were considered and provided for. This was the practice in England and Europe, where earthquakes were rare and masonry buildings had been standing for centuries.

The Napier earthquake showed that New Zealand was different. It was later recognised as being on the 'Ring of Fire' around the Pacific Ocean, which takes in Japan, Alaska, the west coasts of North and South America, and more recently as being part of plate tectonic movements that create earthquakes as well as volcanoes. The horizontal earthquake vibrations induce forces in the structures that are now designed for in accordance with building design codes that started after 1935 and have been progressively upgraded using international experience and data.

For safe public use, those structures built before 1935 may require strengthening for earthquake resistance. The only other option is demolition and construction of a new building. The strengthening process is not only technically very demanding but is also rewarding, as it means buildings of character and quality carry on in useful service and uphold the dignity and heritage of the city's past.

Most of the early buildings used timber, stone or bricks and mortar. They were designed to resist wind forces, which are the more severe horizontal forces in buildings up to two storeys high.

At the start of the 20th century structural concrete became available and reinforced with steel, was used as beams, columns, floor slabs, walls and piles for foundations where needed. An early example of this construction was the 1926 Dilworth Building on the corner of Queen Street and Custom Street. It was

13.1

Heritage Buildings

by
Bryan Bartley
and
Colin Nicholas

Dilworth Building under
construction, 1927.

NZ Architectural & Building
review January 1927

designed by architects Gummer and Ford, who were to the fore in innovative
construction methods of that time, and was built by Fletcher Construction.
The use of electric rather than hydraulic or steam cranes enabled the building
to be constructed rapidly.

Steel framed buildings, also by Gummer and Ford, were built using the
techniques of the modern Chicago skyscraper. An early example in 1918 was
the New Zealand Guardian Trust Building at 105 Queen St. It is eight storeys
high, which was the maximum allowable at that time, and was the highest city
building until the 1960s.

One of the problems of steel framed buildings is fire resistance, so the
steelwork is encased in concrete.

The first tall building in Auckland, designed and built according to the
new earthquake regulations after the Napier earthquake, was the Dingwall
Building at 87 Queen St, also by Gummer and Ford. Their structural engineer
John J. Booth was responsible for the structural design.

John James Booth (1900–1988) born in Ireland, was educated at the University of Dublin and graduated BA. In order to properly look after his family

he decided to leave a troubled home country and travel to New Zealand to seek his fortune. He joined Gummer and Ford, an architectural practice well known for the architectural design of public buildings, and spent the first few years of his structural engineering life designing these buildings. John Booth was truly a pioneer and at the forefront of the new generation of engineers debating and discussing the earthquake problems. At this time he was designing the Dominion Museum for Wellington – a reinforced concrete, three-storey building of awkward shape. He recognised a basic understanding of load paths and ensured integrity in connections as he attempted to carry gravity loads and horizontal seismic loads of 10 per cent of the gravity loading to ground through various frame and diaphragm actions. Not having the luxury of mathematical methods such as moment distribution or mechanical (or indeed electronic) calculators he devised and sought understanding by graphical methods in order to provide sufficient strength and integrity to withstand seismic events to which the cities of New Zealand had been subjected.

NZ Guardian Trust Building under construction, 1915.

After World War II, John Booth started his own firm of engineers and architects, culminating in the firm of Booth Sweetman and Wolfe in partnership with Murray Sweetman and Len Wolfe. Both John Booth and Murray Sweetman were chartered engineers with the Institution of Civil Engineers (London) and became Registered Architects through the New Zealand law change. Much of the infrastructure in the industrial suburb of Penrose in Auckland and the Chelsea sugar refinery, wharf works in North Auckland, Auckland and Gisborne were designed and supervised by the firm. John's son Charles took over the firm in the early 70s, continuing the excellent basis on which sound engineering and architecture was practiced within New Zealand.

Most of the earthquake strengthening makes use of the ability of walls to resist horizontal shear forces (shear walls) and horizontal floors and ceiling panels can distribute the forces to the shear walls. Sometimes when such walls are not available steel frames will be built into the structure to carry the earthquake forces.

The following are examples of the modern earthquake strengthening of heritage buildings: the Auckland Town Hall, the High Court, the Civic Theatre, Auckland War Memorial Museum, Auckland Chief Post Office, Auckland Art Gallery, the Sky Tower. They each have unique features as described in detail in the following chapters.

References and further reading

Booth John J., *Nuts and Bolts: The Autobiography of a Civil Engineer* (unpublished).
Smith, Jack, *No Job Too Big: A History of Fletcher Construction Volume 1 1909–1940*, Steele Roberts Publishers, 2009.

13.2

Auckland Town Hall

by Bryan Bartley, Elizabeth Aitken Rose and Mark Hedley

Auckland became a borough in 1851 with an act of Parliament, but the first council lasted just one year and a second election could not be held because of lack of interest. Auckland became a municipality for the second time following the passage of the Municipal Corporations Act of 1867. Council affairs were administered from different offices until the Town Hall was opened in 1911.

The architects J. Clark & Sons, of Melbourne, won a competition to design the Baroque revival structure, reminiscent of the Lambeth Borough Council Hall in London. Clad in Oamaru stone on a base of Melbourne bluestone, it was built by Ferguson & Malcolm of Auckland. Apart from civic offices, the building contained the great hall (modelled on Leipzig's Gewandhaus Concert Hall) and concert chamber, seating almost 1,600 and 500 people respectively.

Plans for a monumental civic centre on the old market lands adjacent to the town hall were abandoned in the 1920s. The Civic Administration Building (1966) was later erected to ease office pressure and the Aotea Centre (1990) to provide for modern performing arts and a conference venue.

Valued for its heritage and contribution to Auckland's artistic and civic life, the town hall was refurbished in the mid 1990s. Because it was constructed of un-reinforced masonry, it did not meet current seismic protection standards, particularly as a place of assembly.

The structural engineering firm Kingston Morrison Ltd (now Sinclair Knight Merz Ltd) was appointed to strengthen the building. The design problem was strengthening the structure to resist the horizontal vibration forces caused by an earthquake of maximum severity for the Auckland region.

While much of the building could be treated with the usual methods the great hall presented very challenging problems requiring innovative techniques. The hall is a space four storeys high with long high walls on each side of masonry with brick inside. Fortunately they were buttressed to 1.2 metres thick between the windows. To hold the top of the walls together a diaphragm of multi-layered plywood was constructed in the roof cavity as a strong, light floor above the ceiling and connected to the walls.

Support for the mid-height of the walls was a more serious problem and solved by constructing a large horizontal steel truss under the seats of the circle. This truss was in the shape of a horseshoe round the hall, open at the stage end and connected on the long sides to the walls, while the ends were connected via further horizontal trusses to the end walls (see drawing below). The flexibility of these trusses is matched to that of the walls so they work in harmony. The organ loft was a problem as it was packed with 2,000 organ pipes (now

Above: Auckland Town Hall during construction, 1911.

Sir George Grey Special Collections, Auckland Libraries 7-A3941

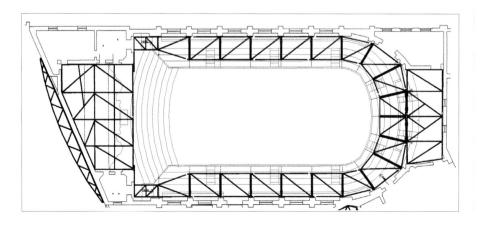

Left: Great Hall strengthening truss.

Courtesy Trevor Robertson, Sinclair Knight Mertz

5,000 after the re-build) and their controls and console so the structure could not pass through it.

A new construction method, which was driven by the constraints of heritage work, was adopted for the strengthening of the mezzanine concrete floors in the main entrance. This entailed thin, carbon fibre-reinforced polymer strips, which were glued to the underside of the concrete slab. This resulted in an improvement in strength without

Above: Strengthening the mezzanine floors in the main entrance.

Courtesy Sika Ltd & BBR Contech (NZ)

Right: Auckland Town Hall from the air during strengthening and refurbishment.

Courtesy Downer and Mike Farralley

significantly changing the depth, so that the architectural features and ceiling heights remained unaltered.

The triumph of this project is that in the great hall there is now no sign any of these important structural changes. The success of the methods used to strengthen the Town Hall is a great credit to all involved but particularly to the innovative design team who met the requirements of the city council economically and effectively.

References and further reading

'Major overhaul for city's top conservation priority', *New Zealand Design Trends*, Vol. 14, No. 6.

Robertson, Trevor, *The Strengthening of the Town Hall*, Proceedings 12th World Conference on Earthquake Engineering 2000, Paper 1155.

The red brick and stone courthouse, formerly known as the Supreme Court, was designed by Edward Rumsey, a student of Sir Gilbert Scott, who was a restorer of English Gothic churches. The Gothic influence can be seen in the castellated towers and in the portrait heads and gargoyles carved by Prussian immigrant Anton Teutenburg of judges and dignitaries of the time. He was a ship's carpenter and it was arranged that he would stay ashore for one round trip and carve the portrait heads in wood to be later cast in concrete. Some of these original heads were displayed in the foyer.

Construction began in 1865 and was finished in 1867. Mathews and Bartley completed the construction when the first builder went bankrupt. The old colonial building was incorporated in a new law court complex developed by the Department of Justice.

The task of strengthening the building and bringing it up to modern earthquake standards was particularly complex. There were only limited locations for new strengthening walls, which place great demand on the floor diaphragms to transfer earthquake loads to the new walls. Consequently steel plate diaphragms were constructed and sandwiched between the original floor and the new floor overlay.

13.3

Auckland High Court

by
Elizabeth
Aitken Rose

The High Court building from Anzac Avenue, 1921.

Sir George Grey Special Collections, Auckland Libraries 1-W1753

The central tower was an engineering challenge for Sinclair Knight Merz Ltd, as earlier modifications had left the tower with very little gravity support for three of its sides. A giant frame was erected within the tower, extending down to foundation steel where it was anchored to the base rock.

Two pohutukawa trees behind the High Court mark the entrance to the former New Zealand Parliament House (1854–1865), used during Auckland's brief reign as capital of the colony.

13.4

Civic Theatre

*by
Elizabeth
Aitken Rose
and
Mark Hedley*

Demolishing the original Civic Theatre brick proscenium wall.

Courtesy Downer and Mike Farralley

The Mighty Civic has enchanted Auckland's citizens since it opened in 1929. It was one of the last great atmospheric picture palaces to be built in Australasia and one of a small number surviving in the world. The cinema was built for the New Zealand impresario Thomas O'Brien, in a remarkably short eight months, by Fletcher Construction Co. and the Super Construction Company (Sydney).

The structure was reinforced concrete beams and columns with brick infill and a steel trussed roof. The 10 major trusses, up to 42.75 metres in length, were imported from England. One hundred plasterers moulded the Indian fantasy temple garden in the foyer and the romantic minarets of a Persian Palace in the 2,750-seat auditorium. A sunset machine and cloud projector transformed the sky-blue ceiling, which darkened into a night lit by 800 stars (24 watt blue bulb 'stars' imported from Germany). Other features included a Wurlitzer Organ that rose, revolving, out of the floor, a rise and fall gondola orchestra pit and the Wintergarden cabaret on the lowest level.

In 1994 when the lease reverted to the Auckland City Council, it was decided to restore and strengthen the building to convert it into a lyric theatre while retaining the 'Palace of Illusions' effect. The task was particularly complicated and was described as being like the 'reconstruction of a wedding cake while keeping the icing intact'.

New concrete shear walls were constructed alongside the original brick walls on new foundation footings. A new and much larger stage, fly tower facility, modern amenities and technologies were installed. The conversion of the Civic to a lyric theatre required some changes to the features in the auditorium. The most significant of these was the raising of the Opera boxes two metres and moving the proscenium arch both horizontally and vertically by two metres. These ornate structures were made from flimsy film-set construction – moulded decorative plaster fixed to rough timber framing with plaster wadding. In order to keep

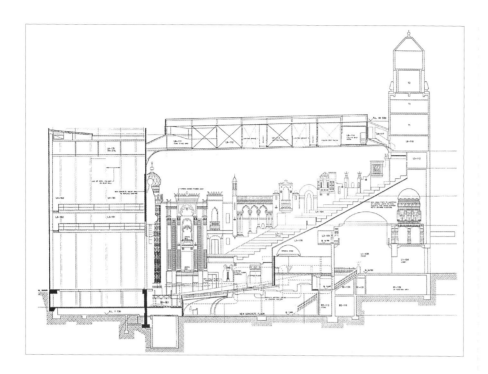

Cross section of Civic Theatre.

Courtesy Jasmax

the ornate 8.5 tonne proscenium arch intact it was braced, lifted and moved forward in one piece to float above the auditorium while a new shear wall was built and the original brick wall behind was demolished.

Great care was needed in the construction of the new wall and the

Interior of Civic Theatre.

Courtesy Gerald Lopez

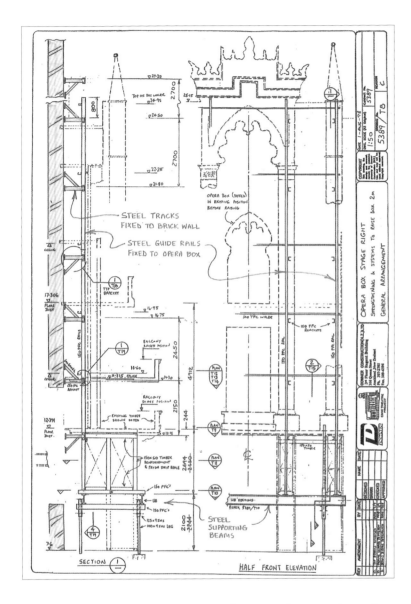

Opera Box raising.

Courtesy Downer

demolition of the existing brick wall so that damage did not occur to other parts of the building. As the new concrete wall was built from the bottom up, the ends of the existing brick wall had to be progressively detached from the rest of the building, necessitating temporary support ties to support it from the new concrete shear wall. Demolition of the existing brick wall then commenced using a large set of hydraulically operated jaws suspended from the tower crane. The brick wall was nibbled down in small bites, with work pausing briefly while the temporary support ties were sequentially released and removed.

The Opera boxes were estimated to weigh about 15 tonnes each and were raised by first constructing steel guide rails and tracks fixed to the wall behind. Steel supporting beams were introduced near the base and the framework of the Opera boxes was firmly tied to this steelwork. With hydraulic jacks in place the original supports were cut free from the brick wall and the Opera boxes jacked up and locked off in their new positions. In this way the steel guide and track system used to raise the opera boxes became the permanent strengthening structure.

The project cost $41.8 million. Holmes Consulting Group were the engineers, Jasmax and City Design the architects and Downer the contractors.

References and further reading

Jones, Martin, *Civic Theatre Building,* New Zealand Historic Places Trust, Register No 100, August 2001.

Smith, Jack, *No Job Too Big: A History of Fletcher Construction Volume 1 1909–1940,* Steele Roberts Publishers, 2009.

'The illusion lives on' and 'Bravo behind the scenes', *New Zealand Architecture Design Trends,* Vol. 16, No. 3.

The Auckland War Memorial Museum was originally built in 1929 as a memorial to the soldiers who were killed in the First World War. Auckland's first purpose-built museum was a two-roomed cottage in Grafton Road established in 1876. This was followed by a second, larger building in Princes Street. It was the energetic and distinguished botanist Thomas Cheeseman, curator of the Auckland Museum from 1874, who pressed for a new building. In 1913 the Museum Council, with Cheeseman's help, requested government support for a museum to be built in the Domain.

A worldwide architectural competition was held to design the museum. From 70 entries, the winner was Grierson, Aimer and Draffin, an Auckland firm. The structure was awarded the New Zealand Institute of Architects gold medal award in 1929. The building was extended between 1956 and 1960 to include memorials for the 4,000 Aucklander's who lost their lives in that war as well as to accommodate the need for additional collections space. It was recognised in 1994 that strengthening and refurbishment were needed when major improvements were undertaken.

A major structural change was made when the Grand Atrium was added between 2004 and 2007. This was Stage II of the museum's refurbishment. It followed Stage I, which involved a series of shear walls and the refurbishment of gallery spaces in the main building. The Grand Atrium was constructed within the internal courtyard created in 1960 when the semi-circular addition was built at the rear.

The new structures increased the museum's exhibition space by 60 per cent,

13.5

Auckland War Memorial Museum

by
Mark Hedley

Aerial view over Auckland War Memorial Museum, May 1966.

adding world class exhibition halls, educational facilities, collection and retail space and car parking whilst still preserving the museum's architecture and facade. Strengthening work included a large shear wall between the Grand Atrium and the main museum, linking the two sides of the building.

A major challenge was the construction of a truck dock entrance to a new underground loading bay. The entrance necessitated the removal of a large chunk of the museum's foundation beam. This was achieved by forming new concrete beams under portions of the foundation which were carefully exposed at strategic points.

Self-compacting concrete was then injected into the confined spaces so that it flowed under the museum's existing beams. When it had hardened, the beams were post-tensioned with high-strength stressing wires, providing a strong concrete frame to support the building.

Above: Aerial view of the Grand Atrium, 30 July 2005.

Courtesy Hawkins and Terry Fong photographer

Right: Construction of the truck dock required removal of some of the foundation beams.

Courtesy Hawkins

One of the main structural elements in the Grand Atrium is the large steel space frame spanning in two orthogonal directions, which supports the wave-like copper dome roof. It also supports the timber bowl-shaped 'learning space' that is suspended below the frame. During construction, the space frame provided convenient support for the contractor's tower crane so that work could proceed unimpeded in the void below.

The work was described as the construction of a seven-storey building within the confines of a heritage building. The Grand Atrium was completed in 2007 by Hawkins Construction. The architect was Noel Lane and the engineers, Holmes Consulting Group.

References and further reading:

Auckland Museum History of the Museum
http://www.aucklandmuseum.
com/159/history-of-the-museum
New Zealand Historic Places Trust,
Auckland War Memorial Museum,
Register No. 94.
Thomas, Grant and Khrapko, Michael, *The Auckland War Memorial Museum Underpinned with Modern Technology*, New Zealand Concrete Industry Conference, Christchurch Convention Centre, Christchurch, September 2006, Technical Papers (TR34).

View of the Grand Atrium, nearing completion, July 2006.

Courtesy Hawkins and Terry Fong photographer

13.6

Auckland Chief Post Office

by
Mark Hedley

Auckland's Chief Post Office (CPO) was built in 1909–1912. The site was part of the land reclaimed from the sea when headlands including Britomart Point were levelled in the 1870s. The railways, with the original Queen Street Station, occupied the land when the decision to build the CPO was made. This was contentious at the time, with some officials recommending that the land was needed for an extension of the railway network. The railway station was eventually relocated to Beach Road in 1930.

The CPO architecture was Edwardian Baroque designed by Claude Paton and John Campbell, the first government architect, who also achieved distinction for his design of Parliament Buildings in Wellington. The building was founded on concrete driven piles and the walls were brick masonry faced on the outside with Oamaru stone and Coromandel granite. All floors except the ground floor and basement were timber. The building was opened on 20 November 1912 in front of a crowd of more than 8,000 people. It was used as Auckland's Central Post Office from 1913 until 1989 and by 1992 had fallen into a state of disrepair before being purchased by Auckland City Council in 1995 as part of the plan for Britomart Transport Centre.

In 2002–2003 the CPO was refurbished and strengthened and became part of the new Britomart Station, marking a return of the railway station to its original site. Unlike the Town Hall, which was preserved to carry out its original function as a place of assembly, the CPO building was significantly modified so that the ground floor could serve as a transport hub.

The walls of the building were predominantly un-reinforced brick, 600 millimeters thick near the base reducing to 150 millimeters thick at roof level – not designed for earthquake loads. Strengthening work consisted of concrete ring beams cast around the perimeter of the building at each floor

Construction commences on the Auckland Chief Post Office, August 1909.

Sir George Grey Special Collections, Auckland Libraries 7-A348

level and new concrete walls cast against and tied into the existing brick walls. The timber floors were reinforced with steel beams and cross-bracing, which in turn were anchored into the new concrete walls. The parapet around the roof was a feature common in heritage buildings and vulnerable to earthquake loads. This was strengthened by drilling closely-spaced steel bars vertically down through the parapet and grouting them (bedding them in mortar-filled holes) into the wall below.

Major surgery was required to change the usage of the ground floor and the basement. The ground floor was lowered and changed from a 'banking lobby' to a public space for inner-city commuters. The lower floor provided for egress from the building to Queen Street at footpath level and allowed the steel column bases with their gussets (angle brace plates) and holding-down bolts to be displayed.

The basement, which had periodically flooded due to the high ground

Auckland Chief Post Office under construction, September 1911.

Sir George Grey Special Collections, Auckland Libraries 1-W946

The Chief Post Office during strengthening work in 2003.

Courtesy Downer

water levels, was lowered, sealed against water and strengthened with massive concrete walls. Its new use required pedestrian walkways to be formed right through the original foundations. As the foundations and piles were exposed for the first time, it was discovered that one of the piles was not actually connected – it had been driven about a foot too low and the beam cast straight over the top!

A major construction challenge to the adaptation of the CPO to its new function was to cut a hole in the rear

Above: Alterations and strengthening work in 2003.

Courtesy Downer

Right: Drawing of the opening required in the rear wall of the CPO.

Courtesy Mark Hedley, Downer

Bottom right: The new beam and columns supporting the CPO rear wall.

Courtesy Mark Hedley, Downer

Below: The pile at the extreme left was never connected!

Courtesy Downer

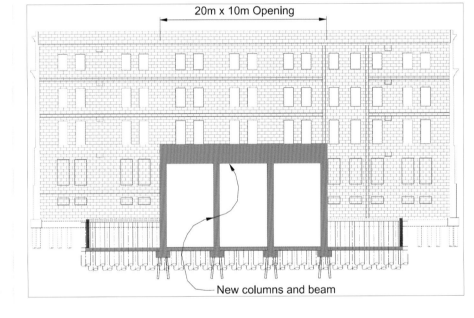

20m x 10m Opening

New columns and beam

The refurbished and strengthened CPO building in 2011.

Courtesy Mark Hedley, Downer

wall 20 metres x 10 metres and replace the brick with new columns and beams.

The wall structure, weighing 350 tonnes, had to be rigidly held in place above the new beam with support structures while still allowing room to build the columns and beam underneath. The result was a wide-open-space entrance from the train station, allowing natural light into the enclosed public space.

The strengthening works were completed by Downer in 2003. The architects were Jasmax and the engineers were Opus International Consultants.

References and further reading

Auckland's Refurbished Former Central Post Office, http://www.resene.co.nz/homeown/trendsideas/post_office_203818.htm

CPO Building, Former Chief Post Office 1912 heritage building Britomart Auckland http://www.britomart.org/buildings-spaces/cpo-building

Maylin, Melvyn and Shanmuganathan, Sulo, 'Britomart Underground Railway Station', *Sesoc Journal*, Vol. 16, No. 1, 2003.

13.7

Auckland City Art Gallery

*by
Mark Hedley*

Auckland City's Art Gallery complex located at the corner of Wellesley Street and Kitchener Street comprised six interconnected buildings when strengthening work started in 2008. The original building with the clock tower was built in 1887 and was expanded to include the Council Chambers building in 1913 and the East Gallery in 1916. A Central Gallery extension was built in 1971 and two further extensions in 1981. The three more recent structures were demolished to make way for a new 5-level structure featuring a glazed atrium nestled into the pohutukawas of Albert Park.

The newly refurbished and extended structure provides increased gallery space, new art storage facilities and expanded shop and café facilities. Modern air conditioning plant has been concealed in the roof and basement spaces and new plumbing, security systems and fire protection installed throughout.

Auckland Public Library and Art Gallery on the occasion of its opening, 25 March 1887.

Sir George Grey Special Collections, Auckland Libraries 7-A15181

To improve its strength under earthquake, it was necessary to tie the walls of the building together with a strengthened floor. However, it was important that the existing heritage timber floors were retained, even if they were no longer seen. The method employed was to drill and grout steel ties into the perimeter brick walls and overlay the floors with layers of plywood and metal strips to form a rigid diaphragm. The strengthened floor was then finished with 19 millimetre oak flooring. Whilst this system has been used in North America, it had not been used before in New Zealand. Special testing was therefore undertaken by Holmes Solutions to determine the factors to be used in the seismic analysis and to verify compliance with the New Zealand Building Code.

Amongst the other areas to receive special attention were the clock tower, the dormer windows and the roof. The clock tower was strengthened with a ring beam and steel bands to tie the clock tower back into the main building. The dormer windows were strengthened by drilling holes down each side wall of the dormer. Steel bars six metres long were then inserted and grouted in place. The roof shingles were systematically removed and replaced so that new plywood sheets could be installed to create a stiff roof diaphragm.

Construction Supervisor Mike Farralley, who has specialised in strengthening heritage buildings for over 30 years, described work on the Art Gallery

as some of the most difficult and exacting that he had done. Mike supervised the restoration of several heritage buildings in Wellington before moving to Auckland in 1995 to oversee work on five successive buildings for the city:

Above: The Art Gallery from the air, with the new extension under construction 2011.

Courtesy Hawkins

Left: The floor strengthening system had not before been used in New Zealand.

Courtesy Hawkins and Stuart Oliver Holmes Consulting Group.

The Art Gallery from
Kitchener St with the
new extension,
2011.

Mark Hedley

the Town Hall, the Civic Theatre, The Chief Post Office, the War Memorial Museum and the Art Gallery. 'One of the most important things is controlled demolition of the parts that need to be replaced. You need to understand the load path and provide the right temporary support so that damage is not caused to the heritage fabric,' said Mike.

The work was completed in 2011 by Hawkins Construction. The architects were Francis-Jones Morehen Thorp from Australia and the engineers, Holmes Consulting Group.

References and further reading

New Zealand Historic Places Trust, *Auckland City Art Gallery*, Register No. 92.
Oliver, S. J. and Mackenzie, C. S. M., *Auckland Art Gallery: A Celebration of the New and Old*, Proceedings of the 9th Pacific Conference on Earthquake Engineering, Auckland, 14–16 April 2011.

Introduction

Sky Tower is an iconic structure that, since its official opening in July 1997, has come to define Auckland's skyline. Standing 333.6 metres above its foundations and 326 metres above street level, it is the tallest free-standing structure in the Southern Hemisphere.

13.8

Sky Tower

*by
Dale Turkington*

The Sky Tower.

Beca photo

Characterised by its tall and very slender appearance, Sky Tower has been likened to 'a hypodermic needle' piercing Auckland's skies. While opinions on the structure have varied over the years, the distinctive tower undeniably stands out from the rest of the cityscape and has become a beacon and a brand icon for Auckland and for New Zealand. At night, it makes a stunning statement, when the whole structure is lit up in a variety of colours symbolic of current sporting events, commemorative occasions or charitable causes.

As a commercial undertaking constructed as part of the Sky City casino/entertainment development, Sky Tower draws revenue from tourism as well as from telecommunications and broadcasting operations. It is New Zealand's most visited attraction, welcoming around 500,000 people every year. From each of its three circular observation decks, visitors can get a 360-degree view of Auckland and, on a clear day, one can see up to 82 kilometres in any direction.

A remarkable feat of engineering, Sky Tower's height, long design life and special nature placed it beyond the scope of standard building design codes. The intensive, fast-tracked programme called for a concerted, collaborative effort from the team of client, architect, engineer, contractor and cost consultant. Construction of the foundations for the tower began in September 1994 and it was completed two and a half years later, on budget and three months ahead of programme.

The speed of construction, the owner's requirement for efficiency and the striking concept of the architect presented many engineering challenges that needed to be overcome.

Today, standing proud among the World Federation of Great Towers, Sky Tower is testimony to the ingenuity and skills of its designers and constructors.

Construction Facts

The Sky Tower is made from 15,000 cubic metres of concrete. 2,000 tonnes of reinforcing steel and 660 tonnes of structural steel were used, including 170 tonnes in the mast and 260 panes of glass.

The mast had to be lifted into place using a crane attached to the structure, as it would have been too heavy for a helicopter to lift. To then remove the crane, another crane had to be constructed attached to the upper part of the Sky Tower structure, which dismantled the big crane, and was in turn dismantled into pieces small enough to fit into the elevator.

At one stage there were around 1,000 people working on the construction site. A design team of 140, including engineers, architects, surveyors and others worked on the building at the peak of construction.

The Brief

The client, Sky City Ltd, had a demanding brief. The company wanted to create 'an international quality tourist attraction and an effective, marketable telecommunications facility, within budget and ahead of programme'. Sky Tower had to create a dramatic yet functional landmark for the big-budget

Sky City casino and entertainment development, and the entire project was on a 'hyper-fast track' programme.

As a landmark structure, Sky Tower was designed for an unusually long life of 100 years. This longevity meant it had to be developed with high design standards and durability, as well as low maintenance requirements.

The likelihood of unusually severe events assailing the tower, such as wind, fire and earthquake, is greater than for more standard structures, designed for a shorter lifespan. This meant safety was paramount, and the engineering design team had to incorporate a high standard of Life Safety for both staff and visitors to the tower in their design.

The Structure

The main structural element is the shaft, 12 metres in diameter with a wall thickness varying from 500 millimetres to 350 millimetres. Inside the shaft, a number of internal concrete walls enclose the lift and emergency stairway shafts, and these were cast integrally with the main shaft.

The shaft is supported on eight raked 'legs'. These stiffen the base of the tower and assist in transferring overturning loads to the foundation. A post-tensioned concrete collar transfers the load between the collar and shaft.

There are three openings in the mid-region of the shaft that allow visitors to see the view from the lifts as they travel inside the shaft. The pod area, on the upper floors of the tower outside the concrete shaft, is constructed using structural steel-reinforced concrete and plain reinforced concrete, with aluminium cladding. A series of hangers and struts were incorporated into the design to avoid using large cantilevers in the mid-pod region.

The concrete shaft ends at a height of 228.6 metres above its foundations. Above this level, a structural steel framework, the pedestal, rises 15 metres to support a concrete ring beam, which in turn supports the steel mast.

Structural Design Elements

Shaft Concrete

The tower is constructed of reinforced, high-performance concrete. A great deal of effort and research went into developing this specially formulated concrete mix to provide a very durable, hard, dense and impermeable material for a long life, with minimal maintenance. It is a tribute to the strong team involved, including the client and the builder, Fletcher Construction, that their focus on getting the concrete mix just right has resulted in Sky Tower maintaining its

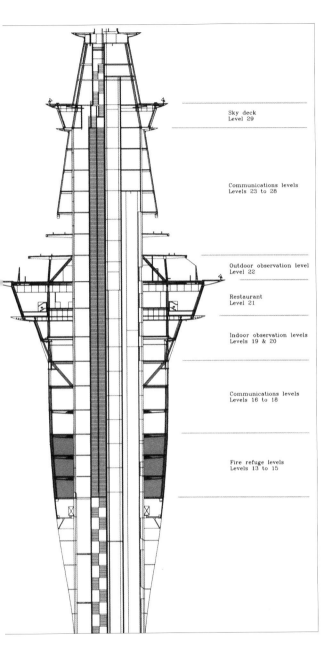

Sky deck
Level 29

Communications levels
Levels 23 to 28

Outdoor observation level
Level 22

Restaurant
Level 21

Indoor observation levels
Levels 19 & 20

Communications levels
Levels 16 to 18

Fire refuge levels
Levels 13 to 15

Above: Drawing of pod
structure.

Beca Group

Top right: The Pod area
completed.

David Xu, Beca

'freshly poured' appearance over the years. Its dense surface shrugs off moisture quickly, minimising the build-up of bacteria and organic material.

The mix incorporated silica fume at the rate of eight per cent by volume of cementitious content, with a very high standard of surface finish. The concrete also had to be capable of being pumped to heights of 250 metres and allow adequate placement.

The structural requirements were for a minimum 28-day compressive strength of 45 megapascals (mPa – a maximum of 70 mPa was set to ensure ductile performance was not jeopardised) and a maximum shrinkage of 750 microstrains at 56 days. The testing programme carried out before and during construction confirmed that the specification requirements were successfully achieved.

Foundation Pad

The tower is supported on a 2.5-metre-thick foundation pad, 24.5 metres in diameter, which is laid on siltstone rock. Helping to support the weight of the pad, 16 grooved piles drilled over 12 metres deep are arranged around the perimeter. The tops of the piles are restrained by a ring beam which also confines the rock within the circle of piles. The piles and ring beam are independent of the pad except for a closely-bound reinforcement cage on the centreline of each pile.

The foundation pad was placed in one continuous pour using a standard concrete mix design. The side forms and top of the concrete were insulated with polystyrene to control heat dissipation. Thermocouple sensors placed in various locations within the pad, near the surface and at mid-depth monitored the temperatures for 35 days, and generally the difference in temperature between the core and surface was maintained below the specified maximum of 20°C (the differential was exceeded only at the external corners of the pad).

Construction of the legs and their relationship to the collar.

Gillian Law Beca

The Legs

Precast off site, the reinforced concrete legs were constructed using the same high-quality concrete mix as that of the shaft, using a permanent spun concrete tubular former (a typical pipe section with amended end details). Because these can be seen and touched at street level, it was important to provide a durable and blemish free surface.

To provide a high degree of compression redundancy, the legs are arranged in two concentric cages and are confined with two concentric spirals, one to each cage.

The Collar

The collar is clamped to the shaft using continuous cable loops with in-line stressing anchors, which are stressed from inside the shaft. It would have been easier to anchor the cables on the outside of the collar, but having the anchorage pockets hidden is more aesthetically pleasing.

The capacity of these cables exceeded those readily available, and the anchorage blocks and other features were specially developed for this project. In keeping

Above: Ducts and anchorage boxes from outside the shaft.

Construction Techniques

Below: Fins immediately below the pod cladding.

James Lord, Beca

with the appearance of the rest of the structure, the collar's precast external shell was constructed using the same concrete mix as used in the legs and shaft.

The permanent connection of the legs to the collar had to be left until the collar had been fully constructed and stressed. By this time, the shaft had reached a height of 157 metres. The connection was achieved by extending reinforcement from the legs into ducts in the base of the collar. A 600 tonne-capacity flat jack was placed on the top of each leg and inflated to achieve a 500 tonne preload in the legs. These jacks were interlinked to ensure none could be overloaded if the tower swayed during this operation.

The preload was held for five days to allow some creep to occur. Then, over a calm 12-hour period with little wind, the reinforcing ducts in the collar and the gap between the legs and the collar soffit were pressure-grouted. Finally the jacks were similarly grouted. While the creep will continue, it is expected that long term, under gravity loading, the load in the legs will be similar to that as if they had been constructed integrally with the shaft.

Fins

Eight precast concrete fins radiating from the shaft provide support for the lower pod levels. The fins were individually constructed and attached by stressing through the shaft wall and tying adjacent units together with reinforcement, in post-grouted ducts.

The Pod

Like the rest of the structure, the pod was designed with redundancy in mind. The robust structure was designed so that, even if a column or other critical element was lost, it would still support the design load and the tower would stand.

It is composed of a combination of composite of structural steel and reinforced concrete, and conventional reinforced concrete, with an efficient design that uses a series of hangers and diagonal struts back to the shaft support. Floor slabs act as rings around the shaft, resisting the horizontal strut force.

The Mast

Proportioned rather like a giant fly rod, the 92.6 metre communications mast provides space for a host of antennae and other communications equipment, and also acts as a structurally efficient cantilever for the tower.

It is constructed of five steel tubes, ranging in diameter from 4 metres to 0.5 metre. Each tube has several segments bolted together using gusseted flanged connections and a perimeter ring of fully tensioned high strength bolts. The segment lengths were chosen to fit within the lifting capacity of the 7 tonne crane. The tubes have access hatches, cable ducts and access platforms at five levels.

In designing the mast, consideration of fatigue was of particular interest, particularly between the mid-heights of the two upper sections. The design team carried out fatigue analysis in accordance with the procedures set out in the New Zealand standard NZS 3404:1992 [4], assuming a 100-year design life. Guidance on appropriate detailing was also obtained from the British standard BS 5400 [5], and it was also used as an alternative code for verification.

To ensure excellent fatigue performance, a number of measures were implemented, including the use of notch tough ductile steel (a special grade of steel that resists crack propagation in areas of high stress such as corners and notches) and good fatigue-resistant details with smooth weld transitions.

Crane lifting the first mast section into place.

NZ Herald

Seismic Design

Designed to exceed the current New Zealand design codes and standard seismic requirements, Sky Tower 'broke the mould' for seismic design.

Although Auckland is a relatively low seismic hazard area for New Zealand, the tower was designed for a worst case scenario – to remain essentially undamaged in a massive earthquake with a magnitude of 8.0 points on the Richter scale, approximately 20 kilometres away (an earthquake occurring on the inferred extension to the Kerepehi fault, which passes to the east of Auckland City). The tower shaft and foundations have been designed with a dependable (reliable) strength to resist these loads, in recognition of the

catastrophic effects a tower collapse would have in the unlikely event of a large earthquake.

A site-specific, probabilistic seismic hazard analysis was used to define the Maximum Credible Earthquake (MCE) for the project, modelling individual seismic sources. This hazard analysis was innovative for New Zealand at the time, as the more common practice was using a uniformly distributed seismicity model. The tower was analysed using both spectral model and time-history techniques.

Finite element analyses were carried out to determine the actions in the shaft coupling beams under lateral loading. To endure non-brittle behaviour of the shaft in circumstances of extreme seismic overload, detailing provisions for ductility have been incorporated.

Wind Design

Auckland City relies heavily on the communications infrastructure on the mast atop Sky Tower. As such, one of the most interesting aspects of the wind design was for the mast (see Liquid Dampers below).

The tower has been designed to remain essentially undamaged when subjected to design wind speeds with a return period of 1,000 years. The entire structure is designed to be able to move as much as a metre in these conditions, and it performs very well in high winds (within 10 per cent of its predicted performance at design). While movement inside the tower can be unsettling for people (for example, swaying of the lift cables), the tower has rarely needed to be shut in high winds due to its excellent performance – and then only for the comfort of visitors.

Statistical investigation of wind data for the design was undertaken by Auckland Uniservices Limited. They compared wind data from three sites in Auckland with the wind speed and return period relationships defined in the New Zealand loadings design code NZD 4203, concluding that it was reasonable to use this code for the non-directional wind speeds for the design of the tower.

The investigators also carried out a series of wind tunnel tests using a model of the site and surrounds to determine wind velocity profiles up the tower and also the cladding design pressures. The code-derived velocity profile was found to be more conservative than these test results and was therefore used for design.

Boundary Layer Wind Tunnel Laboratory (BLWT) in Ontario, Canada, carried out dynamic, computer-based analyses of the tower to establish wind loading response for the tower as a whole. Analyses were performed to determine design forces and actions including the fatigue spectrum for the 100-years minimum life expectation of the steel mast, accelerations in the habitable sections of the tower, the effect of additional damping to the mast and the effects of vortex shedding on both the mast and tower.

Liquid Dampers

While the mast has been designed to meet all performance requirements without the need for additional damping, tuned liquid dampers provide additional insurance against the possibility of increased fatigue stress demands from potentially damaging mast motions. They also provide a higher level of comfort for technicians working inside the mast, as mast accelerations are reduced, improving conditions for installing and servicing antennae.

These liquid dampers have been placed at three positions in the mast: at the top and bottom of the upper section and immediately below the junction between the third and fourth sections of the mast. The dampers consist of donut-shaped tanks filled with a mixture of water, methanol, a biocide and an anti-corrosion agent.

The tank levels have been 'tuned' to match the frequencies of the first two mast modes involving significant mast response, and are the second and third modes of vibration for the tower as a whole. All structures have numerous modes of vibration, e.g. first mode for the tower is the oscillation where the top of the tower swings back and forth and second mode is where the tower is stationary at the top but the tower oscillated back and forth near its middle (approximately). The majority of the mass and 'action' for Sky Tower's mast participates in the first three modes. Therefore, we put 'tuned mass dampers' in positions to best dampen the excitation from these modes.

As the mast moves, energy is dissipated from the form drag, due to the sharp edged baffles that intercept the sloshing fluid. The effect is to raise the damping in the steel mast modes from about 0.3 per cent to in excess of 1 per cent. As the size of the dampers in the upper section of the mast is restricted, the extent to which the damping could be increased is limited. However, the level of damping achieved is expected to greatly improve the in-service performance of the mast and its attachments.

Fire Engineering

Sky Tower posed a brand-new fire engineering design challenge. Its sheer height means that a mass evacuation of occupants to the ground level is impractical. With 1,267 steps from the base of the tower to the viewing deck, it would pose a very challenging physical ordeal even for fire service personnel, and severely hinder their ability to effectively fight the fire once they got there.

As New Zealand's first and highest tower, research into other unique towers, such as the CNN and Eiffel towers, and close collaboration with the contractor to find the safest and most effective options was invaluable. The design was reviewed by a world renowned structural specialist.

The solutions included incorporating an intrinsically safe 'fire refuge' within the pod section, including a command centre that provides four hours of protection. Both passive and active fire protection features have been maximised to ensure there would be enough time for safe egress to the fire refuge, and a dedicated and well protected fire service lift has been included for staged evacuation.

Electrical Services and Lighting Protection

As a commercial venture that had to be marketed as a sophisticated broadcast and communications centre, Sky Tower needed high quality building services infrastructure with a host of special features within the electrical services systems. Not the least of these was a power supply system that minimises the practicable frequency and duration of operational outages. A high degree of redundancy was also built into the electrical distribution system.

A state-of-the-art lightning protection system and coordinated surge protection systems help to minimise the risk of lightning or other transient induced damage of critical electronic equipment. Multiple earthing systems provide for life safety and also avoid electromagnetic interference to the broadcasting and communications equipment.

The lighting included an aviation warning lighting system developed in conjunction with the Civil Aviation Authority, and it took a great deal of illumination engineering expertise to find an effective means of flood-lighting this tall spire rising into the night sky. The initial spectacular lighting design, while since replaced by more modern LED systems, inspired a fascination with Sky Tower's appearance by night that still endures today.

The design of all these systems required substantial research into the latest available technology at the time as well as an unprecedented level of design detailing to meet the performance objectives.

Conclusion

Sky Tower's success story as a landmark project can be attributed to the close collaboration of the architect, contractor, client, cost consultant and engineer throughout the project, focused on a shared vision of excellence. The tower's careful balance of function and form has created a legacy that will continue to be enjoyed by future generations of Aucklanders and the visitors who will marvel at the scenes from its viewing decks high above the city.

When a thing is done well, it is often emulated. The Macau Tower in the People's Republic of China is based on Sky Tower, paying tribute to its outstanding architectural and structural achievement.

However, for the Auckland communities who see its familiar outline every day, Sky Tower is simply a beacon that says, 'I'm home'.

Project Team

Owner: Sky City Ltd
Contractor: Fletcher Construction Ltd
Cost Consultants: Rider Hunt Holmes Cook Auckland Ltd
Architect: Craig, Craig, Moller Architects
Engineer: Beca, Carter, Hollings & Ferner Ltd

References and further reading

Flay, R. G. J., *Wind Speeds and Return Periods for Sky Tower Structural Design*, Uniservices Report 4511.00, June 1995.

Jury, R. D., Sharpe, R. D., Turkington, D. H., *Consideration of Earthquakes in the Design of Sky Tower*, Proceedings of the Pacific Conference on Earthquake on Earthquake Engineering 1995.

Jury, R. D., Turkington, D. H., *Sky Tower: NZ's Tallest Structure*, Proceedings of NZ Concrete Society Conference 1995.

Jury, R. D., Turkington, D. H., Irvine, H. M., *Sky Tower Mast – Design Challenges*, Proceeding of the Pacific Structural Engineering Conference 1998.

'Lighting an Icon', *NZ Lighting Quarterly*, August 1997.

'Protecting Sky Tower', *NZ Electrical Focus*, June/July 1997.

Turkington, D., *Sky Tower: A Balance of Concrete for the Future*, Proceeding of the Australian Concrete 97 Conference 1997.

Wemyss, M. R., *Keeping Sky Tower Cool*, Proceedings IRAHCE Technical Conference 1996.

Alec Aitken, BE (Civil), FIPENZ

Alec Aitken began his career as a clerical cadet with the Pubic Works Department in 1938, hoping to get an engineering cadetship. After serving in the army
and RNZAF in the Pacific during World War II he returned to undertake a
BE (Civil) degree at Auckland University, which he completed in 1950. After
working in various Ministry of Works offices he moved to the Waikato hydro
projects, first at Whakamaru and then as Engineer-in-Charge of the Waipapa
project until 1961. He continued working for the Ministry of Works in various
senior positions in Rotorua, Whangarei and Wellington before being appointed
to Auckland as District Commissioner of Works in 1973. He was responsible
for all projects between North Cape and Mercer, including acting as government representative on a number of boards and committees in the Auckland
region. Alec retired in 1981 after 43 years of service and in 1983 joined the
Auckland Engineering Heritage Committee, serving 12 years as Chairman
until 1998. During that time he has investigated many heritage engineering
projects in our region. Alec has resided in Birkenhead for 36 years and was
born and educated in Auckland.

Elizabeth Aitken Rose, BA, MTP, MNZIP

Elizabeth Aitken Rose lectures at the University of Auckland in urban planning,
specialising in planning history and theory, cultural policy and heritage. Prior to
this, she worked for the Paris-based Organisation for Economic Co-operation
Development, the Ministry of Works and Development and the Wellington
Hospital Board. As the daughter of Alex Aitken, she grew up in an environment
steeped in engineering and was vicariously involved in the construction of some
of New Zealand's major infrastructure projects.

Bryan Bartley, ONZM, BE (Civil), Dist FIPENZ, FAusIMM, Hon FIOQ

Bryan obtained his engineering degree in Auckland and then worked for two years in the City Engineer's office for the Auckland City Council. He joined Winstone Ltd in their quarry activities for nine years, then at Gammon Malaysia Ltd in Malaysia for two years. He returned to Winstone Ltd in 1963 and after a further 22 years of service retired as General Manger, Winstone Central Engineering Services.

He held the position of Executive Vice President for Professional Practice on the Council of IPENZ.

Bryan was co-inventor with the late Jim Macdonald in the very successful range of BARMAC rock crushing machines. There are still 4,500 carrying the BARMAC name and about 1,200 copy machines. He was active with the UK-based Institute of Quarrying and from Chairman of the New Zealand branch was elected as a Vice President then International President for the one-year term.

His service to education was as IPENZ representative on the Council of UNITEC, with the last seven years as Chairman and as a member of the Executive Committee of the Association of Polytechnics. Heritage activities have been as President and Hon. Life Member of the Civic Trust Auckland and a board member of the Auckland Heritage Trust. In recent years he has been a member of the IPENZ Heritage Committee.

John N. Duder, BE (Civil), FIPENZ, MICE, JP, ONZM

After graduating from Auckland University John started his career as a water resources engineer with Sir Alexander Gibb & Partners of London, building an irrigation scheme in Nigeria. Then he worked as a World Bank engineering observer on the massive Mangla and Tarbela Dams of the Indus basin project in Pakistan. Back in New Zealand in 1970 he was the designer's representative on the Tongariro hydropower development for the next three years. For over 30 years he was responsible for hydro, river and coastal engineering works in New Zealand, SE Asia and the Pacific with Tonkin and Taylor Ltd, consulting engineers.

A sometime Director of Tonkin & Taylor Ltd and of Watercare Services Ltd, and a former Trustee of the Auckland War Memorial Museum, he is currently practising as a civil engineering consultant. John is an active Rotarian; he has served 9 years on the Devonport community board and over 30 years on the Spirit of Adventure Trust Board. He was co–founder of the New Zealand Coastal Society and is its first life member. As an active sailor, he is currently a board member of the 'R Tucker Thompson Sail Training Trust'.

John Fitzmaurice, BE (Civil), MS (Harvard), FIPENZ, Life Member Water Environment Federation, Life Member Water NZ

John is a consulting engineer in environmental engineering. He holds the degrees of Bachelor of Engineering (Civil), University of New Zealand, and Master of Science in Sanitary Engineering from Harvard University. He joined the Auckland Metropolitan Drainage Board as a graduate engineer, rising to Design Engineer (Special Works), leaving after 12 years to be a consulting engineer. Over the next 30 years he played a major role in the design of many of the main sewerage schemes in New Zealand. He was involved in the planning for upgrading the North Shore Treatment Plant and directed the oceanographic survey for offshore effluent disposal for the scheme. John has been a Deputy Commissioner of the Environment Court of New Zealand and for some years a member of the Audit Group for Project Manukau, the upgrade of the Mangere Wastewater Treatment Plant.

Mark Hedley, BE (Civil), NZCE, MIPENZ, CPEng (Structural), IntPE

Mark Hedley started work as a design draftsman for Tapper, Cotter, Brown & Partners in 1973. He left to attend Auckland University, completing his BE in 1982. He was employed by Brian Wilson for 16 years as a structural engineer working on a range of interesting projects such as crib walls, bridges, GRP structures, pipelines, buildings, wharves, hydro and underwater diving inspections. He started work for Downer in 1998 as project engineer for the Civic Theatre restoration and later designed temporary support structures for the Britomart and CPO. His current role is Senior Design Engineer for Downer, designing temporary works for major projects. He also takes a lead role in the Company's graduate programme as a mentor and trustee of the scholarship fund.

Sir John Ingram, CBE, BE (Mech), DistFIPENZ, DistFInstD

John Ingram, following service with the RNZAF, graduated BE(Mech), University of New Zealand (Canterbury) in 1950. He joined Boving & Co Ltd., London, water power engineers, becoming Australasian manager living in Melbourne in 1954. The family returned to New Zealand in 1962. After seven years as managing director of Cable Price Corporation Ltd in Wellington, he joined New Zealand Steel Ltd, became managing director and led the company through its loss-making period to a time of sustained profitability. He later led negotiations with the government for the five-fold increase in steel production and the establishment of an integrated flat products works. He retired in early 1987, about the time the expanded plant started up.

John was president of IPENZ (1976/77) and a director or chairman of a number of companies, including the National Bank of New Zealand and Auckland Uniservices Ltd. He is a Fellow of the University of Auckland and has worked in the areas of conservation, the environment and people with disabilities.

Lady Rosemary Ingram has supported Sir John in his writing and involvement in our book while he suffered numerous operations and poor health.

Les Jones, BE (Civil), FIPENZ

Les Jones began his career as a draughting cadet for the Ministry of Works and went on to complete a BE Civil in 1960. After gaining experience in various sections of the MOW, in 1969 he became Resident Engineer of Western Diversions, Tongariro Power Development. During this time he oversaw the construction of two dams, 17 kilometres of tunnel, and three kilometres of canals. In 1970 Les was Chief Estimator for McConnell Dowell Constructors, where some of his successful tenders included the ironsand offshore ship loading system and the civil contract for the Warkworth satellite communication station. In 1974 he became the Resident Engineer for the construction of the Mangatangi Dam built by the Auckland Regional Authority; this 75 metre-high earth dam is the largest water supply dam in New Zealand. 1976 saw Les as Superintendent at Mangere Sewage Treatment Plant and in 1983 he became Chief Engineer, Drainage, Auckland Regional Authority, with responsibility for all major wastewater reticulation, treatment and stormwater in the Auckland Region. In 1987 his final position was Chief Engineer of Auckland Harbour Board.

John La Roche, MNZM, BE (Civil), FIPENZ

John La Roche graduated from Auckland University in 1962 and worked in London for Ove Arup and Partners before returning to New Zealand where he was involved in the design and supervision of engineering projects around Auckland. In 1968 he joined the water treatment company, Paterson Candy International, being involved in the design and commissioning of new water treatment projects including large plants for Hamilton and New Plymouth cities. In 1975 he moved to the bulk water department of the Auckland Regional Authority where he became responsible for the design of water treatment plants.

In 1988 he and others established the voluntary charity Water for Survival, raising funds for water supply and sanitation in developing countries. John took early retirement in 1992 and managed the charity with his wife, providing assistance to over 500,000 under-privileged people. Water for Survival joined Oxfam in 2003 leaving John with time to join the IPENZ Auckland Engineering Heritage committee where he became Chairman in 2007.

Mike Lancaster, BE (Hons), FIPENZ

Mike Lancaster gained his engineering degree at Canterbury College for the University of New Zealand in 1952. He then joined the Ministry of Works and Development. Apart from two years on leave in United Kingdom (1955–1957) his whole career was spent with Ministry of Works and Development. As Resident Engineer in Auckland between 1967 and 1973 he was responsible for the construction of the central section of the Auckland motorways. In 1974 he was appointed Project Engineer for Auckland Rapid Transit. Later in 1981–1988 he was District Commissioner of Works for Auckland and Northland. With the removal of the Auckland Harbour Bridge tolls, he inherited the control of this structure.

Bryan Leyland, MSc, FIEE (rtd), FIMechE, FIPENZ

Bryan Leyland started his engineering career as a cadet engineer the Auckland Electric Power Board in 1956. He graduated after five years and, shortly after, left New Zealand for his 'overseas experience'. This lasted nine years, during which he worked in the UK, Mauritius, Cyprus, West Africa and finally Malaysia. He returned to New Zealand in 1970 and worked for Lloyd Mandeno on various hydropower schemes. Not long after Lloyd died, he set up his own consulting firm which specialised in hydropower and power systems in general. He is now semi-retired and runs a small consulting business from his home in Point Chevalier.

Neil Mander, MNZM, BE (Electrical), FIPENZ

Neil Mander began his telecommunication career with the New Zealand Post Office (NZPO) in 1959 as a Technical Assistant with a bursary to study for the Bachelor of Engineering (Electrical) degree at the University of Auckland. After graduating he continued with the NZPO, which became New Zealand Telecom, rising to the rank of Supervising Engineer.

He was involved with the installation, maintenance and operation of domestic and international broadband transmission systems. The international systems included the COMPAC, the later TASMAN international submarine telephone cables and the Satellite Earth Station at Warkworth. Domestic systems included analogue coaxial cable and microwave radio systems and the first generations of digital technology over paired cable and fibre optic cables.

He accepted early retirement from NZ Telecom in 1991. Since then he has been heavily involved as a volunteer with organisations in the not-for-profit sector, for which he was awarded the MNZM in 2007.

Judy McDonald, MA (Hons), NZLA Cert

Judy McDonald graduated from the University of Canterbury in 1962 with a degree in English literature and languages, and also holds a library qualification. She spent several years teaching in New Zealand and England, including a period as Head of the English Department at Papakura High School, before moving in 1980 to Manukau Institute of Technology. In her role as Liaison Officer, and later Institutional Research Manager, she worked closely with engineers at trade, technician and professional levels. She has a profound admiration for the achievements of the engineering profession.

Andrew Marriott, BE (Civil), MIPENZ, CPEng (Structural and Civil), IntPE

Andrew Marriott attended Auckland University completing his BE in 1987. He was employed by McGuigan Syme Partners for three years as a structural engineer working on a range of interesting projects such as retaining walls, bridges, residential and commercial buildings. He worked in England for five years as a Heritage Engineer on projects such as Warwick Castle, Worcester Cathedral and Chequers. On his return to New Zealand he worked for McGuigan Syme Partners for two years, Chester Consultants for 15 years and eight years as a director on a diverse range of projects. In 2008 Andrew formed his own company, Marriott Consulting Engineers, to focus on Heritage Engineering. He has worked on Waitangi Treaty House and many other listed heritage buildings and monuments. Currently he is the Christchurch City Council's Heritage Engineer, advising on all listed buildings in the Canterbury region. Andrew joined the IPENZ Auckland Engineering Heritage committee in 2000 and was Chairman from 2003 until 2007.

Rhys Thomas, BE (Civil), FIPENZ, JP

After service with the RNZAF as a navigator, Rhys studied at Canterbury College for a BE degree with the University of New Zealand, graduating in 1950. He was initially employed in general civil engineering and structural engineering followed by managing a consultant's Northland branch office. In 1963 Rhys was a founding partner of the multi-discipline firm Fraser Thomas, with development work in South Auckland, Northland and later in the Pacific and South East Asia. His public commitments included service in the Territorial Force Engineers and Infantry, retiring after 14 years with a senior Brigade rank; he also has 25 years' involvement in secondary and tertiary education governance. He was IPENZ representative on the council of the Manukau Institute of Technology. He is the IPENZ member on the Musick Point Trust, in which he has taken a keen interest, and was a founding member of the Auckland Chapter for Engineering Heritage.

Dale H Turkington BApSc, ME, FIPENZ

Dale Turkington's engineering career commenced with the completion of an Engineering Diploma in Civil & Structural from the British Columbia Institute of Technology in 1972. He went on to earn a Bachelor of Applied Science from the University of British Columbia in 1980 and a Master of Engineering (with Distinction) from the University of Canterbury in 1987. Dale worked for a number of engineering consulting firms in Canada, including the internationally recognized bridge firm Buckland & Taylor Ltd and was Manager of Bridge Engineering for CrippenConsultants Ltd. He has worked within the Beca Group of companies in New Zealand, Singapore and Australia for over 20 years in various management and leadership roles. Dale has been responsible for the design management and construction of a number of major infrastructure and commercial projects in New Zealand, Australia, Canada and South East Asia, including the Sky City/Sky Tower Complex, Macau Tower Entertainment Centre and the new Auckland Hospital. He was on the Board of HERA (Heavy Engineering Research Association) from 2002 to 2007, serving as Chair in 2006–2007. Dale also led the Construction Industry Council's Design Documentation Working party; the guidelines created have been recognized by the International Federation of Consulting Engineers as 'worldbest practice'.

David Veart, MA (Hons), LLB

David was educated at Onehunga Primary and High schools. He originally trained as a lawyer at Auckland University and then attended Auckland Teachers'Training College, graduated and later taught in Auckland, Wellington and London. In 1981 he returned to Auckland University and retrained as an archaeologist, obtaining a MA in Anthropology.

In 1984–87 he worked as an archaeological contractor for the NZ Historic Places Trust and from 1987–2010 has been employed by the Department of Conservation and is currently the Auckland Area Historic Programme Manager. During this time he has helped manage the large-scale remnants of New Zealand's engineering heritage at places such as the coastal defence forts at North Head, Fort Takapuna and Stony Batter and has worked on sites as varied as whaling stations in Tory channel and the Hapuawhenua railway viaduct.

He was brought up in a family that had worked in the New Zealand gas industry for two generations and grew up next to gas holders and played in gas works. He is currently a member of the IPENZ Heritage Committee. He has also published a book on the history of cookery in New Zealand, *First Catch Your Weka*, which was a finalist in the 2009 New Zealand Book Awards.

Colin Zeff, MSc (Ergonomics), BE (Mech)

Colin gained his engineering degree from Canterbury University in 1962. He went on to study at Loughborough University in the UK with a keen interest in design and man/machine relationships. He returned to New Zealand to a design teaching position at the University of Canterbury before moving into the timber industry where he held various engineering and technical positions for over 30 years.

He was involved in the development of manufacturing plywood, particleboard and MDF in New Zealand as well as technical developments in timber milling and processing. He held the position of Chief Engineer at Henderson and Pollard Ltd for several years and then at Carter Holt Harvey Timber.

Colin was one of the founders of the Forest Industry Engineering Association (FIEA) and served several years as its President. In 1996 he started his own consultancy business, serving the timber processing industry, but gradually turned his attention to his lifelong interest in heritage engineering and, in particular, railways and tramways.

He currently shares his time between the consultancy and managing the Museum of Transport and Technology's (MOTAT) tramway and tram collection.

ACKNOWLEDGEMENTS

The IPENZ Engineering Heritage Committee wishes to express grateful thanks to the many people who have contributed to our book.

Dr Norm Clark, Vice President, Engineering Services and Environment, and Vicki Woodley, External Affairs Officer at New Zealand Steel, for their generous contribution towards the cost of publication and for providing most of the illustrations for Sir John Ingram's article on 'Steel from Ironsand'.

Bernie Chote, General Manager, Winstone Aggregates, for his encouragement, support and a generous contribution towards the cost of publishing and printing.

Robert Durant, Managing Director Beca Corporate Holdings, for his company's generous sponsorship and the support of Beca staff in providing illustrations and copyright clearances.

Graham Darlow, General Manager Engineering Division, Fletcher Construction, for the generous contribution from his company towards the cost of publishing this book.

Cos Bruyn, Chief Executive Officer of Downer, for his support and generous contribution to support the cost of this publication, as well as the many photographs of Downer's work in building, refurbishment and strengthening projects described so well by Mark Hedley.

Sir Ron Carter for writing the Foreword and his many helpful suggestions.

Keith Giles of Sir George Grey Special Collections (SGGSC) at Auckland City Library for providing help and very many images of historic photographs from the wonderful photographic collections that he is responsible for. He went well beyond our expectations in assisting us.

Harvey Brahne, Sarah Padey and the Auckland Council Archives team for the many images of old plans and pictures that have added so much colour and interest to the writing.

Sue La Roche for her work editing and enhancing images, preparing designs and the keyword index. Her expertise and computer knowledge has been invaluable to the project as a whole.

Professor Jack Woodward for reviewing our writing and providing helpful advice and greatly needed encouragement.

Judy McDonald, as a non-technical person and English specialist, volunteered to edit our manuscript. She made our writing much more readable, but most of all, she gave us encouragement and boosted our confidence when it was most needed.

Norman Firth, a committee member and very experienced technical editor, for his excellent work on the second edit of all the manuscript.

Barbara Pendry, Rachel Hughes, Alistair Shanks, Paul Bickers and Mark Bourne of Watercare Services for the water supply and drainage images from the Watercare collection as well as many helpful comments about our writing.

Dorothy Neilson of Fletcher Challenge Archives for her help in providing images of Winstone Lunn Avenue Quarry and the Portland cement works. She also provided a copy of the book *History and Growth of Wilson's Portland Cement in New Zealand*, which was of great help in our writing.

Bob Norman for agreeing to the use of his writing about Auckland Harbour Bridge from his book *You Can't Win 'em All*.

Roger McRae, General Manager, and John Oey, Estimating Manager, McConnell Dowell Constructors, for illustrations of the slurry pipeline construction at New Zealand Steel and the building of the Warkworth Earth Satellite Station.

Grant Thomas and Hawkins Construction for pictures of the Auckland Museum and Art Gallery refurbishments. Also Roger Onion and Mike Farrelly for background information and pictures of the Town Hall, Civic Theatre and Chief Post Office.

Hunter Gillies and Jasmax for diagrams and assistance with the Civic Theatre and Chief Post Office chapters.

Beca Carter Hollings and Ferner and Dale Turkington for the writing and pictures of the Sky Tower construction.

Bruce Ringer of Auckland Council South Auckland Research Centre for his help in providing information and images of Mangere Airfield, Mangere Bridge and the Tamaki River Bridge.

Alan La Roche and the Howick Historical Society for providing historic images and information on the first Tamaki River Bridge at Panmure.

Kirsty Webb, Local History Librarian at Takapuna Library, for assistance with early pictures of the Takapuna Steam Tram, Chelsea Sugar Works and Devonport Gas Works.

Jim Muir from Opus International Consultants for obtaining approvals to use old Ministry of Works illustrations.

Colin Nicholas for writing the information about John Booth.

Debbie Francis, Librarian, Institution of Civil Engineers, London, for sending *The Civils: Story of the Institution of Civil Engineers* and pictures of the Institution building in London.

Sharon Anderson, External Relations Manager, Faculty of Engineering, University of Auckland, for a picture of the first engineering school at Auckland University.

Dr Roger Blakeley, Chief Planning Officer, Auckland Council, for permission to use illustrations from the De Leuw Cather report.

Jens Madsen and Craig Dowling for providing Ports of Auckland images for use in the book.

Anne Stewart Ball for information about her great-grandfather James Stewart and his building of early railways.

Kirsty Pocock, Manager Publications Australasian Institute of Mining and Metallurgy, for permission to use J. G. Williams' drawing of the Kawau Copper Mine.

Wayne McDonald, as Regional Director Auckland and Northland, NZ Transport Agency (now retired), for permission to use website pictures of Auckland Motorways.

Porthcurno Telegraph Museum, Penzance, United Kingdom for providing pictures of cable-laying ship *Mercury*.

John B. Rose, author of Akarana Ports of Auckland, for permission to use illustrations from his book.

Russell Stone, author of *Logan Campbell's Auckland: Tales from the Early Years*, for permission to use parts of his writing about the Albert Barracks.

Wynne Colgan for permission to use his writing from the NZ Historic Places Trust book *The Past Today*.

Mr H. J. Brown for permission to use his drawing of Albert Barracks in relation to Albert Park.

John Webley for providing Rhys Thomas with information about early Auckland railway stations from writing by the late Gerry Walker.

The Musick Point Trust and the Auckland Suburban Radio Club for assisting Rhys Thomas in his writing about Musick Point.

Antony Ellis, New Zealand Fine Prints for permission to use the colour picture looking up Queen Street, Auckland, in 1852.

Jan Frazer, Auckland Airport, for providing a recent aerial picture of Auckland Airport and a copy of the book *Where New Zealand Touches the World*.

Bryce Williamson and New Zealand Institute of Chemistry for pictures of Dr Nigel Evans, Dr Richard Cooper and Peter Bates.

Robyn La Roche of La Roche Design for her work in converting all the coloured images into CYMK format for the publisher.

Des Peate for permission to use photos of himself and Denis Mansergh.

To our publisher, Jenny Haworth, of Wily Publications, for her genuine enthusiasm and for coming from Christchurch to talk to us in Auckland. Her knowledge of publishing has helped develop this book to its final stage. Also to her team: Quentin Wilson for his skill in page design, layout and in developing concepts suggested for the front cover; Antoinette Wilson for her skill in editing; Choice Company in Taiwan for the print job.

Acheron, HMSV 88
Aero Club of New Zealand 203
AETC (Auckland Electric Tramway Company) 121, 122, 124
Agnew, W Y 63
Albatross (ferry) 118
Albert Barracks 28, 175, 211-216, 329
Albert Park Shelters 216
Alex Alison 118
Allum, Sir John 57, 149
American Concrete Institute 158
Anzani engine, 204
Arapuni Power Station 241
Ardmore Filter Staton 45-47, 59, 209
Aspdin, Joseph 281
Atkinson, Henry 32, 230
Auckland Chief Post Office, 290, 300, 301, 303
Auckland City Art Gallery 304, 306
Auckland City Council 43, 44, 48, 50, 52, 55, 59, 77, 86, 103, 107, 123, 142, 145, 146, 158, 159, 161, 164, 208, 209, 216, 217, 219, 235-237, 294, 300, 320
Auckland City Destructor 234, 236, 237
Auckland Electric Power Board 239, 323
Auckland Gas Company 58, 229-231, 233, 282
Auckland Grammar School 107, 278
Auckland Graving Dock 30, 89, 90
Auckland Harbour Bridge Authority, 149, 150, 153, 155-157
Auckland Institute and Museum 25
Auckland International Airport (& Mangere) 110, 113, 164, 186, 206-210
Auckland, Lord 16
Auckland Metropolitan Drainage Board & District 57, 64, 66, 71, 79, 321
Auckland Railway Station 138-140, 143, 144
Auckland Regional Authority (ARA) 210
Auckland Regional Transport Network 146
Auckland Regional Transport Network Limited (ARTNL) 146

Auckland Tramways 120, 121, 123, 124, 237, 239
Auckland Uniservices Limited 315
Auckland War Memorial Museum, 42, 43, 231, 233, 290, 297, 299, 320
Awanui Station 181
Axis Fergusson Container Terminal 100

Babcock and Wilcox boilers 238
Bacons Lane 218
Baldwin Locomotive Works, 125
Balfour, James 89
Bandpass filters 197
Barmac Crusher 108, 109
Baroona, 119
Barre Johnston, J Ltd 234
Barrowclough, A O 174
Bascule Bridge 138
Bates, Peter, 250, 259, 330
Batten, Jean 206, 207
Bauld, Ross 76
Bay of Islands 87, 131, 138, 212
Bayswater wharf 125
Bazalgette, Joseph 51
BBR Contech (Construction Techniques Ltd) 160, 292
Bean Rocks Lighthouse 89
Beattie, James Forbes 278
Beca Carter Hollings & Ferner Ltd 72, 160, 271, 318
Beca Steven 82, 86
Bell, Alexander Graham 176
Betio Islet, 185
BHP 95, 255, 257-259, 261
Bickers, Dr Paul 85
Big Muddy Creek 37-39
Binnie and Partners 48
Birkenhead 47, 78, 79, 111, 117, 118, 264, 267, 268, 319
Bitumix Ltd 72
Black, Professor James 23
Bloodworth, Thomas 68
Blow, David 76
Bluescope Steel Ltd 255, 256

Boddam, Captain Edmund Tudor 221
Bon Accord Harbour 279
Booth, John and Charles 288-290, 329
Borrie, E F 56 Boundary Layer Wind 315
Boundary Layer Wind Tunnel Laboratory (BLWT) 315
Bowen Reserve 216
Boylan and Lundon 264
Brassey and Peto of Bristol 22
Brian Perry Civil 160
Brickell Moss Partners 70
Broadhead, C F 231
Brodie, Corporal Alexander 175
Bromley works 67, 70
Brown & Caldwell 65, 67, 71, 72
Browns Island 55-65, 67, 68, 70, 77, 79, 184
Brush Electrical Engineering Company Ltd 122
Buffalo, HMS 117
Burt, Mr E J 164

Cairns 196
Calliope Dock 30, 91, 92
Calvert, John T 65
Cameron, General 175
Campbell, Sir John Logan 121
Canada-United Kingdom cable, CANTAT 195
Candy Filter Company 41, 45, 46
Canterbury University 22, 23, 25, 44, 246, 321, 323-326
Carlaw, James 33
Castor Bay 79, 80
Caudron 205
Cautley, Major Henry 220
Chandler, David 60
Chapman, V J 59
Char House 265
Cheeseman, Thomas 297
Chelsea Bay 78
Cheltenham 120
China Hill 115
Chironomus zealandicus 69

City Design 59, 158, 292, 296, 315
Civil Aviation 185, 186, 208, 209, 317
Clearwater Construction 82, 83
Clevedon 282
Cleveland Bridge & Engineering Ltd 149
Coates, Hon J G 40
Collett, Mr W R 171
Collom, Charles C 63
Colonial Ammunition Co 107
Commercial Bay 88, 89, 93
COMPAC 188, 195-197, 323
Connell Wagner-DC Limited 85
Constitution Hill 217-219
Container Terminal 98, 100
Cook, Captain James 41, 246
Cooper, Dr Richard 250, 259, 330
Cormack, Gavin 174
Cosseys Creek 45
Cousins and Aitken Limited 122
Coxs Creek 52, 53
Craig Craig Moller Architects 318
Cumberland, K B 59
Curtis, Sir Barry 75
Curtiss flying boat 205
Customs Street West 237

Dairy Flat 111
Davis, Sir Ernest 56, 70
DC Street Construction Company 183
DCS and Cousins & Cousins 122,
    125-126
De Leuw Cather 112, 164, 329
Devonport 30, 78, 117, 118, 120, 199, 232,
    233, 320, 328
Devonport Steam Ferry Company 117
Dexter, Reuben 204
Diamond, HMS 91, 92
Diamond, John 194
Dickson, Arthur J 58
Dilworth Building 287, 288
Dingwall Building 288
Dobson, Edward 22
The Domain 27, 29, 48, 114, 297
Dominion Portland Cement Company
    283, 284
Dorman Long Ltd 149
Dow, John 70
Downer & Co 44
Downey, David 80
Drury 110, 127-132, 135, 136, 175, 176
Duchess of Argyle 88
Duck Creek 264-266, 268
Duder, Thomas 117
Duffield, Bruce 45
Dun Mountain 120
Dunedin 11, 43, 120, 126, 176, 282

E W Alison 118
East Tamaki 99, 111
Eden Gardens, 278
Ellerslie 111, 121, 122, 136
Emu Rock 117
Energy-Wise Companies 258
Epsom 122, 241
Equiticorp 255, 256
Esmonde Road 81
Etude et Enterprises 63, 68, 70, 174
Evans, Dr Nigel 250, 259, 330

Fairmile launches 119
Fanning Island 195, 202
Farralley, Mike 292, 294, 304
Ferguson & Malcolm 290
Ferro Concrete Co 93
Ferrymead Museum 176
Firth, Cyril 43-45, 48, 50
Fisher, Sir Woolf 247, 249, 259
Fitzmaurice, John R 320
Fletcher Building Ltd 286
Flocor 72
Flying Schools 203-206
Flynn, Ted 209
Fort Britomart 135, 138, 139, 212, 214,
    215
Foster, Leo 271
Frankton 137
Fraser Chalmers 273
Frazer, Sir Francis 57
Freeman Fox and Partners 149, 152
Freemans Bay 18, 88, 93-95, 101, 140,
    230, 237
Fujitsu 193
Fullers Engineering Co 284
Fulton Hogan 83, 84

Galbraith and Cull 246
Gatx-Fuller 285
Gaunt Street 96, 122
Geho Pump 262, 263
George's Tunnel 33-35
Gilberd Hadfield Pile Co Ltd 165
Gilbert and Ellice Islands (now Kiribati
    and Tuvalu) 185
Gilmour, R (Bob) 70, 71
Glenbrook 245, 247, 248, 251, 256, 258,
    259, 261, 262
Glenora Park 203
Gloucester Park 164, 165
Going, Bob 205
Golden Bay 104, 284, 286
Goodman, W T G 234
Goosman, Sir Stanley 111
Grafton Bridge 158-161, 163, 282
Graham, Fred 206

Grand Atrium 297-299
Gray Watts and Beca 271
Great South Road 105, 110, 121, 129
Green & McCahill Ltd 71
Greenlane Road Tram Barn 241
Grey, Sir George 17, 19, 28-30, 32-34,
    36-40, 47, 52, 54, 55, 88-97, 106, 107,
    117-123, 125, 128, 129, 132-134, 136-
    141, 143, 151, 154, 158-160, 169, 171,
    176, 178-180, 182, 196, 203-205, 207,
    210, 212-214, 219, 228, 229, 232, 236,
    238, 239, 266, 267, 279, 280, 289, 291,
    293, 297, 300, 301, 304, 327
Grierson, Aimer and Draffin 297
Gummer and Ford 142, 287-289
Gunson, James 205

Halco Drills 275
Halcrow, Sir William 61, 63
Hall, Alan 283
Hall's Corner, 125
Hamer, W H 93
Harbour Preservation Society 57, 58
Harding, Samuel 128
Harrison, Alan 76
Hart, G A 56
Hauraki Gulf 55, 58, 73, 79, 118, 184, 223
Hawkins 75, 298, 299, 305, 306, 328
Hawkins, Graeme 75
Hazard, Dick 228
Hazard, W H 226, 228
Heale, Theophilus 279
Heard, Mr 262
Hellaby, Sir Alan 253, 260
Henry, Mr 32
Herne Bay 121, 122
Heskett, Mr J A 246
Hicks, Ron 69, 76
High Court 290, 293
Historic Places Trust 161, 187, 211, 216,
    226, 228, 236, 264, 268, 296, 299, 306,
    326, 329
Hobson, Captain William/Governor 16,
    27, 87, 212
Hobson Bay 52, 63, 76, 77, 87, 141, 142
Hobson Bay Sewer 76, 77
Hobson Street 52, 121, 213, 239-241, 243
Hobson Wharf 94, 95, 239
Hobsonville 111-113, 199, 206
Holcim's Westport 286
Holmes Consulting Group 296, 299, 305,
    306
Hora Hora 240
Howick 105, 106, 171, 172, 174, 213, 328
Hughes, Dr T J 40
Huia Dam 41, 45
Humber 153

Hume Industries Ltd 67
Hunter, Mr 271
Huntly 238, 247, 248
Hunua 43-45, 47, 48, 108
Hurstmere Road 125
Hutchinson, George 45
Hyde, Professor C G 79

ICI (Imperial Chemical Industries) 228
Ihumatao 66
Incline, The 38
Ingram, Sir John 12, 245, 259, 261, 321, 322, 327
Intelsat (International Telecommunications Satellite organisation) 191, 194
Iris Moana (the Fairmile launch) 119
Ishikawajiama-Harima Heavy Industries 152

James, John 282, 288
Jane Gifford 88, 119, 283
Jasmax 145, 295, 296, 303, 328
Jellicoe Street 104
Jervois, Sir William Drummond 220
Johns, Clive 68
Johnsonville 111
Johnstone's Hill 115, 116
Jones, Martin 296
Judd, Mr 264

Kaimai tunnel 137
Kaipara 73, 119
Kaitaia 138, 176
Kamo 283
Kapetaua 89
Kapuni 232
Karaka 62, 92, 114
Karangahape Road 107, 120
Karanghake Gorge 240
Kaskowiski (Russian cruiser) 220
Kawakawa 131, 139
Kawau Island and Company 278, 281
Kelly's Creek 34
Kelly Tarlton's Underwater World 53, 54
Kennedy Park, Campbells Bay 80
Kerepehi 313
Kerr Stuart Company Limited 125
Kerr Taylor, Alan 264
Kersner, Frank 67
Kestrel (ferry) 118
Khyber Pass Road 28, 29
Kidd, Alfred 121
Kings Wharf 94, 231, 236, 238-241, 243
Kingsford Smith, Sir Charles 207
Kingsland, 121, 140, 241
Kingston Morrison Ltd 290
Kirk, Norman 258

Knox, Edward 264
Kobayashi, Dr 194
Kohimarama, 205
KRTA Ltd 48
Kumarasingham, Sanjay 76
Kumeu 138, 199

Labour, Federation of 61, 94
Lake Lollipop 262
Lake Pupuke 125
Lane, Noel 299
Langlands and Company 38
Lavender Flat 60
Leach, Professor Tom J 59
Lee, Jack 60
Leigh Fisher Associates 209
Levick, Harry 230
Lewis, Frank 76
Ligar Canal 28, 51, 52
Limestone Island 282-284, 286
Liverpool Street 242, 243
Low and Motion 29
Ludzack Ettinger (MLE) process 82
Lylie, Mr 226
Lyttelton 195

MacAndrew, James 23
Macau Tower 317, 325
Mace Development 98
Madajag, Mario 145
Madang 196
Mairangi Bay 80
Makaurau 12, 75
Mandeno, Lloyd 65, 240, 241, 323
Mangatangi 45, 322
Maungaturoto 111
Mangere Bridge 59, 110, 111, 161-167, 328
Mangere Wastewater Treatment Plant 12, 48, 73-75, 321
Mansergh, Dennis 46
Mansion House 279
Manukau County Council 69, 164, 174
Manukau Harbour 12, 38, 39, 57, 62, 64, 73, 87, 92, 96, 104, 127, 162, 164, 165
Manurewa 203, 204
Manurewa 110, 111,
Maori Trust Board 144
Marsden Point 103, 109, 254
Mason Bros Ltd 70
Massey University 25
Mathew, Felton 87
Matthews, Marmaduc 205
Maunsell AECOM 58, 85
McConnell Dowell 85, 189-192, 194, 260, 262, 322, 328
McCoy, Mike 76
McDonald, D 79

McGiven, Kevin 76
McLaren Falls 240
McLean, J & Son 158
McMillan and Lockwood 72
Mead, Arthur 44, 47
Mechanics Bay 88, 93, 119, 129, 131, 135, 182, 186, 213
Melbourne 56, 90, 117, 129, 154, 155, 171, 226, 271, 290, 321
Meldrum 234, 235
Mercer 135-137, 319
Mercury Energy 239, 243
Mestayer, R L 52
Metcalfe, Henry 38
Milford 78, 125
Mills, Gordon 70
Mindril E500 diamond drills 274
Moana, Iris 119
Moersch, Professor 159
Moore, R F 158, 163
Morehen, Francis-Jones 306
Moriaty, Edward O 29
Morse code 176, 186, 195
Motonui (the Fairmile launch) 119
Motuketekete Island 280
Motukorea Channel 55, 79
Motutapu Island 223
Mowbray, Neil 65
Mt Eden 68, 106, 107, 180, 226-228, 278
Mt Roskill 109, 121
Mt Smart Stadium 278
Mt Taranaki 246, 247
Mt Wellington 106, 111, 269, 270
Muir, James 264
Mumbles Train 120
Muntz metal 172
Murchison 19
Murdoch, G J 50
Muriwai Beach 199
Murray, Andrew 57, 174
Musick, Captain Edwin 182-187
Mynott, W L 59, 64, 71

Napier 19, 176, 282, 287, 288
Nathan, L D 264
National Roads Board 111, 153, 156, 164, 168
Neville, Mr A 209
New Zealand Coastwatcher Unit 185
New Zealand Flying School 204, 206
New Zealand Guardian Trust Building 288
New Zealand Herald 32, 51, 86, 141, 160, 168
New Zealand Parliament House 293
New Zealand Portland Cement Company 282-284, 286

New Zealand Steel Ltd 248, 252, 253, 255, 256, 258, 261, 321
New Zealand Wireless and Telegraphy Act 181
Newmarket Viaduct 113, 168-170
Ngai Tai 186, 187
Ngapuhi 212
Ngairo (ferry) 118
Ngaroma (the Fairmile launch) 119
Ngati Mahuta 258
Ngati Maru Rununga 26
Ngati Paoa 186
Ngati Whatua 77, 186
Nihotupu Dam, Upper and Lower 32, 36-44
Nippon clip-ons 113, 152
Nordberg crusher 272, 273
Norman, Bob 152, 157, 328
North Head 78, 220-223, 248, 326
North Shore 51, 55, 61, 62, 68-70, 78-86, 90, 91, 117, 124, 126, 157, 199, 232, 264-266, 321
Northcote 78, 87, 113, 118, 150, 154, 199, 200
Northern Roller Milling Company 237

O'Brien, Thomas 294
Oakleigh River 284
Oamaru stone 290, 300
Okahu Bay 12, 53, 54, 76
Opaheke 127
Opus International Consultants 114, 162-164, 166, 167, 169, 303, 329
Orakei 53-56, 58, 60, 61, 63, 65, 66, 68, 69, 76, 77, 89, 204
Orenstein & Koppel 260
Ormond, J D 162
Orpheus, HMS 87
Orr, Peter 76
Osborne, E J 79
Osprey Inn 28
Otahuhu 110, 117, 171, 175, 176, 213, 243
Owen, R E 77

Paeroa 137
Palmerston North Sewage Treatment Plant 72
Pandora, HMS 280
Papakura 73, 203, 206, 324
Papatoetoe 110, 111, 207
Parnell 106, 129, 131-135, 138, 140, 142, 144, 217, 281
Parr, James 55
Paton, Claude 300
Peacock, Mr 206
Pearl Harbour 184, 223
Pearse, Richard 203

Peate, Des 46, 47, 330
Petricevich, Michael 82
Phillips, P A 28
Point Chevalier 112, 113, 121, 241, 323
Pond, Mr J A 282
Ponsonby 29, 30, 120-122, 331
Port of Onehunga 87, 94
Porter, James P 60
Portland, Isle of 281
Ports of Auckland 87, 88, 94, 98, 100, 104, 329
Price, A & G Ltd 139
Princes Wharf 94-98
Project CARE 82, 83
Puketutu Island 62, 66

Queen Street 15, 17, 27-29, 51, 52, 89-91, 93, 102, 107, 117, 120, 121, 123, 131, 138-141, 144, 146, 162, 178, 201, 234, 237, 242, 287, 300, 301, 329

Railway to Nowhere 131
Railway Wharf 94
Rangiriri 175
Rank-Cintel 193
Rawn, A M 65
Regional Authority 43, 48, 50, 70-73, 77, 79, 80, 98, 99, 111, 112, 116, 155, 157, 210, 322
Reid, Henry CE 282
Resource Management Act 73, 75, 256
Richter scale 313
RNZAF (Royal New Zealand Air Force) 207, 208, 210, 319, 321, 325
Robinson, Erle 76
Robinson, Sir Dove-Myer 58
Roche lime 281
Roland, Theo 76
Rosedale wastewater treatment plant 83, 84
Ross Creek Dam 43
Rough, Captain 87
Rowntree, John 60, 64
Royal Flying Corps 204, 205
Royal Society of New Zealand 25
Rukuhia swamp 137
Rumsey, Edward 293
Russell, P N & Co 171
Ruston Hornsby diesel engine 224
Rutherfurd, Ernest Shaw 283

Samoan Clipper 182, 183
Sargent, M R (Murray) 70, 71
Savory, Reg 209
School of Mines 23, 26
Scotland, J W H 205
Scott, Robert Julian 22

SEACOM 188, 196, 197
Seccombe's Well 29
Semple, Robert 110
Sharp, Ron 45
Shore Road 69, 122, 199
Shortland Street 140, 177, 179
Siemens Company 120
Sikorsky S42B (flying boat) 182
Simmons, A T 59
Sinclair Knight Merz Ltd 290, 293
Singapore Crusher 270-272, 276
Singleton, Steve 83, 85
Skinner, Tom E 61
Sky City 308, 309, 318, 325
Sky Tower 290, 307-309, 313, 315-318, 325, 328
Slater, James 216
SLRN (Stelco-Lurgi-Republic Steel-National Lead) 248
Smeaton, John 22
Smeatonian Society of Civil Engineers 22
Smithson, Bruce 45
Southgate, John 281
Spiller, Dr Donald 69
Stewart, James 25, 89, 127, 128, 161, 329
Stirrat, Mr A G 254
Stokes, Captain 88
Stokes Point 88
Stone, Russell 216, 329
Stonefields development 277
Stony Batter 223-226, 326
Strand, The 114
Strowger 177
Super Construction Company 294
Supreme Court 280, 293
Sweetman, Murray 289

T Rex 114, 115
Taharoa 12, 247, 249, 258
Tainui hapu Ngaati Te Ata 258
Takapuna 78, 79, 81, 113, 124-126, 199, 200, 233, 326, 328
Takapurawha Point 53
Tamaki River 92, 96, 111, 117, 127, 162, 165, 171, 172, 328
Tank Farm 103, 138
Taranaki 43, 161, 167, 232, 243, 246, 247
Tauranga 94, 118, 137, 176, 240
Tayler, Henry 278
Taylor, G Midgley 52, 53
Taylor, John & Sons, London 65
Taylor, Nancy M 219
Taylor Woodrow 210
Te Awamutu 137, 175
Te Kaha 77
Te Rohe Potae 137
Te Toka a Kapetaua 89

Telecom 186, 323, 324
Telex 176, 188, 196, 201
Telford, Thomas 22, 26
Teredo worm, *Teredo navalis* 162, 172
Teutenburg, Anton 293
Toroa (ferry) 118
Torrens, Tom 45
Town Hall, Auckland 290-292
Trans-Atlantic Telephone Cable (TAT-1)
    195, 197
Transit New Zealand 114
Transpower 243
Twinch, Allan 76
Tyler, James 38, 39, 159, 216
Tymms, Sir Frederick 209

Vickerman, H H 79
Vogel, Sir Julius 22, 135, 136

Waihi Gold Mining 246
Waihoritu 27, 28
Waikato River 45, 48, 49, 73, 92, 113, 127,
    135, 137, 163, 225, 239
Waitemata 16, 27, 47, 51, 55, 58, 61, 64,
    70, 87, 92, 104, 117, 119, 155, 181, 190,
    243, 264, 266

Waiuku, 92, 163, 258
Waiwera Viaduct 115, 116
Walker, Greville 65
Walsh brothers 203-206
Ward, R I 22
Wark, Mr J N 230
Warkworth 188-190, 192, 202, 281-283,
    286, 322, 324, 328
Watercare Services Limited 47-49, 77
Watkins, H H 55, 78
Watt, Hugh 209
Weaver, William 22, 128, 171
Wellesley Street 28, 29, 199, 218, 304
Welsby, Peter 76
Western Springs 29-32, 40, 41, 48, 50,
    90, 241
Westfield 59, 60, 134, 142, 144
Westhaven 104, 118, 149
Whangarei 94, 138, 191, 282-286, 319
Whau River 92
Whitaker, Sir Frederick 264
Whitmore, Sir G S 222
Whitney, Major John 226
Wiles and Jones 194
Wiliam Lanaglands/Langlands and
    Company 38

Wilkes Barre Company 284
Wilkins and Davies 70, 165, 210, 285
Williams, Andrew 83, 85
Wilson, Don 45
Wilson, H Munro 33
Winstone, George 284
Winstone, Mr Percy 270
Winstone Ltd 269, 328
Wiri 99, 112, 164, 278
Wm Scollay and Co Ltd 193
Wolfe, Len 289
Woods, Dave 76
Woodward-Clyde 82
Woodward, Geoff 70
Works Infrastructure 9, 114, 229
Worley 58, 62, 79, 80, 85, 231, 233
Worley, Ralph P 58, 62, 79
Worley, Rupert 231
Wrigg, Alfred 234
Wrigg, Henry 28, 29
Wright, Howard 203
Wynyard, Robert H 88

Zhenhua Port Machinery Company 99
Zinders 232